NOBEL PRIZE LIBRARY

———

CARDUCCI

DELEDDA

ECHEGARAY

ELIOT

Nobel Prize Library

PUBLISHED UNDER THE SPONSORSHIP OF THE

NOBEL FOUNDATION & THE SWEDISH ACADEMY

Giosuè Carducci

Grazia Deledda

José Echegaray

T. S. Eliot

ALEXIS GREGORY, *New York*, AND
CRM PUBLISHING, *Del Mar, California*

CONTENTS

Giosuè Carducci

1906

"Not only in consideration of his deep
learning and critical research, but above
all as a tribute to the creative energy,
freshness of style, and lyrical force which
characterize his poetic masterpieces"

Illustrated by MICHEL CAUVET

PRESENTATION ADDRESS

By C. D. AF WIRSÉN

PERMANENT SECRETARY
OF THE SWEDISH ACADEMY

FROM THE unusually large number of poets and authors proposed for the Nobel Prize this year, the Swedish Academy has chosen a great Italian poet who for a long time has attracted the attention both of the Academy and of the entire civilized world.

Since antiquity, Northern men have been drawn to Italy by her history and her artistic treasures as well as by her sweet and gentle climate. The Northerner does not stop until he has arrived in the eternal city of Rome, just as the war for Italian unity could not stop before Rome was conquered. But before arriving in Rome the visitor is fascinated by the beauty of so many other places. Among these, in the Apennines, is the Etruscan city of Bologna, which is known to us through the *Songs of Enzo* by Carl August Nicander.

Since the Middle Ages, when a famous university made it known as learned, Bologna has been of great importance in the cultural history of Italy. Although in ancient times it was renowned as an authority on jurisprudence, it has now become especially famous for its poetic marvels. Thus, it is today still worthy of the expression *"Bononia docet"* (Bologna teaches). For its greatest poetic attainments of the present, it is indebted to the man to whom the Nobel Prize has been awarded this year —Giosuè Carducci.

Carducci was born on July 27, 1835, in Val di Castello. He himself has given an interesting account of his impressions from his childhood and youth, and he has been the subject of several good biographies.

In order to judge properly the development of his mind and his talents, it is important to know that his father, Dr. Michele Carducci,

[3]

was a member of the Carboneria (a secret political society working for Italian unity) and was active in the political movements for Italian liberty, and that his mother was an intelligent and liberal woman.

Michele obtained a position as a doctor in Castagneto. The young poet thus spent his earliest years in the Tuscan Maremma. He learned Latin from his father, and Latin literature was to become very familiar to him. Although Carducci later opposed Manzoni's ideas with great fervor, he was also strongly influenced for a long time by his father's admiration for the poet. At this time he also studied the *Iliad* and the *Aeneid,* Tasso's *Gerusalemme,* Rollin's Roman history, and Thier's work on the French Revolution.

It was a time of great political tension, and one can well believe that in those days of discord and oppression the young poet's fiery imagination absorbed everything which had to do with ancient liberty and the impending unification.

The boy soon turned into a little revolutionary. As he himself recounts, in his games with his brothers and friends he organized little republics which were governed by archons or consuls or tribunes. Vigorous brawls frequently broke out. Revolution was considered a normal state of affairs; civil war was always the order of the day. The young Carducci stoned a make-believe Caesar who was about to cross the Rubicon. Caesar had to flee and the republic was saved. But the next day the little patriotic hero got a sound trouncing from the conquering Caesar.

Not too much stress need be laid on these games, since they are frequent among young boys. But Carducci did, in fact, embrace strong republican sympathies in later life.

In 1849 the family moved to Florence, where Carducci was enrolled in a new school. Here, in addition to his required studies, he first read the poetry of Leopardi, Schiller, and Byron. And soon he started writing poetry—satiric sonnets. He later studied at the Scuola Normale Superiore in Pisa, where he seems to have shown a great deal of energy in his work. After finishing his studies he became a teacher of rhetoric in San Miniato. Because of his expressions of radical ideas, the grand-ducal government annulled his later election to a post at the Arezzo elementary school. Afterward, however, he taught Greek at the lyceum in Pistoia. Finally he obtained a chair at the University of Bologna, where he has had a long and highly successful career.

These in brief are the general lines of his external life. There has been no lack of struggle in his career. He was, for example, even suspended for some time from teaching in Bologna, and on several occasions he was involved in lively polemics with several Italian authors. He suffered great personal tragedies, of which his brother Dante's suicide was undoubtedly the most painful. But his family life and his love for his wife and children have offered him great consolation.

The fight for Italian liberty was extremely important to the development of his sensibility. Carducci was a passionate patriot; he followed the war with all the fire of his soul. And no matter how much he may have been embittered by the defeats at Aspromonte and Mentana, and no matter how much he was disillusioned by the new parliamentary government, which was not being organized in accordance with his desires, he was, nevertheless, overjoyed at the triumph of his sacred patriotic cause.

His ardent nature was tormented by anything which in his opinion interfered with the fulfillment of the work for Italian unity. He was not one to wait patiently; he continuously demanded immediate results and felt a strong aversion to diplomatic delays and the diplomatic *festina lente*.

In the meantime his poetry blossomed abundantly. Although he is also the author of excellent historical and literary criticism, we should be concerned above all with his poetry, for it is through his poetry that he has won his greatest fame.

The volume *Juvenilia* (1863) contains, as the title indicates, his youthful work of the 1850's. Two qualities characterize this collection: on the one hand, its classical cast and intonation, sometimes carried to the point where Carducci salutes Phoebus Apollo and Diana Trivia; and on the other, its profoundly patriotic tone, accompanied by a violent hatred of the Catholic Church and of the Pope's power, the strongest obstacles to Italian unity.

In strong opposition to ultramontanism, Carducci in his songs evokes the memories of ancient Rome, the images of the great French Revolution, and the figures of Garibaldi and Mazzini. At times, when he

[5]

believes Italy's state hopeless and fears that all of its ancient virtues and valiant deeds have been vitiated, he plunges into the profoundest despair.

This bitterness helps to explain Carducci's numerous attacks on various authors and on other people; Carducci was generally violent in his polemics. But in *Juvenilia* there are also poems with a more positive content, like the song to Victor Emanuel, written in 1859 at the moment when it became obvious that a war with Austria would soon break out. In this song he jubilantly celebrates the monarch who bore the banner of Italian unity.

True patriotism is expressed in the sonnet "Magenta" and in the poem "Il Plebiscito," in which he renews his enthusiastic praise of Victor Emanuel. The most beautiful of the poems in *Juvenilia* is probably the poem to the Savoy cross.

The later collection called *Levia Gravia* (*Light and Heavy,* 1868) contains the poems of the sixties. A certain sadness can be heard in many of these poems. The long delay of the conquest of Rome contributed much to Carducci's bitter feelings, but there were a great many other things which Carducci passionately regretted in the prevailing politics of the day. Carducci had expected more from the new political conditions than they could offer. Yet we encounter some very beautiful poems in this collection. Carducci was familiar with fourteenth-century poetry, and a great many echoes of this epoch are heard, for instance, in *"Poeti di Parte Bianca"* ("Poets of the White Party") and in his poem on the proclamation of the Italian kingdom.

Only in the *Rime nuove* (*New Rhymes,* 1877) and in the three collections of the *Odi barbare* (*The Barbarian Odes,* 1877–89) do Carducci's full lyrical maturity and accomplished stylistic beauty appear. Here we no longer find the same disdainful poet who fought with sword and fire under the pseudonym of Enotrio Romano. Instead, the character of the poet seems wholly transformed; sweeter, softer melodies are to be heard. The introductory poem *"Alla Rima"* ("To Rhyme") is extremely musical, a true hymn to the beauty of rhyme. Its ending excellently characterizes Carducci himself. Evidently Carducci understood his own temperament, which he compares with the Tyrrhenian Sea. But his uneasiness is not continuous, and notes of real joy resound in the enchanting poem *"Idillio di Maggio"* ("A May Eclogue").

"Mattinata" ("Morning"), which clearly recalls Hugo, is also lovely, as are the songs entitled *"Primavere Elleniche"* (Hellenic Springtimes").

"Ça Ira" ("The Rebellion"), a section of the *Rime nuove,* is composed of a series of sonnets. Although it is not of great poetic value, it does represent Carducci's more or less unreserved apotheosis of the French Revolution.

The poet's greatness is more fully revealed in his *Odi barbare,* the first collection of which came out in 1877, the second in 1882, and the third in 1889. There is some justification, however, for criticism of the work's form.

Although Carducci adopted ancient meters, he transformed them so entirely that an ear accustomed to ancient poetry will not hear the classical rhythms. Many of these poems attain the pinnacle of perfection in their poetic content. Carducci's genius has never reached greater heights than in some of his *Odi barbare.* One need only name the fascinating *"Miramar"* and the melodious and melancholy poem *"Alla Stazione in una Mattinata d'Autunno"* ("To the Station on an Autumn Morning"), products of the most noble inspiration. The song *"Miramar"* is about the unfortunate emperor Maximilian and his brief Mexican adventure. It excels as much in its moving tragic tone as it does in its vivid nature imagery. The Adriatic shore is depicted with perfect mastery. This song exhales a certain feeling of compassion which is rare in Carducci's treatment of Austrian subject matter, but which he expressed yet another time in the beautiful song on the Empress Elizabeth's sad fate in *Rime e Ritmi* (*Rhymes and Rhythms,* 1898).

Many contrasts clearly are to be found in a violent and rich poetic nature like Carducci's. Disapproval from many sides has thus been mixed with the just admiration for this poet. Yet Carducci is without doubt one of the most powerful geniuses of world literature, and such disapproval, voiced also by his compatriots, has not been spared even the greatest poets. No one is without defect.

The blame is not, however, directed at his sometimes passionate republican tendencies. Let his opinions remain his own possession. No one will contest his independent political position. In any case, his hostility toward the monarchy has subsided with the years. He has come more and more to consider the Italian dynasty as the protector of Italian independence. In fact, Carducci has even dedicated poems to the Queen Mother of Italy, Màrgherita. A venerable woman revered by almost all factions, her poetic soul has been celebrated by Carducci's grandiose art. He has paid her beautiful and affectionate homage in the magnificent song *"Alla Regina d'Italia"* ("To the Queen of Italy") and in the immortal poem *"Il Liuto e la Lira"* ("Lute and Lyre"), in which, through the Provençal *sirventes* and the pastoral, he expresses his admiration of the noble Princess. The petty, obstinate republicans, because of these and other tributes, have looked upon Carducci as a deserter of their cause. He justly responded, however, that a song of admiration dedicated to a magnanimous and good woman has nothing whatever to do with politics, and that he reserved the right to think and write whatever he pleased about the reigning Italian family and its members.

The reasons for the antagonism of his friends and political partisans toward him are of a completely different origin. This antagonism is occasioned less by his ferocious assaults on persons of differing political opinions than by his over-enthusiastic paganism, which often assumes a biting tone toward Christianity itself. His anti-Christian sentiments have above all produced his much discussed hymn to Satan.

There is a good deal of justice in many of the attacks on Carducci's anti-Christianity. Although one cannot perfectly approve of the way in which he has tried to defend himself in *Confessioni e Battaglie* (Confessions and Battles) and in other writings, a knowledge of the attendant circumstances helps to explain, if not to justify, Carducci's attitudes.

Carducci's paganism is understandable to a Protestant, at least. As an ardent patriot who saw the Catholic Church as in many ways a misguided and corrupt force opposed to the freedom of his adored Italy, Carducci was quite likely to confuse Catholicism with Christianity, extending to Christianity the severe judgments with which he sometimes attacked the Church.

Still we must not forget the genuine religious sentiments expressed in some of his poems. It is helpful to remember the end of *"La Chiesa di Polenta"* ("The Church of Polenta"), which stands in healthy contrast to *"In una Chiesa Gotica"* ("In a Gothic Church").

And as to the impetuous *Inno a Satana* (*Hymn to Satan,* 1865), it would be a great wrong to Carducci to identify him, for example, with Baudelaire and to accuse Carducci of poisonous and unhealthy "Satanism." In fact, Carducci's Satan has an ill-chosen name. The poet clearly means to imply a Lucifer in the literal sense of the word—the carrier of light, the herald of free thought and culture, and the enemy of that ascetic discipline which rejects or disparages natural rights. Yet it seems strange to hear Savanarola praised in a poem in which asceticism is condemned. The whole of the hymn abounds with such contradictions. Carducci himself in recent times has rejected the entire poem and has called it a "vulgar sing-song." Thus, there is no reason to dwell any longer on a poem which the poet himself has disavowed.

Carducci is a learned literary historian who has been nurtured by ancient literature and by Dante and Petrarch. But he cannot be easily classified. He is not devoted to romanticism, but rather to the classical ideal and Petrarchan humanism. Regardless of the criticism which can justly be launched against him, the irrefutable truth remains that a poet who is always moved by patriotism and a love of liberty, who never sacrifices his opinions to gain favor, and who never indulges in base sensualism, is a soul inspired by the highest ideals.

And insofar as his poetry in the aesthetic sense attains a rare force, Carducci can be considered worthy in the highest degree of the Nobel Prize for Literature.

The Swedish Academy thus pays respect to a poet who already enjoys a world-wide reputation, and adds its homage of admiration to the many praises already given him by his country. Italy has elected Carducci senator and repaid the honor he has brought her by assigning him a lifelong pension amounting to a considerable sum.

There was no formal Acceptance Speech by Carducci.

POEMS

By GIOSUÈ CARDUCCI

Translated by Emily A. Tribe

SONNET XXXVI

Alone my bark sails o'er the storm-tossed sea,
Amid the white-winged gulls' lamenting cries;
The thund'rous waves around her threatening rise,
And on her flash the lightnings ceaselessly,

While towards the shore for ever lost to me
Memory looks back with straining tearful eyes;
Hope, vanquished by the weary view that flies,
Droops o'er the splintered oar despondently.

But on the stern erect my Genius stands,
And scanning sea and sky his song rings clear
Above the whistling wind and creaking mast:

"We sail, sad mariners, for misty lands
Of dumb forgetfulness: howe'er we steer
Our course must lead to Death's pale reef at last."

HYMN TO SATAN

To thee of all being
The first cause immense
Of matter and spirit,
Of reason and sense.

[11]

Whilst in the full goblet
Shall sparkle the wine,
So bright through the pupil
The souls of men shine,

Whilst earth still is smiling,
And the sun smiles above,
And men are exchanging
Their sweet words of love,

Thrills mystic of Hymen
Through high mountains course,
And broad plains are heaving
With life's fertile force,

On thee in verse daring,
From tight rein released,
On thee I call, Satan,
The king of the feast.

Away aspersorium,
With priest who would bind!
Priest, not at thy bidding
Gets Satan behind.

Behold, rust is eating
The edge of the blade
In the hand of great Michael
The faithful displayed.

The displumed Archangel
Descends to the void,
The thunderbolt's frozen
Jehovah employed.

Faint pallid meteors,
Wan stars void of light,
Like rain down from heaven
Fall angels in flight.

In matter aye sleepless
Of forces the spring,
King of phenomena,
Of forms lord and king.

Here only lives Satan,
His power supreme
In a dark eye flashes
With tremendous gleam,

Whether it languidly
Retreats and rebels,
Or bright and audacious
Provokes and compels.

In gay blood it sparkles
That's pressed from the vine,
Whose gift of swift pleasure
Shall never decline,

Which can to our fleeting
Life new strength impart,
Which puts off our sorrows,
To love gives a heart.

'Tis thou that inspirest
The song that doth rise
In my bosom, O Satan,
When that god it defies,

On whom guilty pontiffs
And cruel kings call;
Men's minds thou so shakest
As when lightnings fall.

Ahriman and Adonis,
Astarte, to thee,
Canvas, marble and paper
All lived and were free.

When Venus new risen
From billowing seas
Serenely made happy
Ionia's breeze.

On Lebanon quivered
The trees at thy name,
When to gentle Cypria
Her risen love came.

Thee chorus and dances
In joy celebrate,
Love pure and virginal
To thee dedicate

Mid the palm-trees fragrant
Of Araby's land,
Where whitens the sea-foam
On Cyprian strand.

What matter if fury
Of fierce Nazarene
From ritual barbaric
Of love-feast obscene

Hath set with blest torches
The temples on fire,
And Argolis' idols
Hath hurled in the mire.

In cottages lowly
A refuge dost find,
Amid household Lares
Folk keep thee in mind.

The God and the lover
A woman's warm breast
With his ardent spirit
Once having possessed,

Thou turnest the witch
Whom long searching makes pale
To lend succor to nature
O'er disease to prevail.

Thou to the motionless
Eye of the alchemist,
In sight of the magus
Who dares to resist,

Beyond the dull cloister
Its gates set ajar,
Revealest in brightness
New heavens afar.

In lonely Thebaid
The wretched monks hide
From thee and things worldly
In safety to bide.

Ah, doubtful soul standing
Where life's roads divide,
See, Satan is kindly,
Heloise at thy side!

In vain with rough sackcloth
Thy flesh dost maltreat,
From Maro and Flaccus
He verse will repeat

Betwixt psalms of David;
'Twixt weeping and dirge
He causes beside thee
Delphic forms to emerge.

Amongst those companions
Though garbed in black weeds
With rosy Lycoris
Glycera he leads.

But other the phantoms
When finer the age,
At times he awakens
From Livy's full page,

When tribunes and consuls
And vast crowds that thrill
With ardor and passion
That sleepless cell fill,

He to the Capitol
Thy land to set free
Of Italic pride dreaming,
O monk, urges thee.

And you, Huss and Wycliffe,
No fury of flames
Could stifle your voices'
Prophetic acclaims.

Send forth on the breezes
Your watch-cry sublime
"A new age is dawning,
Fulfilled is the time!"

Already are trembling
Both miter and crown,
And cloistered seclusion
Rebellion breaks down.

Then fighting and preaching
Under the stola
Comes Fra Girolamo
Savonarola.

The cowl Luther cast off,
And freedom he brought:
So cast off thy fetters,
Be free, human thought!

And shine forth resplendent,
Encircled with flames,
Arise Matter, Satan
The victory claims.

A beautiful monster,
A terrible birth,
Runs over the ocean,
Runs over the earth.

Volcano like flashes
Through dim smoke it lowers,
It scales lofty mountains,
Broad plains it devours.

It spans the abysses,
In caverns it hides
And through the deep cleft ways
Invisible glides;

Then comes forth undaunted,
From coast to coast hies,
As from some fierce whirlwind
It sends forth its cries.

As breath of the whirlwind
Spreads out on the vast
Expanse, O ye nations,
Great Satan goes past.

From place to place passes
Beneficent he
On his chariot of fire
Untrammeled and free.

All hail to thee, Satan!
Rebellion, all hail!
Hail, power of reason,
Avenge and prevail!

To thee arise incense
And holy vows paid,
Thou, Satan, hast vanquished
The god by priests made.

MAZZINI

As from the barren rocks above the sea
A marble giant lone doth Genoa stand,
So rose in dark days he, austere and grand,
Unmoved above a heaving century.

From rocks whence would the child Columbus see
New mountains springing from a wave-washed land,
With Gracchus' heart and Dante's thought expand
Glimmering in heaven the third Italy

He sees, toward her he pressed with fixèd eyes,
And forward through a graveyard was his way.
Behind him a dead people on he drew.

To heaven now lifts his face that exile gray,
Benign and grave, where ne'er did smile arise:
"Ideal," thinks he, "thou alone art true."

LOVE'S CANTICLE

In its great days the Pauline fort fair-wrought
  With rampart long and cross-wise glacis rose:
Thus the third Paul sketched it one morn in thought,
  Twixt Bembo's and his missal's Latin prose;

"Blithely from me strays this Perugian flock
    To strange ravines," said he, "for admonition
The Eternal Father hath His thunder-shock,
    I, His Vicegerent, cannon in position:

" 'Coelo Tonantem' Horace sang, and Jove
    Speaks through the rain-clouds o'er the north wind's track.
I to my flock through cannon say: 'Don't rove,
    Back to Engedi, and to Sharon back,

" 'But, since th' Augustan age we now renew,
    See to it, Sangallo, that a fortress bold
For me you raise worthy of Rome and you,
    And worthy our pontificate of gold.' "

He spake: Sangallo all the stronghold's might
    Rounded and shaped like limbs of comely bride,
Then o'er her threw a veil of marble white,
    And with a tower garland crowned her pride.

In Latin couplets Molza sang its praise:
    Gifts more than seven by his mystic powers
In bombs and shells the Paraclete conveys,
    On the Perugians pouring them in showers.

The multitude's—a dog—you know full well,
    On stones he cannot break, he teeth employs:
To whet his iron fangs, historians tell,
    On fortresses he specially enjoys.

Their stones he crunches, then, with joyful bark,
    Himself upon the ruins stretches, till,
Rousing once more he on his way doth hark,
    'Spite blows upon new stones to work his will.

So in Perugia did he. Where the proud
    Mole cumbering the soil, its shade did fling,
Now chatt'ring women, laughing children crowd
    In sunshine there. Love smiles, and smiles the spring.

[19]

The bright sun blazing in the blue immense
 Makes distance white far as Abruzzi's chain,
And with desire of love yet more intense
 Smiles on the Umbrian hills and verdant plain.

The mountains calm rising in rosy light
 Each other contemplate, till they enfold
Themselves in undulating vapors bright
 And cloak their forms in violet and gold.

Perhaps, Italia, 'tis thy fragrant hair
 That stirs, upon the nuptial couch serene,
Beneath the eternal lover's kisses, where
 It spreads across thy breast, two seas between?

For me today, wherefore I can't surmise,
 I feel my thoughts with sapphire radiance glow,
I feel through every vein today the sighs
 From heaven descend, arise from earth below.

Each prospect new within my heart awakes
 An old affection, till my tongue doth move
Of its own self, and into language breaks,
 Cries to the heavens and to the earth: Love, Love!

Do I embrace the heavens, or in the All
 Am I absorbed again? How to divine?
That note I heard did from the poem fall
 That is eternal; now 'tis one short line.

From gloomy hamlets that in Umbria's land
 In mountain gorge to hide themselves delight,
From lone Etrurian citadels that stand
 Above the flow'ry slope on watchful height,

From fields 'mid arms and bones the ploughs uncover.
 Rome still doth threaten in misfortune's spite;
From Teuton towers, seeming aloft to hover,
 Like falcons bent on predatory flight;

From civic halls, that in defiance rise
  Black-turreted, and to confront them dare;
From fanes that stretching upwards to the skies
  Long marble arms, entreat the Lord in prayer;

From little towns that up the hill-side haste;
  And gaily to the city dark repair,
Like villeins, who would plenteous harvest taste,
  Which, after reaping, with their lords they share;

From monast'ries, whose somber sites are resting
  'Twixt towns and cities 'neath their belfries' chimes,
Like cuckoos singing, 'mid the sparse trees nesting,
  The joys and griefs of other lands and times.

From narrow streets, from many a glorious square,
  Where free the art of our forefathers flourished,
As forest oaks, or garden roses fair.
  That for our day a blithesome May hath nourished;

Through crops that deck the plains with tender green,
  Through vines that sloping terraces o'erclimb,
Through lakes and distant rivers' silvery sheen,
  Through woods that clothe the snowy peaks sublime;

Through cottage smoke gay curling in the sun,
  Through clattering wheels of mills that full and grind,
Arise a thousand hymns in unison,
  A thousand voices in one prayer combined:

"Hail, weary peoples of the human race!
  Too much we suffer and too much we hate.
Nothing can die, though all things change apace:
  Love! fair is earth and holy future fate."

What is it that above the mountains shines?
  A new Aurora flushing all the West?
Or do Madonnas trace with glowing lines
  Their rosy path athwart the mountain's crest?

Madonnas fair whom Perugino saw,
   Descending through the April sunsets clear,
Their arms above the Babe in pious awe
   Outstretched, in sweet divinity appear?

Another vision she, an ideal bright
   With justice, radiant with tenderness,
I bless each one who for her falls in fight.
   And each one who for her will live, I bless.

What care I now for priests' or tyrants' sway?
   They older are than are primeval gods.
Ten years ago I cursed the Pope: today
   I with the Pope would be no more at odds.

Oh, poor old man, who knows? Some lone desire
   May him assail; to love his heart may crave.
Perhaps his Sinigaglia doth inspire
   His memory, mirrored in Adria's wave.

Open the Vatican! I'll give its host
   An arm, poor captive to his own decree.
To Liberty, come! I propose a toast:
   Citizen Mastai, drink a glass with me!

THE SONNET

   Dante a cherub's motion to it gave,
   In azure floating, compassed round with gold;
   Petrarca his heart-sorrow to it told,
   River divine, each verse a murmuring wave.

   Tasso for it from Tibur's Muse did crave
   Venusian honey and he made it hold
   Mantuan ambrosia. Alfieri bold
   Smote with its diamond shaft tyrant and slave.

Ugo to it lent notes of nightingale
In cypress groves Ionian; acanthus blooms
To gird it gathered in his mother's land.

Not sixth but last I count me in that band,
Rapture and wrath, plaints, fragrance, art, their tombs
Recalled in lonesome days my verses hail.

THE OX

I love thee, kindly ox; a sense serene
Of strength and peace thou dost infuse in me;
How like a solemn monument art seen
At gaze athwart the fertile fields and free!

The yoke to take contented thou dost lean,
To man's light work thou addest dignity.
He urges, goads, and thou with placid mien
And eye's slow turn dost answer patiently.

Thy spirit through thy nostril moist and black
In vapor issues. Like some glad refrain
Thy lowing dies upon the tranquil air.

Within thy somber eye is mirrored back
The green reflection of the ample plain,
Austerely sweet, and in the silence fair.

VIRGIL

As when the gentle moon low in the sky
O'er the parched fields cool summer dew distills,
The river in the pale light gleaming fills
Its shallow banks as it glides murmuring by.

The nightingale from leafy ambush nigh
Floods the vast calm with his melodious trills,
The wanderer listens, time forgets, as thrills
With thoughts of fair locks loved his memory;

And bereaved mothers who have grieved in vain,
Turn from a grave toward brightening heaven their eyes
And soothe their souls in the dawn's spreading shine.

The mountains smile and smiles the distant main,
And through tall trees the warm wind softly sighs,
Such is thy verse to me, Poet divine.

FUNERE MERSIT ACERBO

O thou who 'neath the flower-clad Tuscan hill
Dost slumber, by whose side our father lies,
Hast thou not heard e'en now a soft voice thrill
The grass upon thy grave with plaintive cries?

It is my little son who at thy chill
Door knocks; he who renews thee in the wise
Great name. The life that thou to bear didst still
So bitter find, O brother, he too flies.

Ah no, 'mid painted flower-beds he played,
Laughed at blithe visions, till the shadow fell
On him, and thrust him downwards to your cold

Lone shore. Receive him thou, for he must dwell
In the dark seats; the sweet sun to behold
He turns, and to his mother cries for aid.

FIESOLE

Where Fiesole saw from her citadel
The livid Arno once stagnate, the place
Where flowers Sulla's city, now slow of pace
Franciscans climb, recalled by clanging bell.

Among the Etruscan ruins lizards dwell,
Their fixed eyes watch through every crannied space;
While Hesper shines in solitary grace,
From cypress groves wind-wearied moanings swell.

The joyous belfry dominates the plain
From moon-shaped curve, as when Italians rose
In the dread year their glories to restore.

O Mino, thou in marble dost attain
To Nature, in thy curl-crowned boys she glows,
Maiden and mother smiling evermore.

S. MARIA DEGLI ANGELI

O brother Francis, how much airy space
Vignola's noble dome doth close restrain!
Where naked on the bare earth thou didst place
Thyself, arms crossed, wrestling with life's last pain.

'Tis hot July. Over the laboring plain
Rises love's canticle. O that some trace
The Umbrian song may give me of thy strain,
The Umbrian sky some brightness from thy face.

On the horizon of that hill-girt land,
Its splendor softened by the mountain haze,
As of thy Paradise it were the portal,

With outstretched arms may I behold thee stand,
Singing to God: "O Lord, to Thee be praise
For Death, sweet sister of our body mortal!"

DANTE

Dante, how comes it that my vows I pay
To thy proud image? Still I meditate
The verse that made thee lean, till sundown late,
And new dawn finds me pondering thy lay.

Yet not for me doth fair Lucia pray,
Nor doth by healing stream Matilda wait,
And vainly Beatrice with her hallowed mate
Godward from star to star pursues her way.

I hate thy Holy Empire: I had cast
With sword the crown from thy good Frederick's head
To earth, there where the vale Olona bounds.

Empire and Church are in one ruin sped;
Thy song above them soars, to heaven resounds.
Jove dies, the poet's hymn unscathed shall last.

CROSSING THE TUSCAN MAREMMA

Sweet country side whose impress I retain
In my wild ways and my disdainful song,
My breast where love and hate ne'er slumber long,
How leaps my heart beholding thee again:

I see familiar forms of hill and plain
With eyes uncertain, as I trace the throng
Of magic visions that to youth belong,
If they should glow with smiles or gloom with pain.

O vain was what I loved and vain my dream,
Ever I ran, but never reached the goal.
Tomorrow I shall fall; but far-off gleam

The hills above the mists that round them roll;
Thy verdant plain where morning showers beam
With laughter, speaking peace unto my soul.

OLD WOE

The pomegranate green in the garden,
    Towards which thy baby hands
    Thou didst reach out, still stands,
The tree of the scarlet flower.

The orchard now lonely and silent
    Renews its green with spring;
    And June once more will bring
Back light and warmth as her dower.

Blossom art thou of my tree, withered,
    Struck by the cruel blast,
    Of this vain life the last
Thou art, and its rarest flower.

Now 'neath the cold earth thou art lying,
    Beneath the dark cold earth,
    The sun brings thee no mirth,
To wake thee Love hath no power.

PANTHEISM

Not to you, ye watchful stars, have I told it,
Nor, all-seeing sun, have I told it to thee;
Her name flower of beautiful things I hold it,
Which only my silent heart echoed for me.

Yet one of those stars my secret's repeating
To another, throughout the darkness of night,
The sun with a smile recounts it on meeting
Just as he is setting, his moon-sister white.

Over shaded hills, on glad plains it is ringing,
As each bush and each flower to tell it compete;
"O sad Poet," birds in their flight are singing,
"Then at length Love has taught thee his dreams full sweet."

I ne'er told it, yet with what god-like clamor
Earth and heaven call out that loved name to me;
'Mid acacia blossoms' odorous glamour
Doth the Great All proclaim: "She loves, she loves thee!"

EVENING GREETING

The stars that wander o'er the sea are saying:
    "O fair moon, do not sleep, we bid thee wake;
Deign, O fair moon, to rise, no more delaying,
    For we would round the world our journey make.
We o'er the chamber would our watch be keeping
Wherein our dark-haired sister bright lies sleeping,
Our sister who, by the magician's art,
Was forced, O mother moon, from us to part."

The pine-trees from the hill-tops are replying,
   From river-banks the alders too complain:
"O stars with tiny bright eyes ever prying,
   Alas, why make ye such discourses vain?
To us she showed herself in May-day splendor,
Betwixt a glorious beech and laurel slender,
A nightingale sings and a rose hath its birth
Wherever her light foot hath printed the earth."

When every star has set upon the ocean,
   On plain and mountain reigns a silence deep;
Earth seems a chamber dark where all emotion
   Of human sorrow sinks at last to sleep.
Short is the night, the little birds awaking
Chirp in the holt; "fair mistress, dawn is breaking."
Thy lattice opened, this first morn of May
Brings thy heart greeting from the world today.

MORNING GREETING

The sun knocks at thy lattice: "Lady fair
Arise," he says. " 'Tis time to love! From choirs
Of roses hymns I bring, and to thee bear
When thou awak'st the violets' desires,
   And from my shining realm to homage pay
   Thy servitors April I lead and May
   And the young year, who on the fragrant flower
   Of thy sweet youth arrests the flying hour."

The wind knocks at thy lattice: "Much," he says,
"O'er mountain have I traveled and o'er plain";
Today the earth in unison doth raise
With dead and living one harmonious strain.
   From every nest, from every greening grove

They cry, "Spring is returning, let us love!"
And from the blossoming graves come murmured sighs,
"Oh love ye, love ye! for behold Time flies."

My thought knocks at thy heart, a garden rare
With flowers filled: "May I come in?" it says.
"A wayfarer am I oppressed with care,
A weary friend, who for refreshment prays.
    Among these blossoms gay I fain would rest
    To dream of bliss that ne'er shall be possesst.
    I fain would rest in holy joy like this
    To dream of never yet obtainèd bliss."

MARTINMAS IN THE TUSCAN MAREMMA

Gray mists climb the shaggy hills,
Fall in rain upon their crest,
'Neath the wind from the North-West
Bellows and whitens the sea.

But from wine that seethes in vats,
Through the town in ev'ry street
Floating odors pungent sweet
Fill all men's hearts wth glee.

Sputt'ring loud with heat the spit
Turns above the glowing brands;
At his door the huntsman stands
Whistling, watches, o'er the lea,

'Gainst clouds of somber rose relieved,
Flocks of birds dark plumaged stream;
How like exile thoughts that seem
Toward the setting sun to flee.

HELLENIC SPRING

(DORIC)

Know'st thou the island fair upon whose strand
The Ionian sea's last fragrant kisses light?
Calm sea where Galatea dwelleth and
     Acis upon the height?

Pelasgian shades of Eryx high above,
Eternal Aphrodite laughs and reigns,
And all the coasts around thrill with warm love,
     When she to bless them deigns,

With love they thrill, with love, both hill and field,
When she of Enna, from the infernal powers,
Is to her mother's tearful eyes revealed
     Once more mid furrow flowers.

"Love! Love!" the waters whisper as they rise;
To green beds Alpheus Arethusa woos
To swim entwined. Achaean harmonies
     Call the Italian Muse.

Love! Love! the towns from poets take the strain.
Through Doric forums, down the flower-strewn street,
Bacchantes hurry forth, and the refrain
     Upon the lyre repeat.

I ask not for the towers of Syracuse
Or Agrigentum high. Loud swells and falls
The Theban hymn; a hundred palms diffuse
     Their shade o'er regal halls.

Where can be found the solitary vale
The fair Nebrodian mountains crown with pine,

Amid whose fountains Daphnis told his tale
    In poesy divine?

"To hold the land of Pelops I'm not meet,
Nor yet to gather store am I destined
Of golden talents, nor with agile feet
    May I outstrip the wind.

"I'll sing upon the solitary crown
Of this high rock, my arms enfolding thee,
Watching the white lambs from afar go down
    To the Sicilian sea."

The while the happy Dorian boy hath sung,
The nightingales were silent—To that shore,
O Argive soul, a fair veil round thee flung
    That Beatrice wore,

I'll carry thee in verse and when the rest
Of noontide leisure all the land hath stilled,
And with their bright effulgence every breast
    By sea and sky is filled,

For thee upon the sun-lit hills I'll wake
The fair-haired Dryads, light of foot and fleet,
And Homer's ancient gods admirers make
    Of thy pure form so sweet.

The other gods are dying, those of Greece
Know not decline; they, in maternal trees,
In flowers, mountains, rivers, sleep in peace,
    And in the eternal seas.

Before the face of Christ their beauty's flower
Naked and pure in marble rigid grew.
In verse alone, O Lina, breathes their power
    Of youth for ever new;

Or if the face of some enamored fair,
Or heart of poet call them up awhile,
From sacred nature they come everywhere
    Forth-flashing with a smile.

Behold the Dryads come on dancing feet,
And: "In what age," the Oreads ask, "art grown
So fair? And from what land, O sister sweet,
    Dost come, to us unknown?

"But in those stars, thine eyes, sad care is seated,
Perhaps the Cyprian hath wounded thee,
A goddess cruel, who fair forms hath treated
    Oft with malignity.

"Among you mortals Helen only may
Nepenthe mix in cups for heroes dressed,
But we well know what hidden mysteries lay
    Enclosed in Gea's breast.

"For thee we'll gather mystic balsams shed
As tears, when lives in lives transmuted are,
And pearls by Amphitrite ocean-fed
    From cruel men afar.

"For thee we'll cull the living flowers that know
The joys and sorrows of the human lot,
They shall o'ertell thee tales of long-ago,
    Loves ne'er to be forgot.

"For thee the rose's plaint they shall recite,
That with desire faints on thy bosom fair,
And hymns repeat, her haughty sister white
    Chants, nestling in thy hair.

"Then to refulgent caves we'll carry thee
With us where amethyst and crystals shine,

Where elements and forms eternally
    In mazy dance combine.

"We will immerse thee in each shining river,
Where swans and Naiads harmony unite;
Their sides in silver on the waters quiver
    As doth the soft moon's light.

"We'll carry thee to peaks which Zeus benign
As father looks on; they to heaven aspire.
There in the temple's consecrated shrine
    Quivers Apollo's lyre.

"To our most fragrant halls we'll welcome thee,
And give thee for a spouse in beauty matched
Hylas, that fairest Grecian boy whom we
    From Death's dark shadow snatched."

Ah me, from that sunsetting of your day
Descended on earth's cradle sorrow's pall!
Grudge not, O maids of Greece, that this one ray
    Of love on me should fall.

That unknown care which her fair bosom stings
I'd purge with Ascrea's honey pure and rare,
I'd lull her pain to sleep with Theban strings
    If I Alcaeus were.

Her gracious being with the vital power
Of those bright hymns I would irradiate;
And her soft locks with the immortal flower
    Of gods incoronate.

And while on hyacinths my arm doth rest,
My branch of laurel shading us above,
I'd murmur as I lean upon her breast:
    "Lady, 'tis you I love."

AT HIGH MASS

"Da la qual par ch'una stella si mova."
"From whom it seemed as though there rose a star."
Guido Cavalcanti.

It was a day of festival, July
Burnt down through fleecy clouds in sultry heat,
Within the church through the triforium high
Fell yellow light on pulpit, desk and seat;
   While through the door, which pointed Gothic arch
On antique granite lions loved to load,
Came sounds of joyous song and rhythmic march
And lowing herds from market-place and road.

It was High Mass; the organ poured a flood
Of music forth, and called upon the Lord.
Far in the background two young soldiers stood,
Their fixed eyes turned to where the altar soared;
   There they 'mid lighted tapers' festal sheen,
'Mid many-hued brocade and pomp of gold,
Their village church as it so oft had been
With flowers decked for Mary's month behold.

Beneath the brown curve of an arched recess,
Between two slender shafts in crimson dressed,
The lady knelt in all her loveliness,
With her fair hands ungloved together pressed.
   The liquid luster gleamed from her dark eye
Beneath her black-plumed hat's protecting shade,
And in a flash of faith her mystery
This flower of youth to God an offering made.

To me, as once to Guido, it had seemed
A star had issued from those upturned eyes,

And from those lips that scarcely moved I deemed
A wingèd angel mounted to the skies.
    The star all tremulous with holy light
Now smiled and smiled, at what I do not know.
The suppliant angel Godward winged her flight,
"Thanks unto Thee, O Lord," her actions show.

Then, as the priest the "Ite" turned to say,
The strong sun broke through the obscuring cloud,
And on the lovely lady cast a ray
To crown her as she rose, her head still bowed.
    A scarlet flush as though of shame then passed
O'er each Byzantine Saint imaged above,
But the Madonna fixed her eyes down cast
Upon her Son, and softly murmured "Love."

BEFORE SAN GUIDO

The tall straight cypresses in double row
    Troop from San Guido down to Bolgheri;
Like giant striplings at a race they go
    Bounding to meet and gaze once more on me.

Straightway they knew me. "Welcome back again,"
    Bending their heads to me they whispering say,
"Why dost thou not alight? Why not remain?
    The evening's cool, familiar the way.

"Oh, sit thee down beneath our odorous shade,
    Where breathes the North-West wind from off the sea.
We bear no malice for thy cannonade
    Of stones once hurled, they wrought no injury.

"We carry still the nests of nightingales,
  Alas! Wherefore wouldst speed so soon away?
The sparrows round us still when evening pales
  Circle in mazy flight. Ah, prithee, stay!"

"Fair cypresses, sweet cypresses so dear,
  True friends of better times now far from me,
How gladly would I tarry with you here,"
  Gazing I answer: "Ah! how joyfully!

"But oh my cypresses, pray let me go;
  This day is not as those, nor is my age.
Today. . . . However can I make you know?
  I'm a celebrity and quite the rage.

"I can read Latin now and even Greek,
  I write and write as many volumes show,
In other qualities I am not weak;
  No more an urchin, hence no stones I throw,

"Especially at plants." All the long file
  Of tree tops with a doubtful murmur swayed
And the declining sun with gentle smile
  Between green peaks its rosy hues displayed.

Between the sun and cypresses 'twas clear
  A kindly thrill of pity for me ran;
Then 'stead of murmurs, words distinct I hear:
  "We know it well, poor friend, thou art a man.

"We know it well; we from the winds have learned,
  The winds that gather up and waft men's sighs,
How in thy bosom feuds eternal burned
  For which nor wit nor skill a balm supplies.

"To us and to the oaks thou mayest confide
  Thine own heart's grief and all that mortal sadness.

Behold how calm, how blue yon ocean wide,
   As therein sinks the sun with smiling gladness.

"How full the sunset sky of birds in flight,
   And how the swallows twitter in their glee;
The nightingales will sing the livelong night.
   Then prithee stay, those evil phantoms flee.

"Those evil phantoms from some dark recess
   Of your hearts battered by incessant thought
Rise, as in graveyards flitting flames distress
   The passer-by, from foul miasma wrought.

"Ah, prithee stay! Tomorrow at noontide
   When 'neath the spreading oak-trees' ample shade
The horses gather closely side by side
   And all the sultry plain's in silence laid.

"Anthems that ever pass 'twixt heaven and earth
   We cypresses will for thee still recite,
And nymphs who in the hollow elms have birth
   Will come to fan thee with their veils of white;

"And Pan, who on the solitary height
   And o'er the plain at this hour lonely fares,
Shall drown in god-like harmony's delight
   The dissonance, O mortal, of thy cares."

And I reply: "Nay, let me go; since me
   Beyond the Apennines Titti expects;
Much like a sparrow-nestling is Titti,
   But her no feather robe from cold protects.

"She must eat more than cypress berries rough,
   Nor do I reap like the Manzonian strain,
A fourfold payment, for insipid stuff.
   Good-bye, my cypresses, good-bye, sweet plain."

[38]

"Then at the churchyard what wouldst have us say,
    Where in her grave thy grandam sleeping lies?"
They fled, and seemed a train in black array
    That hasting and lamenting onward hies.

Then from the hill-top down the road between
    Those cypresses, that from the churchyard leads,
Methought grandmother Lucy, sad of mien,
    To meet me came, tall in her sable weeds.

Sweet mistress Lucy, from whose lips there fell,
    Beneath her silvery locks, the Tuscan speech,
Not such, as the Romantics fondly tell,
    The *stentorelli* could the learned teach.

Versilia's accents musical and sad,
    That in my heart abide like some old strain
Of Mediaeval song, that in it had
    The strength and sweetness of our joy and pain.

Oh grannie, grannie, those were joyous times,
    When you to me, a child, that old tale told,
Tell me, grown wise, of her who in strange climes
    Her lost love sought 'mid perils manifold.

"Full seven pairs of shoes have I worn out
    Of iron made, to find thee once again;
Full seven staves of iron strong and stout
    Have I ground down in that long journey's pain!

"Full seven vials with tears I made o'erflow
    Through seven long years of bitter, bitter weeping!
Thou sleep'st, my desp'rate cries unheeded go,
    The cock crows loud, but still thou wilt be sleeping."

Ah grandmother, how beautiful, how true
    This tale is still. For many, many a year

Have I sought thus, nor ever found the clue,
 Though toiling morn and eve; perchance 'tis here,

Beneath these cypresses, where I to rest
 No longer hope, to dwell no longer crave,
Haply 'neath those above is hid my quest,
 Beside, dear grandmother, thy lonely grave.

The engine snorting sped upon its way,
 While I thus wept within my heart of hearts.
A group of gamesome colts with joyful neigh,
 Pleased with the din, run as the train departs.

But a gray ass nibbling a purple thistle
 Aloof, maintained his meditative mood,
Nor deigned to glance where shrilled the strident whistle,
 But slow and stolid still he chewed and chewed.

A NIGHT IN MAY

Never the calm of a more tranquil night
Was greeted by the scintillating stars
On brink of running stream's translucent waves,
While dewdrops tremble on the pastures green,
Breaks through the shadow cast by rugged hills
The ancient, wandering, solitary moon.

What vaporous mists, O chaste, austere, pale Moon,
Rise through the warm soft air of the deep night
To thee from woodland glades and pine-clad hills?
'Twould seem as rivals to the virgin stars
The nymphs were waking on the pastures green,
And that a tender whispering thrilled the waves.

Never in such a calm upon the waves
Did lovers sail forgetful 'neath the moon,

As I, no lover, now stretched on the green,
For only on the good shines such a moon.
Meseems that from the tombs and from the stars
Spirit friends I see wandering on the hills.

O ye who sleep in the maternal hills,
Ye who, in lonely tombs, beside the waves,
Behold in heaven the passing of the stars,
Ye who, beneath the fixed rays of the moon,
I saw again peopling the silent night,
Go lightly gliding o'er the yielding green.

Alas! how much did I see of my green
Youth on the tops of those illumined hills,
While at their foot seeks refuge vanquished Night,
When I beheld approach me o'er the waves
Clearly depicted by the fulgent moon,
A shape through whose eyes shone the rays o' the stars.

"Remember"—said it to me—then the stars
Were veiled and shadows spread athwart the green,
Suddenly in the heavens sank the moon,
And shrilly chants re-echoed through the hills,
And left alone beside the heaving wave
I felt as from a tomb grow chill the night.

When heaven at night is thickest set with stars
I joy beside the wave, stretched on the green,
To watch the moon descend behind the hills.

THE FIELD OF MARENGO

(SATURDAY IN HOLY WEEK, 1175)

The moon shines on a darkling wood; the wood's a flying crowd
Of horses, men and halberdiers, that stirs and bellows loud;

'Twixt the Bormida and Tanaro upon Marengo's field,
They fly from Alessandria's walls they could not force to yield.

Fires from Alessandria down slopes of the Apennines
Light up the Caesar's headlong flight, Lord of the Ghibellines,
Watchfires of the League from Tortona make reply,
While through the Holy Night arise the songs of victory.

"Close is the Swabian lion mewed by civic Latin blades;
Tell it, O fires, proclaim it to the hills, the seas, the glades;
Tomorrow Christ arises! Thou shalt see how much new fame,
O Sun, we add tomorrow to the sons of the Roman name."

Listening as he leans his head upon his tall broadsword,
Thinks to himself in scorn the Hohenzollerns' gray-haired lord,
"To die by the hand of traders, who ne'er till yesterday
Had girded their vile fat paunches with steel for knightly fray."

While a hundred Rhenish valleys fill the Bishop's vats in Speier,
And a hundred brawny Canons are seated in his choir,
"Ah," groans he sadly, "Who for you, my fair Cathedral towers,
"On Christmas night will sing the Mass, or keep the holy hours!"

Thinks Ditpold, County Palatine, whose flowing flaxen hair
Waves round his neck so supple, like rose and privet fair:
"The Elfin songs rise from the Rhine, borne on the stilly night,
Where Thekla wanders, dreaming dreams, beneath the wan moonlight."

Says the Bishop Prince of Mainz: "I carry here beside
My crozier with its iron top the unction sanctified.
There's plenty for us all—I would, with their Italian load
Of silver, my poor mules were safe across the Alpine road."

Says the Count of Highland Tyrol: "Tomorrow's sun shall greet
But thee, my son, upon the Alps, but thee my dog shall meet;
Henceforth they both are thine, while I, a hart trapped by villeins,
Shall fall before their cut-throat knives, on these gray Lombard plains."

In the middle of the camp stood the Emperor alone
Near his charger, and looked upward to the sky; one by one
O'er his gray head still the stars were passing on, while behind
The black Imperial banner was disputing with the wind.

Kings of Poland and Bohemia arrayed on either hand
Bearing the sword and the scepter of the Holy Empire stand;
Then when the stars grow weary, and the red dawn in the skies
Flushes the Alpine peaks with rose: "Forwards," the Caesar cries,

"To horse, my faithful lieges! Thou, Wittelsbach, display
Before the Leagues of Lombardy the sacred sign today.
Proclaim it, herald, thou, 'The Roman Emperor goes by,
Heir of Julius the Divine and of Trajan's Majesty.' "

Alas! between the rivers, the Tanaro and the Pò,
Spread the blasts of Teuton trumpets how joyously, how fast!
When the stubborn souls and standards of Italia louted low
At the aspect of the Eagle, and Imperial Caesar passed.

ÇA IRA

I

The gay sun shines on the Burgundian hills,
And in the vintage of Marne's vale delights,
And Picardy awaits the plough that tills
Her fallow soil, and harvest new invites.

But like an ax the wrathful sickle smites
Upon the vines, like blood their red juice spills.
The ploughman's eye strains through the eve's red lights,
Across waste lonely lands which autumn chills;

The goad is brandished as it were a lance
Above the team, the driver holding taut
The guiding gear, shouts: "Forward, forward France!"

The ploughshare in the furrow shrieks, fresh wrought
The moist earth reeks, from the dim mists advance
Phantasmal shapes as tho' they battle sought.

II

They are the sons of the toil-compelling earth
Who rise full-armed to reach the ideal height,
To whom for Fatherland the soil gave birth,
Plebeian horsemen blue and red and white.

Thou, Kleber, dark of brow, for home and hearth
A roaring lion foremost in the fight:
And thou, ablaze through perils in thy path,
Hoche the sublime, thou flash of youth and light.

Desaix, who duty chose and left renown
To others; and Murat, tempestuous wave,
Who stooped so low as to accept a crown,

And Marceau, who in radiant death his pride
Of youth and his pure soul to silence gave,
Like one who hastens to embrace his bride.

III

In Cath'rine's guilty Tuileries, where late
The pious Louis to his priests would kneel,
Where Breton knights thrilled to the Queen's appeal,
Her smiles, her tears, secrets revealed of State.

When falls the sultry gloaming, fraught with fate
A shape is seen: nor joy her acts reveal,
Nor grief; she twists her spindle, twirls her wheel,
The stars she reaches with her distaff great.

The crone spins through each night by moonlight wan,
She spins by light of stars, she spins, she spins.
Never she wearies, never taketh rest.

Brunswick draws nigh, a gallows in his van.
Much rope he needeth to chastise the sins
Of France, by rebel spirit strong possesst.

IV

The bearers of ill tidings, post on post,
Came thick as hail: "Longwy has fallen!" cry
From their surrender vile the flying host
Who, dusty, crowding to the Assembly hie.

"We manned the walls, but we were at the most
But one man to two guns; 'twas vain to try
To hold the town, arms failed us, we were lost.
What could we do?" As one voice rose reply:

"Have died!"—Down sunburnt cheeks unwonted tears
Fell drop by drop; then with their heads low bowed
They turned and went, nor cast one upward glance.

The hour of peril passes, the sky clears,
Its wing vibrates upon the tocsin loud:
"Up, people, up! Help, help, O Sons of France!"

V

Hear, hear, ye citizens, Verdun her gates
Has opened to the foe, her daughters base
Receive the foreign kings with flowery fêtes,
And bow before Artois in courtly grace!

They quaff white wine whose sparkling draught elates,
With Uhlan escort mazy dances pace.
Verdun, vile town, confectioners of cates!
Death follow shame! Death only can efface.

But Beaurepaire dishonorable mischance
Refuses to survive: his soul a last
Gaze hurls at us, the future and at fate.

In heaven to take it antique heroes wait.
To children yet unborn the cry has pass'd
"Up, people, up! Help, help, O Sons of France!"

VI

See o'er the Hôtel de Ville the black flag fly,
Avaunt! It cries to love and to the sun.
On the dread silence breaks the minute gun,
With warning roar hear minute guns reply.

With groups severe of antique sculpture vie
The people, whom each hour fresh tidings stun,
And brand men's hearts till all their thoughts are one:
"That Fatherland may live, today men die."

Before the face of Danton, monstrous, wan,
Long files of women furies pass, urge on
Their shoeless sons before them armed with wrath,

And Marat sees in air grim groups come forth
Of men with pikes who pass across the place,
And where they pass, behold! a bloody trace.

VII

A vision white, a sacrificial train
Of Druids, falling on men's souls torments
Them: while Avignon's Papal towers unchain
A whirlwind, which its turgid fury vents.

O suffering Albigenses, your laments,
And Huguenots, your slow protracted pain,
Now boils your martyr blood, boils and ferments,
Making men's hearts intoxicate with bane.

This the tribunal, this the penal fire
The new age borrows from the horrific shade!
O art thou France, who o'er thy trembling sire

Risest to take with ready hand and brave
The cup filled with thy kindred's blood, fair maid,
Then drainst the draught to expiate and save?

VIII

The Alpine winds are mourning; on the shore
The waves bemoan Savoy's ill-fated child.
Here clash of steel and shouts of fury wild.
"Lady of Lamballe, the Abbaye—by yon door!"

Naked she lies, her golden hair defiled
With soil, in the mid street; one outrage more;
A barber in the crowd, hands stained with gore,
Stretched out the tender limbs, and looking smiled:

"A lily is her neck, like pearls between
Carnations red her lips and teeth appear.
How fine her skin, how white, how smooth, how soft!

"Up, eyes the color of the sea, aloft!
Up, curl-crowned head! We'll towards the Temple bear,
And Death shall bid good morrow to the Queen."

IX

Oh ne'er to King of France at his levée
Did such a crowd their salutation bring;
The tower dark appears night-bird of prey,
Who in the noon-tide spreads ill-omened wing.

Philip the Fair, that Mediaeval King,
Extended here the secular arm to slay;
And here the last Knight Templar's voice doth ring
In summons to the last Capet today.

[47]

Now hear the howling of the horrid crew,
Upon the lofty pike the proud head sways,
Knocks at the window. And the King prostrate

Looks down from that sad house of Royal state
Upon the people: to God for pardon prays
For the dread night of St. Bartholomew.

X

Beneath the trampling of barbarian horse
Awakes within his grave again Bayard?
In Orleans' smiling vale, as last resource
Erects the Maid once more her pure standard?

Who comes from Haute Saône, from wind-swept Garde
To where the felled trees bar their singing course
Repairing faulty ramparts? Is it the galliard
Vercingetorix' red-haired Gallic force?

No, 'tis the spy Dumouriez; in his heart
There beats the genius of Condé; he throws
Upon the outspread map one burning glance:

"Those unknown hills which stretch athwart the chart
Shall be new Sparta's bulwark 'gainst her foes—
These hills are the Thermopylae of France!"

XI

In the Argonne, over the eastern hill
The slow dawn breaks with heavy mist and rain;
The tricolor flaps wet above the mill
Of Valmy, craving sun and wind in vain.

Stay, stay, white miller. Destiny doth fill
Thy place today; the future is the grain.
Today the shoeless civic army will
With red blood set the moving wheels in train.

[48]

His sword upraised: "For Fatherland, on, on!"
The epic columns of Sans-culottes close.
The marseillaise, 'mid cannonade of foes,

Above the forests deep of the Argonne,
Archangel of the new-born era soars—
Then Kellerman 'mid noise of cannon roars.

XII

March, famous children of the Fatherland,
To songs', and cannon's harmony advance!
This day of glory did today expand
Vermilion pinions in the valorous dance.

Confusion dire which panic fears enchance
Encumbers Prussia's road with troops unmanned;
Hunger and cold, diseases and mischance,
Back to their refuge chase the exile band.

The pallid sunset flickers o'er the vast
Expanse of mire, the neighboring hills secure
From the sun sinking one faint smile of glory.

Wolfgang von Goethe on the turmoil cast
His eye, said, issuing from a group obscure,
"Today from this place starts the world's new story."

THE IDEAL

When with the step of a goddess, O Hebe,
Thou reachest me smiling my cup of ambrosia,
And from it arising bright vapors
Float round me as onward thou passest.

[49]

Then of time I feel the shadow no longer
On my head, nor of chill care the oppression,
But in my veins floweth serenely
The Hellenic life untroubled, O Hebe.

And the ruined days have arisen, O Hebe,
From the gloom of age below the declivity,
In the sweet light which thou diffusest
For renewal of life are they yearning.

And the new years from the darkness emerging
Turn their ardent brows to thy light, O Hebe,
Which rises in tremulous radiance,
And salutes them all rosily glowing.

Down on these and on those, bright star, thou shinest
From above, thus amid slender aspiring
Shafts in files of black and white marble
Boldly springing in Gothic Cathedrals.

Heavenward rising there on the topmost
Pinnacle poised calmly stands the sweet daughter
Of Jesse, all in a shimmering
Brightness of golden sparkles enveloped.

Thus from her aerial vantage she gazes
On the homesteads, the green plain by silvery rivers
Watered, on fields where waved the ripening
Harvest, and toward the snow-clad Alpine summits.

Around her gathering clouds are floating;
From amid those clouds smiles the radiant maiden
On the blossoming dawns of May days,
And on the sad sunsets of November.

ROME

ODE FOR THE 2630TH ANNIVERSARY OF THE FOUNDATION OF ROME

April with purple flowers crowned beheld thee
Rise up stern from the furrow of Romulus,
On the hill beheld thee, thy gaze turned
Towards the plain that as yet knew no tillage.

After such long succession of centuries,
April still irradiates thee, thou greatest,
Most sublime, the sun and Italy
Salute thee, Flora of our race, O Rome!

If behind the priest the Vestal in silence
Mounts the Capitol no longer, no longer
On the Sacred Way the procession,
Four white horses a-breast, winds triumphal,

Yet this deep solitude here of thy Forum
Surpasses the shout, surpasses the glory,
For all that in the world is civic,
Great, august, that still today is Roman.

Rome divine, all hail! Whoso misconceives thee,
His sense and mind are wrapt in cold and darkness;
In his heart perverse there germinates
Naught but the torpid wood of barbarism.

Rome divine, all hail! With head bowed low before
Thy Forum's ruins, I follow thy footsteps
Sparse, with tender tears I worship thee,
Thou home-land goddess, holy genitrix!

For thee am I an Italian citizen,
For thee am I a poet, Mother of Nations,
Who on the world bestowedst thy spirit
And on Italia didst imprint thy glory.

Behold this country once out of free peoples
Under one single name, by thee united,
Italia, to thee returns, gazes
On thine eagle eyes, to thy breast clinging.

Whilst athwart thy silent Forum thou stretchedst
Thy marble arms to her, and from the fateful
Hill didst point thy columns, thy arches,
Out to her thy daughter bringing thee freedom.

Arches that now new triumphs are waiting,
Now no longer of Kings, of Caesars no longer,
Nor human arms with chains distorted
Bound to the ivory cars of conquerors.

But for thy triumph, people of Italy,
Over dark ages, the ages barbaric,
Monster bearing, wait that from such thou
Wilt with calm justice enfranchise all kindreds.

O Italia, O Rome! That day shall thunder
From a cloudless sky be heard o'er the Forum:
Shouts of glory, of glory, of glory
Shall ascend the blue depths of the heavens.

TO THE STATUE OF VICTORY AT BRESCIA

Virgin divine, didst thou spread thy propitious
Wing over the bowed helmets of the shield-bearers,
Who, with knee pressed against the bucklers,
Await with couched spears the hostile onslaught?

Or didst thou wing thy way before the eagles,
Before the headlong flood of Marsian warriors,
Or repulse with thy shining splendor
The neighing horses of the hordes of the Parthians?

Or with arms folded and foot firmly planted
On the casque of the vanquished, O fierce goddess,
Dost thou inscribe some victorious
Name of the captain on the clipeum?

Is it the name of some archon who glorified
Over despots the holy laws of free men,
Or of a consul, who for boundary,
Name and terror of the Empire contended?

I would see thee upon the Alps resplendent
Amid tempests proclaim to the centuries:
"Oh nations, thus far has Italia
Come, her name and her rights vindicating."

But meanwhile Lydia from the sober blossoms
Brought forth by October 'mid Roman ruins
Chooses some to weave thee a garland;
She then at thy feet laying them gently

Says: "On what things, O sweet maid, didst thou ponder
Beneath the moist earth for these many ages?
Didst thou hear the hoofs of the horses
Of Germans, o'er thy Grecian head trampling?"

Said the goddess: "I did hear," her eyes flashing,
"For not only am I the glory of Hellas,
But am too the strength of Latium,
Throbbing still in the bronze through the ages.

"Times came and went like the fateful gyrations,
Flights of twelve vultures beheld by Romulus:

Then I rose crying: 'O Italia!
With thee are thy gods, with thee are thy dead sons!'

"Rejoicing in the event Brescia received me,
Brescia the strong, Brescia the iron-handed,
Drenched in the blood of her enemies,
Brescia the lioness of Italy."

ODE TO THE FOUNTAIN OF CLITUMNUS

Still from the mountain which undulates with the dim
Groves of darksome ash-trees murmuring with the wind,
And to the distant breezes wafts its odors fresh
    Of wild thyme, and salvias,

Descend at dewy eve to thee, O Clitumnus,
The flocks from the pastures, and to thee the Umbrian
Shepherd boy drives the recalcitrant ewe to plunge
    In thy waters. Meanwhile

From the breast of the sun-embrowned mother who sits
At her cottage door, barefoot, and sings, towards him
The suckling infant turns, and all her chubby face
    In a smile expandeth;

Full of thought, the father, his nether-limbs encased
Like those of antique fauns in hairy goat-skin garb,
The painted wagon drives and tests the growing strength
    Of the fair young oxen.

Of the fair young oxen square-chested, broad and deep,
Their crescent horns erect above their heads expand,
Their dark eyes full and soft, their hide snow-white such as
    Loved the gentle Virgil.

Meanwhile the darkening clouds o'er the Apennine range
Gather like wreathing smoke; grand and austere and green,
From th' encircling hills in graded tiers descending,
    Umbria watches.

Green Umbria, all hail! And thou, Clitumnus, hail
Presiding god! My ancient country stirs my heart,
And on my burning brow, of old Italic gods
    I feel wings brushing.

Who did the shade of weeping willow first induct
To banks of sacred streams? Let winds from Apennines
Despoil thee here, enervate plant, thou well beloved
    Of lowly ages!

Let here to blasts of winter, to strange mystic tales,
And to May's quick'ning pulse the somber ilex thrill
Around whose hoary trunk the clinging ivy twines,
    Youth's blithesome vesture;

Here round the emerging god in closely serried rank
Let giant cypresses, keeping their vigil, stand;
Whilst thou, from 'mid their shade, thine ever fateful song
    Shalt sing, O Clitumnus!

O thou who hast beheld three empires, tell me how
The lusty Umbrian blood-stained in that long strife
Did to the spear-armed velite yield, and how
    Grew strong Etruria;

Tell how in after years from the subdued Cimino
Gradivus by forced marches did descend upon
The leagued Cities, planting on each hill-built fort
    Proud Roman standards.

But thou, Italic deity, did'st bring to peace
Victor with vanquished, the kindred native folk,

That when the Punic fury thundered on the shore
    Of lake Thrasymene,

The cry rose up from all thy caves re-echoing,
From many a winding horn through thy reverberate hills:
"O thou who dost thy snow-white oxen lead to graze
    Near misty Mevania,

"Thou, who the glebe dost plough along the terraced hills
To the left bank of Nar; thou who dost fell the green
Woods above Spoleto, and thou who dost a bride
    Wed in martial Todi;

"Leave thou thine oxen fat amid the reeds, and thou
The ploughshare in the half-drawn furrow leave, leave thou
The ax fixed in the tott'ring oak, and thou the bride
    Leave at the altar.

"And hie thee, hie thee, hie thee! armed with club and spear
With javelin and ax and dart, for Hannibal—
Fierce Hannibal—dire foe, thy household gods insults,
    Threats thy Penates."

Behold how smiled the sun with life-inspiring ray
Through all this valley broad by beauteous mountains closed,
Whence high Spoleto sees hurled back in headlong flight
    To certain ruin

The cruel, huge-limbed Moors and fierce Numidian horse
Mingled in frantic fray, while on them from above
Rain showers of iron darts and floods of burning oil,
    And songs of victory!

Now silence reigns o'er all. I in the lucid pool
Behold the slender spring of water rising clear;
It quivers, and into rippling wavelets ruffles
    The watery mirror.

Sepulchered in the depths a tiny forest laughs,
With outspread moveless branches; then 'twould seem as though
Amethyst with jasper did in sinuous lines
    Mingle their limpid loves:

While flowers like the sapphire sparkle and assume
The cold reflections of the hardest adamant
And splendorously shine, luring us to the depths
    Of the green silences.

At the foot of thy hills, 'neath the shade of thy oaks,
There with the rivers—there is the fount of thy song,
O Italia! There lived the nymphs—lived—and there
    This marriage-bed divine.

The azure naiads rising, tall, wave arms aloft
Fluttering their flowing veils, as loudly they invite
Through the still evening air from all the mountains round
    Their brown nymph sisters;

Beneath the pendant moon the mazy dance they lead,
And as they circle round they chant in merry choir
Of immortal Janus, and how love him subdued
    For fair Camesena.

Of heavenly lineage he, child of the soil a stalwart
Maiden she; their marriage-bed the cloud-capped Apennine;
Their close embrace whence the Italic race was born
    Was veiled in showers.

Now all is silent, oh widowed Clitumnus, all;
And of thy fair temples one sole outpost stands
Yet in thy name, e'en here no longer thou dost dwell
    A white-robed deity.

No more do the strong bulls, proud victims, sprinkled
With waters of thy sacred streams, the trophies bear

Of haughty Rome to altars of ancestral fanes:
    No more Rome triumphs,

Triumphs no more, since when a Galilean came
Auburn-haired. He ascending to the Capitol
Cast down into her arms the cross He held: "Bear this
    And serve!" said He.

Then fled the nymphs to weep in the rivers concealed,
Or closed within the bark of the maternal tree,
Or moaning melted into air as vaporous clouds
    Above the mountains.

When a strange company, in long black habit clad,
With solemn step and slow, through temples white, despoiled,
And broken colonnades, wended their weary way
    Chanting their litanies;

And over fields resounding with noise of human toil,
And over hills remindful of imperial sway,
They passed, a desert made, and then that dreary waste
    They called God's Kingdom.

Where'er the sun-god blessed they have driven away
The crowd of toilers from the holy ploughs, the sons
From expectant fathers and from their blooming brides,
    Hurling their curses.

They maledictions hurled against the wholesome works
Of life, of love, and in delirious madness raved
Conjunctions horrible, connecting pain with God,
    On rocks, in caverns;

Intoxicated then with tortures of the flesh
Into the cities came, whirling in frenzied dance,
Before the crucifix they supplicating fell,
    Impious in abjection.

Hail, spirit of humanity! Whether serene
Beside Ilissus' banks or strong and true
By Tiber's soul-inspiring shores, arise and reign,
    The dark days are passed.

Thou fecund mother of the oxen young, unwearied
To break the glebe and to replant the fallow fields,
And of the wild young colts neighing in lust of war,
    Thou mother Italy,

Mother of corn, of vines, of the eternal laws,
And of the glorious arts that make life sweet to man,
All hail! I sing anew to thee hymns to celebrate
    Thine ancient praises.

Green Umbria's lofty hills, her woods, her waters ring
With plaudits to the song. Before us belching forth
Its smoke in widening rings, the engine's whistling course
    Pants for new industries.

IN THE PIAZZA OF S. PETRONIUS

In the air of winter clear dark-turreted Bologna rises,
White above her the snow-clad hill is smiling.

'Tis the calm sweet hour when the fast-dying sun greets the high towers,
And thy sacred fane, holy Petronius.

The towers whose battlements the wing of time so often brushes,
And the stately temple's lonely pinnacle.

With the icy splendor of adamant the heavens are shining,
And a veil as of silvery gauze is resting

On the Forum, softly rounding off the contours of the dark piles
The bucklered arms of our fathers erected.

Upon the copings of those lofty roofs the sun still lingeringly
Smiles with the paly gold of the wallflower.

And in thy gray stone and in thy bricks of dusky vermilion
Seems to rewaken the soul of the ages.

And in the frozen air a melancholy desire awakes
For ruddy Mays and evenings warm and odorous,

When the women fair and gay were wont to dance in the Piazza,
And consuls came with vanquished kings returning.

Thus the Muse as she departs smiles on the verse in which there trembles
For the beauty gone by a vain yearning.

THE TWO TOWERS

ASINELLA

I sprang from the heart of Italy, 'mid the pealing of anthems,
What time the Alps were cleared of hordes barbarian,
And from the poplar-fringed Pò, through the green country,
The war-chariots returned to the sounding of trumpets.

GARISENDA

I, remembering as I rose, I bowed my head over the ruins
And the tombs, while Irnerio sat bending
Over the huge volumes, and spake with slow accents to the people,
The shield-bearers, of Rome the greatness telling.

ASINELLA

Fair was the day in May when I beheld in glorious freedom
The people o'er the bridge of Reno passing,
And saw thee, O Scion of the Swabian house, thy fair head bending
To the fluttering red cross of Italy.

GARISENDA

O sad month of May, when round the lovely body of Imelda
Clashed the swords of her brothers, and for forty
Long days civil fury ran roit 'mid bloodshed and slaughter,
The towers strong-built were crumbled to powder.

ASINELLA

Dante have I seen raise his young head to gaze on us in passing,
And like the light clouds that over us are floating
Have I seen phantom upon phantom pass over him and pressing
Round him all the centuries of Italy.

GARISENDA

I have seen beneath my shadow the Pope and the Emperor
Come by, the hand of each clasping the other.
Ah, wretched me! God's judgment did not will that I should fall, crushing
Both the fifth Charles and Clement 'neath my ruins.

SIRMIO

Here behold the verdant Sirmio smiles upon the lake's calm waters,
        Fair flower of the peninsula.

The sun looks on her and caresses, Benacus round her closes
        Like a goblet huge of silver,

Along whose shining marge the peaceful olive, broad branches spreading,
        Mingles with the eternal laurel.

This glistening goblet Mother Italy, with arms outstretched upholding
        To the gods supreme presenteth,

And the high gods therein let fall from the heavens above, Sirmio,
        The gem of the peninsula.

Baldo, rugged mountain sire, from the height the fair protecting,
  Watches 'neath his eyebrows shaggy.

The Gu resembles some Titan fallen for her sake in battle,
  Stretched supine yet still threatening.

But towards her on the left from the bay like the crescent moon curving
  Salò her white arms extendeth.

Joyous as a maiden who joining in the dance lets her tresses
  And veil float loose on the breezes;

And she laughs and she scatters flowers with prófuse hand, and proudly
  With flowers her young brow encircles.

And in the distant background Garda raises her dark citadel
  High above the watery mirror,

Singing an ancient saga of buried cities long forgotten,
  And of Queens barbaric telling.

But here, whence thou in simple joyance of the blue, O Lalage,
  Dost send thy soul and thy glances,

Here long ago Flavius Catullus his Bithynian bark moored fast
  To the stones in the sunshine gleaming,

Sat through long days, and in the shifting phosphorescence of the waves
  Saw his Lesbia's bright eyes sparkle,

Saw the faithless smile, the multitudinous passions of Lesbia
  In the glassy wavelets mirrored,

While she in dark suburban alleys wore out the puny weaklings,
  Descendants of Romulus!

While to him from the watery depth the Nymph of the lake was singing:
  "Come, O Quintus Valerius!

"Come! Behold even here to our grottos the sun too descendeth,
      But white and peaceful as Cynthia.

"Here the never ceasing tumult of your busy life appeareth
      But of bees the distant humming,

"And the anxious madding care and the timorous fears in this cold silence
      Fade away in slow oblivion.

"Here the fresh coolness, here gentle sleep, here soft music and the choirs
      Of cerulean water maidens,

"While Hesperus widens the rosy glow of evening upon the waters,
      And the waves on the shore are moaning."

Ah, cruel Love! He the Muses hates; lascivious subdues, tragic
      The poet's fire extinguishes.

But who from thine eyes that prolonged wars are waging, who can from them
      Secure himself, O Lalage?

Cull for the Muses pure three branches of myrtle and of laurel
      And to the eternal Sun wave them.

Dost thou not see from Peschiera flocks of swans already
      Down the silvery Mincio sailing?

Dost thou not hear from those verdant pastures where sleeps Bianore
      The breezes waft the voice of Virgil?

Turn and adore, where a poet great, severe, looks forth, O Lalage,
      From the towers of the Scaligers.

"Up, up, in beautiful Italy," he murmurs and looks smiling
      On the land, the sky and the water.

[63]

ON THE DEATH OF EUGÈNE NAPOLEON

A barbarian assegai one laid low
All unconscious what it did, the life quenching,
Light of eyes on whom floating phantoms
Smiled down from the immeasurable blue;

Lulled on Austrian pillows the other, with kisses
Satiated, in chilly dawns dreaming reveillées
And battle rolls, then drooped he as on
Fragile stem the wan hyacinth droopeth.

Far from their mothers both: the bright abundance
Of their fair young locks the touch seemed awaiting
Of maternal hand, lightly ruffling
With its fond caress; but ah! instead

Into the darkness leaped those young souls,
No sound of their mother-tongue could follow them,
Step by step telling of love and of glory;
Comfortless, lonely, they passed into silence.

Not this, O somber son of Hortensia,
Didst thou promise to thy child before Paris;
But didst pray: May that fate which o'erwhelmed
The King of Rome, be from thee averted:

Peace and Victory came from Sebastopol,
Lulling the young child with their white wings whirring,
And while Europe looked on in wonder,
Like beacon shone the column of Vendôme.

But blood-stained is the mire of December;
But the fog of Brumaire is perfidious;

In that air trees grow not, are barren,
Or bear fruits filled with poison and ashes.

O solitary house of Ajaccio,
Which green branches of tall oaks overshadow,
Above the serene hills still crown it,
And before it the sea ever soundeth.

Here Laetitia—ah, sweet name Italian,
Changed from henceforth into one of ill-omen—
Here was wife, here once happy mother,
Short was the season, alas! and hither

Thou, having hurled against thrones the last thunder,
Thou to the peoples just laws having given,
Thou should'st have withdrawn thee, O Consul,
'Twixt the sea and the God thou believed'st in.

The home-loving shade of Laetitia dwelleth
In the vacant house; by no ray encircled
From Caesar, this Corsican mother
Lived on 'twixt her tombs and her altars.

Her eagle-eyed son, Man of Destiny,
Her daughters bright in beauty as Aurora,
Thrilling with hope her children's children,
Lie all in far-off graves away from her.

See standing here the Corsican Niobe,
In the night, in the porch whence her children
Went forth to their christening, proud standing,
Towards the wild sea her arms she outstretches,

She calls, she calls, if from burning Africa,
If from Britain's shores, if from America,
Any of her tragic brood thrust out
By Death, might in her bosom find haven.

THE ROCK OF QUARTO

Into the calm waves stretches the low reef of
Rocks, while behind them the laurel groves spreading
Broad foliage, breathe out their sweet odors
With rustling murmurs into the evening.

Pure in her silvery splendor the full moon
Is shining in front of them, while beside her
The star of Venus smiling, tinges
All the sky with her shimmering brightness.

Forth from this peaceful nest 'twould seem some lover
Might in his little boat be outward sailing,
Wafted by gentle zephyrs, to the
Sweet discourse of secret love. His lady

Fixedly gazing on the star of Venus.
Italy, Italy, lady of ages,
Lady of poets, lady of martyrs,
Glorious widow, of infinite sorrows.

Sailing from thence thy faithful lover sought thee
Over the sea; round him draping his ample
Poncho's folds from his leonine neck,
The sword of Rome high poised on his shoulder

There Garibaldi stood. They came noiselessly,
By fives, by tens, melted into the shadow
Dark companies, these the avengers,
The thousand avengers of destiny.

As when pirates seeking rich booty steal forth,
So these wander concealed from thee, Italia!
Down thy coasts, for thee death entreating
Of the ocean, of heaven, of their brethren.

From the marble bow of her terraced palaces
Genoa, the Superb, glowed with her bright lights,
While her songs in the moonlight evening
Died away o'er the sea in the distance.

O house where that prophetic genius stirred up
Pisacane to attempt the fatal voyage!
O dwelling where Childe Harold thirsted
For the heroic strife of Missolonghi!

A crown of Olmpian light encircled
The white roofs of thy lofty palaces,
That evening of the fifth of May, when
Sacrifice was victory, O poesy!

And star of Venus, star of Italia,
Star of Caesar, then thou didst smile, and never
With thy radiance didst thou illumine
For Italian souls a spring more sacred.

Since the time when the silent prow of Aeneas
Big with fateful future, Tiber's stream breasted,
And the steep rocks where Pallantium
Had fallen, saw great Rome proudly rising.

SALUTO ITALICO

INSPIRED BY CARDUCCI'S VISIT TO TRIESTE IN 1878

The critic sneers at my verses, of ancient fashion Italic,
Which I with care beat out on my fingers, recalling your numbers

Dispersed, like bees at the strident noise of brazen discs clashing,
They gather together again with multitudinous buzzing.

But ye, O my verses, take your flight from my heart like young eaglets
From their nests on Alpine summits at the first zephyr of morning;

Take your flight and as ye pass with anxious care question the murmur
That the winds down the Julian, through the Rhaetian Alpine passes,

From the green abysses, along by the rivers, send heavily
Laden with epic defiance, with songs of doings heroic.

Like a sigh o'er the silvery waters of Garda it passes,
'Tis a lament from Aquileia o'er the solitudes wafted.

They hear it, those dead of Bezzecca, and wait in expectancy.
"When?" cries Bronzetti, erect 'mid the clouds, a shadow phantasmal.

"When?" gray veterans one to another are sadly repeating,
Who, when their locks were dark, O Trent, one day had bidden thee farewell.

"When?" impatiently chafing, ask the young men who but yesterday
From the towers of St. Just beheld blue gleaming the waters of Adria,

Fly with the new year, O verses of ancient fashion Italic,
To the beautiful Gulf of Trieste, to the hills, to the spirits;

With the rays of the sun that empurple the church of Petronius,
From the towers of St. Just, where the Roman ruins lie scattered;

Bear greeting o'er the gulf to Giustinopoli,
Gem of Istria, to the green port, to the lion of Muggia,

Bear greeting to the god-like laughter of Adria,
Far as where Pola displays her temples to Rome and to Caesar.

Then beside the urn where rest the ashes of Winckelmann, herald
Of the arts and of glory, bewixt two peoples still watching

In the face of the stranger in arms on our soil encamping
Sing, O my verses, Italia, Italia, Italia!

MIRAMAR

O Miramar, over thy white towers
Vexed by skies with rain heavily laden,
Dark with the flight of birds of ill omen,
    Clouds are gathering.

O Miramar, 'gainst thy rocks of granite
From the grim ocean frowningly rising,
Like souls tormented hurtling in battle,
    Gray waves are beating.

Under the shadow of clouds gloomily
Stand those gems of the sea, the turreted
Cities, Pirano, Egida, Paranzo,
    Muggia, watching;

And the sea flings to that rock-built bastion
Up in foam all those bellowing furies,
Whence to both the Adrian shores thou lookest,
    Castle of Hapsburg;

And the heavens over Nabresina
Thunder along the iron-charged coast, while
Trieste below, lightning-crowned, from amid
    Clouds her head raises.

Alas! how on that sweet April morning
All nature smiled, when came the Emperor
Forth, the fair-haired, to set sail, his lovely
    Lady leading.

He upon whose manly form is printed
Command, with calm face, she his fair lady,
With proud eyes blue as the summer sky out
    Towards the sea gazing.

Farewell, O castle, in vain erected
A nest of love for days of happiness;
Other breezes the wedded pair hurry
    O'er the lone ocean.

Kindled with hope they leave the storied hall,
The inscriptions wise, the pictured triumphs.
Dante and Goethe to the Emperor
    In vain are speaking

From animated busts. With enigmatic
Face a Sphinx allures them o'er the waters:
He yields, the volume of the romancer
    Leaving half opened.

But not of love tells nor of adventure
Song or sound of lute that bid him welcome
To the Spain of the Aztecs. What chant comes
    Borne on the breezes,

Through the hoarse lamenting of the surges
From Salvore's melancholy headland?
Do the dead of Venice sing? or ancient
    Fays of Istria?

Alas! on our seas, O son of Hapsburg
Novara's fatal deck ill-omened mountedst,
Mounteth with thee a dark Erinnys
    Thy sails unfurling.

Thou beholdest the Sphinx transform her seeming,
She recedes, perfidiously alluring,
It is the pale face of mad Joanna
    On thy wife gazing.

It is the skull of Marie Antoinette
Ghastly grinning; cavernous eyes glaring

At thee from the yellow face contorted
    Of Montezuma.

In the midst of the close aloe-thicket,
Never stirred by the fresh breath of breezes
Within the dusk temple pyramidal
    Livid flames belching.

Through the dense tropical darkness scenting
Thy blood, the god Huitzilopotli
Howls to thee: "Come!," his glance the broad ocean
    Swiftly o'erpassing.

"Long have I been waiting; the white fierceness
Ruined my kingdom, profaned my temples.
Come, from the fifth Charles thou the descendant,
    Predestined victim.

"No offering with ancestral strain tainted,
Or royal madness would e'er content me;
Thee I waited, flower of the Hapsburgs,
    Thee will I gather.

"To the great soul of Guatimozino
Who reigns beneath the sun's bright pavilion,
Victim I send thee, pure, strong, beautiful,
    O Maximilian!"

ODE TO THE QUEEN OF ITALY

Whence didst thou come, what centuries transmitted
Thee to us so gentle and so beautiful?
Down through the songs of sacred poets
There where I, O Queen, one day beheld thee?

[71]

Was it then, in those steep rock-built fortresses,
Hot Latin suns embrowned tawny Germania
The blue-eyed, and in new minstrelsy
The clash of arms mingled with love's lightnings?

Fair-haired virgins with changing color followed
The sorrowful lay's monotonous cadence;
Lifting humid dark eyes to heaven
They besought for the strong ones God's mercy.

Or was it in that short day when Italy
Was all one blithesome May, and all the people
Were cavaliers, when Love in triumph
Wound 'mid the battlemented houses,

Into the Piazzas, gay with white marble
Statues, with sunshine, with bright colored flowers
And "O cloud," as sang Alighieri,
"Dost in Love's shadow smiling fade away."

As the white star of Venus in young April
Above the highest Alpine summits rises,
And on the snows still golden glowing
In her calm and tranquil radiance breaking

Laughs on the lowly solitary cottage,
Laughs on the fertile valley's lush luxuriance,
And in the shadow of the poplars
Wakens the nightingale and talk of lovers,

So dost thou with the circlet of diamond
Light crowning thy fair hair pass on resplendent,
And proud of thee the crowd rejoices,
As when a daughter goes to the altar.

With a smile mingled with tears of emotion
The young maiden looks on thee, and timidly

Stretching her arms as to an elder
Sister, she calls to thee: "Margherita!"

And around thee flies the Alcaic strophe
Free-born 'mid the fierce tumults for liberty.
Three times it encircles thy tresses,
Brushing them with wings that know of tempests.

Singing it says: "Hail, O illustrious lady,
For whom a crown was by the Graces woven,
From whom the tones of tender pity
Speak in each accent of her voice so gentle.

"Hail, thou kindly Queen! As long as the visions
Of Raphael shall flit through the pure Italian
Light of the evenings, and the lyrics
Of Petrarch shall sigh 'mid the laurels."

RUIT HORA

O longed-for solitude of greenery,
Far from noisy hum of cities,
Two friends divine with us will come thither,
Love and wine, O Lydia!

Behold now in the crystal-clear goblet
Laughs Lyaeus, youth eternal!
While love within thine eyes, O bright Lydia,
Triumphs, and doffs his bandage.

The low sun floods with level beams the bower
Breaking them in rosy brightness
Within my glass. In thy locks his gold shimmers
Tremulous, O Lydia.

In thy tresses dark, O white Lydia,
Faintly a pale rose languishes,
And in my heart a sudden sweet sadness
The fire of love tempers.

Tell me wherefore, beneath the flames of evening
Sends the sea forth mysterious moaning
Below there? And what are the songs, O Lydia,
Those pines sing to each other?

See with what yearning towards the westering
Sun their arms yonder hills stretch out,
They seem, as shadows grow and enfold them,
To crave a last kiss, O Lydia.

For thy kisses I crave, if the shadow,
Lyaeus, joy-giver, o'ertake me;
I crave for thine eyes, O bright Lydia,
If falls Hyperion.

And the hour doth fall; unclose, O rosy
Lips, O flower of the soul, O flower
Of desire, unfold thy close petals,
O dear arms, to me open!

AT THE STATION ON AN AUTUMN MORNING

Oh how those lamps are pursuing each other
Under the tall trees lazily yonder,
On miry road sleepily spreading
Their light through branches dripping with raindrops.

Plaintively, shrilly and stridently whistles
The steam belched from the engine near by. Leaden

The sky, and the morning autumal
Like a huge phantom over all hovers.

Whither and to what goal do these people
Hasten along, closely muffled and silent
To the dark cars? To what unknown sorrows,
To what vain torments of hope long deferred?

Thou, pensive Lydia, givest thy ticket
To the swift sharp clip of the guard; thou givest
Thy best years to Time, the pursuer,
Thy moments enjoyed, thy remembrances.

By the side of the black train inspectors,
Black hooded, pass along coming and going,
Like shadows; dim lanterns they carry
And long rods of iron, and the iron

Brakes rapidly tested like a knell sounding,
Long and lugubrious, while a sad echo
From the depths of the soul responded
Like a spasm of pain in its dullness.

Then the doors harshly slammed to in the shutting
Seem insults; mocking, the call for departure,
The last summons, sounds rapid alarum;
On the panes great rain-drops are beating.

Lo! of his metallic soul now become conscious,
The monster shudders, snorts, pants and opening
Eyes of flame, hurls into the darkness
Long whistles loud, space shrilly challenging.

His hideous length trailing starts the fell monster,
Bears away my love with his wings wide flapping.
Ah, that pale face and farewell flutter
Of veil vanishing into the darkness.

[75]

O gentle face softened in roseate pallor!
O eyes, ye stars that are with peace all radiant!
O pure white brow, by locks abundant
Shaded, in gracious attitude inclining!

Like thrilled the warm air when thine eyes shone on me;
And in thy smile hot summer palpitated,
And the young sun of June delighted
In bestowal of luminous kisses

Between the clustering chestnut curls' warm shadow,
On the tender bloom of the soft cheek; brighter
Than any sun my dreams surround the
Fair form with an aureole of glory.

Now under the rain and into the dark mist
I return, and fain with them would I mingle:
I reel as one drunk, and I touch me
Lest I too might be naught but a phantom.

O what a falling of leaves never-ending,
Chilly, silent, heavy on my soul; methinks
That the world around me forever
Has become all-pervading November.

Better for him who has lost sense of being,
Better this gloom, better this mist low lowering,
I would, I would lay me down in a
Dullness of calm that should last forever.

A SUMMER'S DREAM

'Mid thy battles, O Homer, and resonant swing of thy verses,
Did the heat of the day overcome me, my head sank in slumber
By the banks of Scamander, but to the Tyrrhenian my heart flew.

Sweet things and placid I dreamed of, I dreamed of my earliest years,
Vanished my books and the chamber, made hot with the sun of July,
And reverberant with the rolling of heavy carts on the flint-paved
Streets of the city. Then around me rose the hills that I loved well,
Wild hills that young April reflowered; down the hillside descended
Rippling fresh murmurs a booklet, and babbling grew to a river.
By the river, in bloom of her young years, my mother was walking.
A child by the hand she was leading, on whose white shoulders brightly
Golden locks clustered. The boy walked with short steps, joyous, exultant,
Proud in the love of his mother, his heart moved by the festival
Vast of harmonious melodies life-giving Nature was chanting.
Far above from the hamlet were bells sweetly chiming glad tidings,
Announcing that Christ on the morrow would return to His Heaven.
Over the peaks and the plain, and through the branches, through the breezes,
Through the waters, rang out melodious the Spirit of Spring-tide,
And the apple trees and the peach trees were all white and pink blossom,
While in flowers beneath them the grass laughed in turquoise and yellow,
Downward sloping were the meadows, clothed all in deep crimson clover
And the gentle hills had decked themselves with broom in golden glory,
And a zephyr soft came down from the sea, those bright flowers stirring,
Wafted their odors around. On the sea four white sails came gliding,
Came gliding slowly, rocked backwards and forwards, in sunshine swaying,
Sunshine which mingled earth, sea and heaven in one brilliant splendor.
Happy and blessed the young mother gazed out into the sunlight;
Long I gazed on my mother, and pensively gazed on my brother,
He now so long lies on the flowery hill by the Arno,
She too now sleeps well near the solemn Carthusian hermitage,
Thoughtful, and doubting whether they still breathed the sweet air of our
    earth
Or if those kind ones because of my grief came back from a shore where
Over again they lived happy years amid shadows familiar.
But the dear dream images vanished, lightly passed with the sleeping.
Meanwhile Lauretta with joyous music filled all the chambers,
Bent o'er her frame in silence Bice plied the swift toil of her needle.

BY THE URN OF PERCY BYSSHE SHELLEY

Lalage, I know what dream in thy deep heart arises, know too
What are the good things lost thy wandering eye doth follow.

Vain is the hour that is with us; it strikes and flown is the moment;
Only in the past find we beauty, only in death find we truth,

On the mountain of the centuries the ardent Clio plants her
Agile foot, outspreading to heaven her glorious pinions.

Beneath the soaring Muse the world's vast graveyard illuminated
Yawns revealed, while before her laughs the sun in splendor arisen

Of the new era. Thou thought of my youthful years, O strophe,
Fly back henceforth forever secure, O fly back to the old loves.

Fly through the heavens, the heavens serene, to the beautiful
Island far out in the distant seas resplendent with fantasy.

Siegfried and Achilles, heroes tall and fair, on their spears leaning,
Are wandering here beside the resounding deep, their songs singing.

Ophelia from her pale lover fleeing, to the one gives flowers,
While to the other from the sacrifice comes Iphigenia.

Under a verdant oak-tree Roland high converse holds with Hector,
While Durendal, set round with gold and gems, in bright sunshine glitters.

Andromache once more clasps her son to her comely bosom;
Alda the beautiful motionless stands, on her stern sire gazing.

His gray locks wild, King Lear his woes relates to wandering Œdipus,
Œdipus with uncertain eyes still searches for the Sphinx.

Pious Cordelia calls: "Alas, O white-robed Antigone,
Come, Grecian sister, come, let us together sing peace to our fathers."

Helen and Isolda pensive pace beneath the shade of myrtles,
While the crimson sunset laughs in the flowing gold of their tresses.

Helena watches the heaving waves; King Mark turns to Isolda,
His arms wide outstretching, on his full beard her fair head reposes.

With the remorseful Scottish queen on the shore stands Clytemnestra
In the light of the moon, they in the sea their white arms are plunging.

And the cool sea swollen with warm red blood recoils, while the weeping
Of the unhappy queens all along the rocky marge re-echoes.

O far far away from the paths of the rude toiling of mortals,
Island of fair women, island of heroes, island of Poets!

Island around whose shore the ocean breaks in whitening surges,
And strange birds wing their way wandering through the dark blue vault of
    heaven.

Grand and sonorous, shaking the laurel trees, passes the Epic
As over the billowy plains passes in May the tornado,

Or as when Wagner with his thousand-souled power harmonizes
Resounding brass with voices, the heart of humanity thrilling.

Ah but hither not one later poet as yet hath arisen,
Were it not thou, perchance, O youthful Shelley, thou soul Titanic,

In a virgin form enclosed, snatched from the divine entanglement
Of Thetis, thee Sophocles bore in haste to dwell with hearts heroic.

O heart of hearts, over this marble which holds thy cold ashes
Spring casts her bright many-colored flowers, shedding warmth and perfume.

[79]

O heart of hearts, behold! the sun, divine father, envelops thee,
With his radiant beams of love, thou poor silent heart, thee surrounding.

Freshly in the spacious air of Rome the dark cypresses quiver,
And thou, O poet of the enfranchised world, where dost thou tarry?

Thou, where art thou? Dost thou hear me? Mine eyes all wet with tears are
   gazing
Out to the sad wide plain stretching beyond the Aurelian circuit.

SNOWFALL

Slowly flake by flake, from a sky the color of ashes,
Flutters the snow; no cry of life from the city resounds,

Not the cry of the vendor of herbs, not the rumble of wagons,
Not of songs joyous with love and youth rise the refrains.

Hoarsely hours are groaning from the belfry in the Piazza
Through the air like the sighs of a world remote from the day.

At my clouded window wandering birds are tapping, friendly
Spirits returning are they, come to look on me, and to call.

Oh indomitable heart, be calm! Soon, O ye dear ones,
Soon shall I descend to silence, soon in the shade repose.

GEOFFREY RUDEL

From Lebanon the cool fresh morn
   Sheds rosy tremors on the sea;
By Latin barque the cross is borne
   From Cyprus sailing gallantly.

On deck stands Rudel, Prince of Blaye,
    With fever faint, his yearning eyes
Seek on the heights above the bay
    Where Tripoli's fair castle lies.

When he beholds the Asian strand,
    The famous song he sings anew.
"Love hath for you from far-off land
    Filled all my heart with aching pain."
The circlings of the gray sea-mew
    Follow the lover's sweet complaint;
On the white sails the sun grows faint,
    Obscured by clouds in fleecy train.

The ship in the calm haven drops
    Her anchor fast; Bertrand descends
In anxious care, naught heeds, nor stops,
    Toward the hill his way he wends.
With mourning trappings all bedight
    The shield of Blaye is in his hand,
He hastens to the Castle height:
    "Where is the Lady Mélisande?

"The messenger of love I come,
    I come the messenger of death.
I come to seek you in your home
    From Blaye's good lord, Geoffrey Rudel.
He caught your fame on Rumor's breath,
    Unseen he loved you, sang of you,
He comes, he dies; this poet true,
    Lady, to you sends his farewell."

With pensive mien the lady rose,
    Looked at the squire, some moments stayed,
Then a black veil around her throws,
    Her face and star-like eyes to shade.
"Sir Squire," quoth she, her words come fast,

"Let us go where Sir Geoffrey lies,
    That we may bear the first and last
        Word love may utter ere he dies."

Beneath his fair tent pitched along
    Beside the sea Sir Geoffrey lay,
In low tones sang one tender song
    That told his heart's supreme desire.
"Lord, who didst will that far away
    My love should dwell in Eastern lands,
Grant that I may in her dear hands
    Commit my soul as I expire."

Guided by faithful Bertrand's hand
    The lady came, the last note caught,
Before the entrance Mélisande
    Lingered, her heart with pity fraught.
But soon with trembling hand she threw
    Her veil aside, her face left clear.
Near to her lover sad she drew,
    And murmured: "Geoffrey, I am here."

Stretched on a low divan he lay,
    Turning, then vainly strove to rise;
With a long sigh the Lord of Blaye
    Upon those lovely features gazed.
"Is that the face, are these the eyes
    Love promised one day should be mine?
Around that brow did I entwine
    Vague dreams my waking thought had raised?"

Just as the moon on some May night
    Bursts through the clouds' encircling gloom,
Flooding the earth with silvery light,
    Fills it with growth and with perfume,
So to the enchanted lover seems
    This tranquil beauty to impart

Sweetness divine beyond all dreams,
    Filling the dying poet's heart.

"Lady, what is this life of ours?
    The fleeting shadow of a dream.
Now end the fable's transient hours,
    'Tis only love that knows not death.
To one in agony supreme
    Open thine arms. On the last day
I wait for thee; a kiss now may
    Commend to thee my latest breath."

The lady held him to her breast,
    And bending o'er her lover pale
Upon his quivering lips she pressed
    Love's kiss of greeting and farewell.
The sun broke through his misty veil,
    From sky serene shone on the sea,
The lady's golden locks set free
    Like light o'er the dead poet fell.

PIEDMONT

On the jaggard summits, sparkling in sunshine,
Leap the swift chamois; the avalanche thunders
Down from the glaciers whirling and rolling
    Through the woods pouring;

Out from the expanse of the silence cerulean,
Spreading his dark wings and wheeling in circles,
Slowly descending in stately gyrations
    Flies forth the eagle.

Hail to thee, Piedmont! Thy rivers descending
From far in melodious sadness resounding,
Like to thy epic songs telling the valorous
    Deeds of thy people,

Down to the valleys, full, rapid and blithesome,
Dashing they come like thy hundred battalions;
There to the awakened villas and cities
    Tell they of glory.

Aosta old, by Caesar's walls encircled,
Thou who in Alpine pass above the fashions
Of the barbarian ages proudly raisest
    The arch of Augustus.

Ivrea the beautiful, who her red turrets
In the blue Dora's broad bosom dreamily
Mirrors, and all around is the dark shadow
    Of King Arduin.

Biella, 'twixt the mountain and the growing
Verdure of the plain, down the fertile valley
Gaily looks, boasting arms, ploughs and laborious
    Smoking of chimneys.

Potent and patient Cuneo, and smiling
On the gentle slope standing, sweet Mondovi,
And the land joyful in castles and vineyards
    Of Aleramo;

And from Superga, amid the rejoicing
Choir of the high Alps, Torino the regal
Crowned with victory, and the republican
    Asti reposing,

Fierce with the slaughter of Goths and the anger
Of the red Frederick, from the reverberant

River, O Piedmont, she gave thee the new song
      Of Alfieri.

He came, that great one, as cometh the great bird
From whom was taken his name, o'er the lowly
Townlet he hovers, tawny-haired; restless.
      "Italia, Italia!"

He cried to the ears unaccustomed, to the
Slothful hearts, to the souls supine, "Italia,
Italia!" echoed from the tombs of Arqua
      And of Ravenna.

And under that flight the bones in the graveyard
All the length of the fatal peninsula
Creaked, and were seeking each other to clothe them
      In wrath and in iron.

"Italia, Italia!" and lo, a people
Of the dead arose singing, war they demanded,
And a king in his pallor and in his courage
      Devoted to death

Drew the sword. O year so hopeful in portents,
O spring-tide of the fatherland! O ye days,
O ye last days of the blossoming May time!
      O sound triumphant

Telling of victory first to Italians,
How as a child through the heart didst thou thrill me,
Wherefore in times more propitious, the Vates,
      Gray-haired, of Italy,

Thee I sing today, O king of my green years,
Thee, king so much blamed and so much lamented,
Who passedst away, thy sword in hand bearing;
      Clothed with a hair-shirt

[85]

Thy Christian breast, Italian Hamlet. Under
The fire and the sword of Piedmont, and under
The force of Cuneo, the rush of Aosta,
     The enemy scattered.

Languidly now the last boom of the cannon
Died away behind the flight of the Austrian,
The king on his charger rode down the slope westward,
     Facing the sunset

In the midst of his staff gathering round him,
Glad with dusty smoke and victory, he drew forth
A missive, unfolding it said: "Surrendered
     Is Peschiera!"

O what a cry as with one voice vibrating
Arose from those breasts, of ancestors mindful,
Waving the standards of Savoy: "Long live the
     King of Italy!"

Red in the glory of sunset was glowing
Widely extended the plain of Lombardia,
Beyond, the lake of Virgil, like a veil fluttered
     By a bride coyly

Opening its fold for the kiss of love promised.
Pale, erect and unmoved in the saddle
Sat the king, his fixed eyes beholding the shadow
     Of the Trocadero,

And him the misty Novara awaited
And Oporto, final goal of sad error,
O by the chestnut woods silent and lonely
     House by the Douro,

With the resounding Atlantic to front it,
Fresh with camellias beside it the river,

Which beneath calm so indifferent sheltered
      Sorrow so poignant.

The king lay a-dying, when in the twilight
Between the two lives a marvelous vision
Passed before him, and he beheld the fair-haired
      Sailor of Nizza

Who rode at full tilt from the Janiculum
Gallic outrage to encounter, around him
Shone like carbuncle gleaming in sunshine the
      Blood of Italia.

Over the king's failing eyes came a mistiness,
The shadow of a smile on his lips hovered.
A flight of spirits come from above the
      King's death encircle.

Before all, O noble Piedmont, he who at
Sphakteria sleeps, and first at Alessandria
Gave to the breeze the tricolor, Santorre
      Di Santarosa,

And they to God all together escorted
The soul of Charles Albert: "O Lord, we bring Thee
The king who wasted us, the king who smote us.
      Now he, Lord, also

"Hath died, as we, O God, died for Italia.
Give to us our country. Give to the living,
Give to the dead, by the smoke of blood rising
      From fields of battle,

"By those sorrows which level the palaces
With the cottages, O God, by the glory
Which was in past years, God, by the martyrdom
      Which is in the present,

[87]

"To that heroic dust with life still throbbing,
To this angelic light at length exultant,
Give, O God, the fatherland! Give Italy
    To the Italians!"

CADORE

I

Thou art great. With the rainbow of thy colors
The sun eternally mankind consoleth;
With youth perpetual invested
Nature smiles upon thy forms ideal.

While athwart the gloom of the dark century
Those rosy phantoms passed like lightning flashes,
The people's longing eyes cast upward,
And the tumult of the sword suspended

And he who Rome and Italy had harried,
The stern oppressor, the cold Flemish Caesar,
The paint-brush fallen at thy feet picked up,
Lowly stooping, of himself forgetful.

Tell me if beneath the weight of Austrian
Marbles in the gray silence of the Frari,
Old man, thou sleepest, or wanderest
A soul set free 'mid thy native mountain.

Here where the heavens thee, whose brow Olympian
A century with pleasant life encircled,
Here the heavens limpid and cerulean
Laughing kiss thee through the fleecy cloudlets.

Thou art great. Yet from yonder simple marble
That face of youthful daring and defiance

Cries to my heart more strongly, asking
Me to sing his praise in antique measure.

What is it, god-like youth, that thou defiest?
The onrush of assault, battle, destiny
One 'gainst a thousand didst defiance
Hurl, heroic soul, Pietro Calvi.

So long as through the perennial fleeting
Of centuries, the Piave falls rushing
Through green abysses to the Adrian
Sea, the spoil of the dark forests bearing,

Which long ago to old St. Mark gave towers
Of pine for war amidst the Echinades,
As long as the sun in his setting
The pale peaks of the Dolomites tinges.

While the Marmarole dear to Veccellio
Are aglow with rosy refulgence, a palace
Of dreams in the calm of the evening,
An Elysium of spirits and fairies,

Always, ah always may thy name, O Calvi,
Sound to the covetous terrible, and may
Youths pale, when thy deed they remember,
Spring to arms in defense of their country.

II

I sing thee not, Cadore, on pipes of Arcadia that follow
        Murmurs of breezes and waters,
But in measures heroic I sing thee that down in the valleys
        Follow the sound of the musket.

O second day of May when on the road towards Austria wending
        The gallant Calvi advanced, and
On the low wall leaping that marks the boundary, balls whistling round him
        Stands there, erect, fair, motionless,

[89]

Raises in his right his sword, on its point the pact of Udine,
      His gaze fixed on the enemy,
And in his left hand waves a blood-red kerchief, sign that no quarter
      He would give, nor none expected.

Pelmo and Antelao at the deed from white clouds loftily
      Free in air their hoary summits
Like ancient giants shaking back the dangling plumes of their helmets,
      To watch the fortunes of battle.

Like to the shields of heroes that glitter in songs of the poets,
      To the amazement of ages,
So in pure radiance of splendor sparkle the glaciers on meeting
      The sun as he mounts in the heavens.

With what ardor dost thou embrace, O sun of our ancient glories,
      Man and the Alps and the rivers,
Thou who beneath dark boscage of pine trees the stubborn clods piercing
      Touchest the dead to revive them.

"Smite, O sons, o'er our bones," cry the dead voices, "smite, O our children,
      The ever-returning barbarian;
Fall on him, O ye rocks, from snow-clad heights which our blood hath crimsoned,
      O'erwhelm him, ye Avalanches!"

Thus the voices of the dead from mountain to mountain resounding
      Of those who fought at Rusecco.
And from farm to farm, from village to village, the sound in fury
      The winds bore onwards, increasing.

Joyously fly to arms these youths whom Titian gladly had painted,
      Down they come, singing: "Italia!"
On their balconies of dark wood, with carnation brightly crimsoned
      And geranium, stand the women.

Gay Pieve nestles 'mid the smiling hills, and hears the rushing
     From below, of the Piave.
Auronzo, that broadly spreads itself on the plain 'twixt the waters
     Beneath the dark Ajarnola,

And the sunny Lorenzago, above the shelving meadows
     Midmost dominates the valley,
And all the verdant Comelico scattered over with hamlets
     Hidden 'mid pine-trees and fir-trees.

Other towns and other homesteads 'mid pastures and forests
     Send forth their sons and their fathers.
Loud resound the horns of the shepherds, all seize their guns, they brandish
     Their pruning-hooks and their lances.

From behind the altar comes the ancient banner that at Vellé
     Saw another flight of Austrians,
Welcomes now the valiant. With a roar the lion old of Venice
     Greets the new sun and new perils.

Hark, a sound from the distance! It comes down the valley, draws nearer,
     It rises, rushes, increases.
O sound that laments and summons, that cries, entreats and enrages,
     A sound persistent, terrible.

What is it? The enemy asks, to the encounter advancing,
     With his eyes seeking the answer,
" 'Tis the bells of the people of Italy, bells that are tolling
     Today for your death or for ours."

Alas! Ere seven years have passed, on yon plains, from Mantua's trenches
     Death shall snatch thee, Pietro Calvi!
Thou didst come to seek Death's cold embrace as to his tryst some exile
     Comes to meet his bride in secret.

As he once on Austrian arms had gazed, so now on Austria's scaffold
     Looked he serenely, undaunted.

[91]

Grateful to the hostile judgment that sent him to join as a soldier
    The sacred legion of spirits.

Never, ah never a nobler soul didst thou launch forth from its prison
    To the future of Italy,
O Belfiore, dark fosse of Austrian scaffold, Belfiore
    Refulgent alter of martyrs!

Should thy name ever fade from the heart of a son of Italia,
    May for him, wretched, ignoble,
Th' adulterous bed bring forth such scum as from his Lares ancestral
    Would spurn him forth into the mire.

And to him who fatherland denies may unclean, suicidal
    Forces swarm in his blood, and breeding
In his heart, in his brain, from his lips ugly and blasphemous
    May a green toad breathe out venom.

III

Now my song returns to thee, as the eagle,
Satiate with victory over the dragon,
Poising above his aerial
Nest on peaceful wing returns to sunlight.

So my song to the Fatherland devoted
Comes appeased to thee returning, Cadore.
Slowly from the pine-trees are wafted
Murmurs in the pale light of the young moon.

For thee a long caress on the magical
Sleep of the waters. For thee with fair children
All thy country-side is blossoming,
And from the overhanging cliffs bold virgins

Singing mow the ripening hay, their rebellious
Tawny tresses beneath black kerchiefs twisted,
While from their blue eyes sparkling flashes
Rapidly they cast around them; as the

Wagoner drives on his team of three horses,
Dragging along the precipitous pathways
Pine-trees scattering pungent odors;
All Perarolo to the weir hurries.

'Mid giddy heights with vaporous mist encircled
Thunder the echoes of the chase, the chamois
Falls before the shot aimed so surely.
So when country calls, falls the enemy.

I would ravish the soul from thee, Cadore,
Of Pietro Calvi for the peninsula.
On the wings of song I would send it
A herald. "Ho, thou but half-awakened,

"Lo, not for adulterous dreams, nor perfidious
Slumbers are the Alps a pillow propitious.
Arouse thee! have done with vain shouting.
Arouse thee! the martial cock is crowing."

When Marius shall scale the Alpine passes
Once again, and on the two seas shall Duilius
Gaze appeased; then I, O Cadore,
Will ask of thee the soul of Veccellio.

In the Capitol with her spoils resplendent,
In the Capitol by her laws made glorious,
Shall he depict Italia's triumph,
Newly arisen among the nations.

SANT' ABBONDIO

The Heavens as adamantine crystal clear
    As though from the beyond transfused with light,
The scintillating Alpine snows appear
    Like human souls by burning love made bright.

From cabins that 'mid clustering bushes peer
    Rises the smoke in wreaths of blue and white
By light winds wafted. The Madesimo here
    Falls in cascades 'twixt banks with emerald dight.

The Alpine girls in scarlet garments clad,
    Holy Abbondio, in thy feast take part
With stream and pine, in songs both soft and glad.

What laughs so gaily in the valley there?
    Peace, oh my heart, be at peace, oh my heart!
Life is so short, and ah! the world is fair.

NEAR A CERTOSA

From the sad persistent greenness 'midst the leaves that still are clinging
Red and yellow to the acacia, one its downward way is winging.
    No wind stirs but a light tremor,
    As it were a soul that passes.

Under mist like veil of silver flows the streamlet onward brawling;
Disappearing in the streamlet through the mist a leaf is falling.
    From the cemetery what faint sighs
    Through the cypresses are breathing?

Suddenly the white cloud parted, through the rift is sunshine streaming
O'er the moisture of the morning, while above the blue is gleaming.
    Now the austere grove rejoices,
    Since it feels the winter coming.

Ere in its icy chain the winter shall bind up my soul, on me,
Shed the effulgence of thy smile, O sacred sun of Poesy!
    Thy great song, O father Homer,
    Ere the shadow me enfoldeth.

THE SONG OF LEGNANO

I

In Como bides the Emperor Frederick.
A messenger to Milan rides full speed,
The New Gate enters, nor draws rein but cries:
"Ho, men of Milan, give me escort due
To Sor Gherardo, consul of your town!"
The consul stood in middle of the square,
The messenger bent o'er his saddle bow,
Whispered brief words and spurred him on his way.
Consul Gherardo straightway gave the sign
And trumpet blasts convened the Parliament.

II

'Twas blast of trumpet called the Parliament,
Because the palace had not risen anew
On tall pilasters, rostrum was there none,
No tower was there, no bell swung from its crown,
Among the blackened ruins, where now thorns
Grew green among low cabins built of wood.
There in the narrow public place the men
Of Milan held their Parliament, beneath
The sun of May; from windows and from doors
The women and the children waiting watched.

III

The consul speaks: "My lords of Milan, hear!
With spring in blossom come the German hordes,
As is their wont; their Easter feast consumed
In their own lairs, the greedy boors descend
Upon our valleys; through the Engadine
Two excommunicate archbishops lead.
The fair-haired Empress to her lord hath brought

Besides a faithful heart an army new;
Como holds with the strong and leaves the league";
"Down," shout the people, "Down with Como, down!"

IV

"My lords of Milan," says the consul, "hear!
In Como Frederick musters troops and goes
To join the false Pavians and the lord
Of Monferrato. Men of Milan, choose;
Or will ye from your ramparts new await
And watch in arms, or to the Caesar send
Your messengers, or seek with spear and sword
The Barbarossa in his camp?" "We'll seek
With sword and spear," shouted the Parliament,
"With spear and sword the red-beard in his camp!"

V

Now Albert of Giussano forward steps,
By head and shoulders he o'ertops the rest
Of those who round the consul crowd, his form
Amid the Parliament rose like a tower
Stalwart and tall; his helmet in his hand
He holds, around his brawny neck and on
His square-set shoulders broad his long dark locks
Fell free; upon his frank and open face
The sun beats sparkling in his eye and hair;
His voice is like the thunder heard in May.

VI

"O men of Milan, brothers, people mine,
Do ye remember those March Kalends dark?"
Says Albert of Giussano, "To Lodi rode
Your wan-faced consuls, who with naked swords
Upheld in hand unto the Emperor swore
Obedience. Three hundred strong we rode,
On the fourth day we laid down at his feet
Our thirty-six fair standards, kissing them;

Master Guitelmo offered him the keys
Of famine-stricken Milan. All was naught!"

VII

"Do you remember that sixth day of March?"
Says Albert of Giussano: "he would have
The men-at-arms, the people, standards, all
Beneath his feet. From the three city gates
Forth came the people, came the battle-car
Prepared for war, the people cross in hand,
Before him the Carroccio's trumpets sound
Their last fanfare. The Carroccio's lofty mast
Before him bent, lowering the Gonfalon,
Until it swept the ground, he touched its hem.

VIII

"Do you remember? Clad as penitents,"
Says Albert of Giussano, "bare-foot, cords
About our necks, our heads with ashes strewn,
We knelt in mire, with outstretched arms implored
For mercy. All there wept, the lords and knights
Who round him stood wept too, but he, upright
Upon his feet, beside th' Imperial shield,
In silence stood unmoved, looking on us
With that cold gaze of his, diamond keen.

IX

"Do you remember, on the morrow, how,"
Says Albert of Giussano, "on the road
Returning to our shame, we saw behind
The gate the Empress gazing at us? Then
We cast our crosses at her feet and cried
'O fair, O pious Empress, lady true,
Have pity, pity on our women!' She
Retired within and he on us imposed
That gates and walls be leveled to the ground,
So he with his embattled host might pass.

X

"Do you remember? Nine days did we wait,"
Says Albert of Giussano, "how Archbishop, counts,
With servile suite of vassals went away;
The tenth day came the herald: 'Go ye forth
O wretched men, go forth and with you take
Your wives, your children and your goods. Eight days
The Emperor gives you.' Then with groans we ran
To Sant' Ambrogio, to the altars clung
And to the tombs. They chased us from the church,
Our wives, our little ones, like scurvy curs!

XI

"Do you remember that Palm Sunday sad?"
Says Albert of Giussano. "Ah, that was
The passion of our Lord and of Milan!
From the four holy suburbs of our town
Three hundred towers of her encircling crown
We saw fall one by one; then through the dust
Of ruins we beheld our houses razed,
Demolished, blasted; files of skeletons
In some huge graveyard standing they appeared;
Below, the bones still smoldered of our dead."

XII

Thus speaking Albert of Giussano raised
His two hands, covered up his eyes and wept,
There in the midmost of the Parliament
Like to a little child he sobbed and wept.
Then through the throng of all the Parliament
There ran a roar, as 'twere of savage beasts,
While from the doors and from the balconies
The women, pale, disheveled, with their arms
Outstretched, their wide dilated eyes turned towards
The Parliament, shrieked: "Kill the red-beard, kill!"

XIII

"Behold," says Albert of Giussano, "Now
Behold I weep no more. Our day has come,
O men of Milan, and we needs must win.
Behold, I dry mine eyes, and, looking up
To thee, O fair sun, shining in God's heaven,
I take an oath: Tomorrow, ere the night,
Our dead in Purgatory shall hear good news
Which I myself will bear."—"Nay," cry the people,
"To th' Imperial heralds trust it rather!"
Sinking 'neath Resegone smiled the sun.

THE LIFE AND WORKS OF
GIOSUÈ CARDUCCI

By PAUL RENUCCI

THERE ARE poets whose writings can be enjoyed without any reference to the events of their private life or the historical context in which they lived—but Giosuè Carducci is not one of them. Quick to react to the latest scandal, prone to controversy rather than to a quiet, secluded life, ready when the occasion arose, to make up for the brevity of his meditation by the thunder of his language, Carducci was a sounding board in the very heart of a century that was unusually rich in events.

Carducci was both poet and professor —an active teacher who reached a wide audience and whose contributions to literary criticism are hardly less impressive than his poetical output. Few creative artists have been forced so constantly to keep in mind the history of their predecessors; few poets took so lively an interest in the production of their fellows. These influences are apparent in the erudition that characterizes many of his poems, in his experiments in scholarly versification, and in his occasional use of an archaic or Latinized vocabulary.

Giosuè Carducci was born on July 27, 1835, at Val di Castello, in the northwestern corner of Tuscany. His father, a physician without private means, was forced to practice where he could, and the family moved about a great deal. Their longest single period was spent at Bolgheri, where they stayed for about nine years. Carducci later called his childhood "a dreary springtime," divided between a home over which his father's ill humor cast a cloud—he was both irascible and melancholy—and the forests of the sparsely cultivated countryside, where wild boar still roamed.

But Doctor Michele Carducci led a hard life. His patients were mostly penurious peasants, and his political opinions did not help him obtain a more profitable practice: they combined the "philosophical" spirit of the eighteenth century, a pinch of anticlericalism (which, his son tells us, was counterbalanced by an admiration for the extremely Catholic writer Alessandro Manzoni), and a large dose of patriotism. In a word, Dr. Carducci was less a revolutionary than a crank, but that was more than enough to make him unpopular with the good society of the Tuscan villages, and to estrange him from a lower class easily shocked by nonconformist attitudes.

The political events and revolutions of 1848–1849 worsened the hostile atmosphere in which the Carduccis lived; they had to move three times in less than two years. At Laiatico, an incident occurred that gives a good idea of the character of the man from whom young Giosuè inherited his aggressive impulses and his taste for violent outbursts. The year was 1849. The revolution had failed in Tuscany as everywhere else, and the people of Laiatico were celebrating the Grand Duke's homecoming. A plaster statue of the sovereign was carried in procession through the village and all the men doffed their hats as it passed—all but Doctor Carducci. He flatly refused to do so; when he was urged to kiss the "idol," his refusal became still more forceful. This was greeted with a chorus of protests and threats, to which he replied by smashing the statue with his walking stick. In the free-for-all that followed he was badly mauled.

After that, Laiatico was no place for the Carducci family, and they moved to Florence. Young Giosuè, who was just fourteen and had never had any other teacher than his father, was sent to the establishment run by the Piarists—a religious order that took its name from the charitable institutions known as *Scuole Pie* (pious schools). Apparently his father's instruction, supplemented by extensive, if indiscriminate, reading, had been more than adequate: after only three months at school, the boy passed his first examination with splendid marks.

The doctor's first plan for Giosuè was to prepare him for a career in the army, but he soon changed his mind and the boy continued his studies along civilian lines; he completed two years of study in rhetoric and another in science. He was a brilliant scholar and passed his final examinations "a pieni voti e pluralità di plauso" (with full marks and multiple applause).

Carducci's passion as a youth was reading. After Manzoni's *The Betrothed*,

a work his father greatly admired, he tackled the great epics, the *Iliad,* the *Aeneid,* Tasso's *Gerusalemme Liberata,* the poems of chivalry, such as Ariosto's *Orlando Furioso.* From these he went on to the ancient Greek dramatists and to the Italian authors of the early nineteenth century. During this first phase of his literary studies he seems to have been attracted most by epic and satirical poetry.

But reading, however omnivorous, did not satisfy him. He began to write verses that mirror the course of his literary explorations. He tried his hand at an epic poem in eight-line stanzas on the capture of Bolgheri by King Ladislas of Naples, a series of three-line stanzas on the death of Julius Caesar, and a translation in the same verse form of Book IX of the *Iliad.* He also wrote verse epigrams deriding certain teachers and schoolmates. Two sonnets written when he was fourteen years old were inspired by less martial or bad-tempered sentiments—*"A mia Madre"* (To My Mother) and *"La Vita"* (Life).

In April 1851, his father, who had found life in Florence no less difficult than elsewhere, was given the job of medical officer at Celle. He was hired for a trial period of six months at the modest stipend of one hundred lire a month, with the promise of a twenty-lire raise every month. His new post was far from easy for him at the start, for his reputation as a dangerous revolutionary had preceded him (he was only given the job because there were no other candidates). But Doctor Carducci must have mellowed to some extent. He disarmed his potential enemies, behaved with discretion, and demonstrated his professional skill, which had been questioned. On June 30, 1851, he was officially and permanently appointed to the job. It did not make him a rich man, but at least he was able to have his family with him. So when Giosuè went to Celle for his holidays, the whole family was there.

They were unpleasant holidays, if we are to believe what he said about them later. His mother was diffident and resigned; she took consolation in religion for the ill humor of her husband, for whom wine now meant more than politics. (Giosuè too later became known as a knowledgeable Chianti fancier.) Giosuè missed his Florentine friends and the libraries where he had spent so much of his time. He called Celle a snake pit, and the girls he met there hideous she-devils. At first all he did was read in total isolation, or meditate as he roamed the neighboring hills. Finally, when he was bored almost to extinction, he taught the village boys to read and to sing patriotic songs.

Most important of all, he began to write poetry again. His father's newfound political moderation had been accompanied by a revival of religious fervor, and following in his footsteps, young Giosuè wrote pious poems in honor of Saint Elizabeth and Saint John the Baptist. In 1853, he sent Father Barsottini, his teacher at the Piarists' school, some verses he had written on the first Crusade—inspired by Tasso's *Gerusalemme Liberata*. On the strength of that effort, Father Barsottini recommended him for the examination for admission to the Scuola Normale Superiore at Pisa. He was accepted and entered that establishment on October 17.

Carducci's success in the examination for admission was one of the great joys of his life, as is evident from letters he wrote to his friend Enrico Torquato Gargano and to his fiancée Elvira Menicucci, whom he was to marry six years later. He saw in his studies the prospect of three years of independence and material security. But his hopes were dashed to the ground. It was not that the security or independence failed to measure up to his expectations, but he found his professors mediocre, pedantic, and ill-acquainted with Italian literature which they considered politically dangerous. Lectures dealt almost exclusively with ancient authors, and for all other literary matters Carducci was forced to fall back on conversations with fellow students in coffee houses or on the banks of the Arno and on books he read for his own pleasure.

It was during this time that he made a number of friends who had some influence on his intellectual development. One was his Florentine fellow student Enrico Nencioni; another was Ercole Scaramucci, seventeen years his senior, historian, numismatist, philanthropist, and connoisseur of Italian literature. When Scaramucci died before his time, his young friend delivered his funeral oration in tears from the pulpit of Celle parish church. In the oration Carducci praised his friend as a devout churchman, a deadly enemy of "anarchy," a friend of the lower classes who "nonetheless did not throw himself into the mire of the riffraff," a patriot without the "sinister fury of a demagogue or the pitiful, worthless daydreams of the Utopians" (a term that clearly alluded to the advocates of Italian unity). This was strange language for a young man who had taught to the village children patriotic songs, and Carducci might have struck less conservative notes if he had not been speaking from a pulpit. What is surprising, however, is not that he was willing to adopt such conventional language but that he did it so thoroughly, and without attempting to discover a middle ground between his praise of Italian unity and his condemnation of the same ideal.

This first public manifestation of his immoderate temperament must be remembered. Carducci's life includes many other instances of sudden transitions from one attitude to its opposite in politics, religion, and literature. Careful reflection was never his strong point. A short time before, he had delivered the inaugural address at the Academy of the Muse Lovers in Florence, where he was accustomed to meet a certain number of his fellow students. There he recapitulated the history of Italy in the same terms he later used in the *"Canzone di Legnano"* (Song of Legnano). Extolling his countrymen's martial valor, he sang the praises of the revolutionaries who had "fought like lions" and exhorted young Italians to shun the allurements of their century, "the vilest of all," and to behave like resolute patriots.

At the beginning of the 1854 summer vacation, Carducci went to Celle to be with his family, only to find the villagers up in arms against his father. Doctor Carducci had moderated his opinions but not his moods. He had given the mayor a box on the ear on account of a professional grievance, and had been convicted of assault by the court of Montepulciano. As a result, he was forced to give up his post and leave the village. The best job he could find was that of surgeon in the nearby commune of Piancastagnaio. The post was badly paid (once again, Dr. Carducci got it only because there were no other applicants), and the move was a hard blow to the family fortunes. By June 1855, Giosuè was in such a state of poverty that he could not pay the 34-lire fee for his final examinations. Luckily he was on friendly terms with Pietro Thouar, editor of the magazine *L'Appendice*. Thouar got him out of his difficulties by offering him the sum he needed in payment for articles for the magazine. To earn more money, Carducci compiled an anthology of Italian poetry for use in schools. *L'Arpa del Popolo, Scelta di Poemi Religiosi, Morali e Patriotici* (The People's Harp, a Selection of Religious, Moral and Patriotic Poems, 1855) was divided into three parts—God and Religion, Man, and the Fatherland—and its contents ranged from Dante's *Vita Nuova* to contemporary popular verse, the *stornelli* or rhymed couplets that Carducci and his friend Scaramucci had picked up in the country around Celle. Carducci's intention was to include only those poems that were capable of rousing "good and useful sentiments" in the people; he excluded, without a pang, those "that foster superstition and make men egoistic and indolent."

In 1855, Carducci also obtained his doctoral degree. After passing the final examination, he went to visit his father at Piancastagnaio. He found the people neither more up-to-date nor more likeable than those at Celle, but the village's location did much to make up for its inhabitants. Carducci fell in love at first sight with the vast prospect to the south of the valley of the Paglia River, the pleasant temperature (Piancastagnaio lies about 2,600 feet above sea level), the crystal-clear brooks, and the encircling mountains. In these natural surroundings he soon recovered his strength and serenity after a year of intense toil.

But his vacation was more eventful than he had bargained for, for a cholera epidemic struck the region. It was a sore trial for his father. Giosuè showed great courage. From mid-August to mid-September he assisted his overworked father day and night, enforcing the application of the rules of hygiene in people's homes and drafting a set of sanitary regulations for the municipal authorities. Through their zeal, father and son made themselves popular at last with the local inhabitants, won praise in official quarters and even received some sums of money, small but welcome.

In November, Giosuè went back to Pisa, where he studied for his teacher's examination and exchanged many letters with Thouar, Gargano, and other friends.

A coterie was forming around Thouar's magazine *L'Appendice,* and from letters written by Carducci in 1855–1856, it appears that the group's original purpose was to defend classicism against both the excesses and the weaknesses of romanticism. The *Appendice* group fought in the name of *Italianità* (a blanket term for the Italian spirit and tradition), represented in literature by Dante, Petrarch, Alfieri, Parini, Monti, Foscolo, and Leopardi. The coterie's joint volume *Poesie Liriche Italiane* (Italian Lyric Poems) contained notes on "good authors" for the benefit of young girls, indicating an interest in feminine education that was remarkable for the period.

At the examination qualifying him as a schoolmaster, Carducci made an eloquent lecture on the medieval poetry of the court and chivalry. Soon afterward he visited his family, who had moved once again. Angered when he was refused a raise in salary, Dr. Carducci had left Piancastagnaio for Santa Maria del Monte, not far from the village of San Miniato al Tedesco, where Giosuè had just been appointed a high-school teacher at a wage of sixty-five lire a month.

In 1856 Carducci enjoyed a quieter vacation than he had the previous year. He continued to write poetry and diatribes against romanticism, along with his friends in Florence. *L'Appendice* had just printed *"Diceria"* (Gossip), an article by Gargano protesting against the invasion of Italian bookshops by foreign authors. The Florentine press attacked the article, and the coterie counterattacked in a pamphlet entitled *Giunta alla Derrata* (Something Extra). Carducci drafted most of the pamphlet, in a mood more antiromantic than ever.

Carducci was unhappy from the start as a high-school teacher at San Miniato al Tedesco. In *Le Risorse di San Miniato* (The Resources of San Miniato), he gives a vivid account of his first year in that little town. At times he exaggerates a note or a color, and by and large he seems to have given us rather less than the whole truth. But there is another side to the story. He acted in so aggressive and extravagant a way that complaints were laid against him. A quarrel in a café earned him a reproof from the subprefect. His provocative behavior and his anticlericalism (which he expressed in disrespectful attitudes in church and by gorging himself with sausages on fast days) nearly caused his dismissal. He was reported to the minister of education, who called for a formal censure. When the time came to execute the minister's order the authorities showed less rigor; Carducci got off with a warning. But the episode cost him a post at the Arezzo high school that he was anxious to obtain; it was his by right as the result of a competition but was refused him, allegedly on the intervention of the philologist Pietro Fanfani, who was shocked by Carducci's misbehavior.

When Carducci published his *Rime* (*Rhymes*) in 1857, he did so partly to pay the debts he had incurred as a young man. The collection comprised twenty-five sonnets, two ballads, and a eulogy for Giacomo Leopardi and Pietro Giordani. The subject of love is given little space. The warmest sentiments, in fact, are for patriotism and an admiration for the great poets of the distant past, whom he took as his models. The classical form of his verse frequently clashes with his romantic state of mind. The critics attacked Carducci with lack of personality, and they were not entirely wrong. In *Rhymes,* neither the subject matter nor the mode of expression is new. If the poems seemed daring it was because of the poet's insistent exaltation of Italy, still split up and in part subjected to foreign rule, and because of his vehement antiromanticism. Many of the poems were later republished in the definitive edition of the *Juvenilia* of 1880, revised and improved.

In Autumn, 1857, Carducci settled in Florence, and he stayed until early in 1860 without any official post. Those difficult years were saddened by the suicide of his brother Dante in 1857 and his father's death in 1858. Giosuè supported the rest of the family by editorial work. In 1859, he married and in the following year was appointed to the Pistoia high school. He was there only a short time. In 1860 Terenzio Mamiani entered the Italian Cabinet. The new minister remembered the young writer, whose *Rhymes* he had read and appreciated. When the poet Giovanni Prati refused the offer of the chair of rhetoric at Bologna University, Mamiani offered it to Carducci, who jumped at the promotion. Thus, at the age of 25, Carducci became a university professor. He remained in his post at Bologna until his retirement in 1904.

His appointment to a post both honorable and permanent ended Carducci's financial and familial anxieties. From this point on, his life was devoted to his family—he had three daughters, to whom he gave names that were either literary (Beatrice, Laura) or political (Liberty), and one son, Dante, who died in 1870 at the age of three—his intense and fruitful work as a professor, his poetry and his politics.

Politics caused him more trouble than pleasure. In 1863, he was briefly suspended from his post—and its salary—for attending a republican banquet and signing an address to Giuseppe Mazzini. In 1876, he was elected republican member of Parliament but he never assumed his seat. A law limited the number of professors in that body; and since too many had been elected, Carducci was one of those eliminated. Two years later, the Queen of Italy paid an official visit to

Bologna. The poet, who till then had been considered an indomitable republican, wrote an ode—*"Alla Regina d'Italia"* ("To the Queen of Italy"), printed among the *Odi Babari* (*Barbarian Odes*, 1877, 1882, and 1889). The poem seemed servile to some readers, but in fact, it was the Queen he wanted to honor rather than the monarchy.

This particular ode marked the beginning of a period of political appeasement. In 1886, Carducci ran for parliament again, but this time as a member of the loyal opposition party, rather than as a candidate on the republican ticket. He was not elected, and had to be satisfied with a seat on the Bologna Town Council until, in 1890, he was appointed senator in recognition of both his fame as a writer and of his evolution toward political moderation. That evolution was so complete that in 1891 he agreed to sponsor the banner of a monarchist association. The act so infuriated his republican students that they held a hostile demonstration, during which Carducci was slightly injured. His literary reputation followed a more serene course: along with a number of national distinctions, it won him the honor of the Nobel Prize in 1906, the year before he died.

Carducci had arrived in Bologna afire with enthusiasm, and with a memory packed with the works of his favorite authors, but he was hardly prepared for the duties of a university professor. The first five or six years of his professorship were devoted almost entirely to filling the gap in his training. He intensively explored the vast field of Italian literature, and it was not long before his lectures were among those most popular at the university. As a scrupulous philologist and a brilliant speaker, he exerted an influence that was felt by many more than those who attended his lectures. The eloquence of both his prose and his verse caused Carducci to be chosen frequently as official orator at commemorative ceremonies. Gradually, his fame reached the farthest corners of Europe, but he himself traveled little. He seldom ventured beyond the limits of Tuscany, Emilia, or the adjoining provinces. He never crossed the sea or even the Alps. The only foreign city he ever saw was Trieste, which he visited in 1878, when it still belonged to Austria. All his knowledge of foreign nations, and even of Southern Italy (except for Naples) and the Italian islands, was drawn exclusively from books.

Carducci's poetical output covers well over half a century. In 1848, before he was thirteen years old, he wrote one of the first of his verses—a sonnet to God. His last poem, a quatrain entitled *"Il Castello di San Martino"* (The Castle of San Martino) is dated November 10, 1902. Considering this lengthy span, the quantity of his output may seem modest: it is all contained in the first four volumes of the thirty that make up the definitive edition of his works.

One of the outstanding features of the poems is that so few are devoted to personal themes. There are exceptions, but as a rule Carducci was sparing of autobiographical details, personal confidences, or intimate effusions. Only rarely do we catch a glimpse of a man in love or tempted by love. Here and there we find a father grieved by his infant son, "Pianto Antico" (Ancient Tears), or a middle-aged man in a position of authority haunted by childhood memories, *"Davanti San Guido"* (Before San Guido), both found in *Rime Nuove* (New Rhymes, 1877). But Carducci's aversion to romanticism and its excessive use of "I" and "me" prevented him from wearing his heart on his sleeve.

Carducci often needed an occasion, an anniversary, a publication, a ceremony, a spectacle or the like to rouse his inspiration; the events of the outside world in-

cited him to delve into his inner self. But the occasion seldom served merely as a pretext: it decided the tone of the poem, sometimes its structure, usually its conclusion; and the initial invocation often developed into an implicit dialogue. An example taken almost at random is *"Alle Fonti del Clitumno"* (At the Springs of the Clitumno), one of the *Barbarian Odes*. Here Carducci is not only a poet who re-creates in his imagination the virtues of ancient times on a spot that once was sacred. He carries on a ceaseless dialogue, in which he addresses the stream, greets Umbria, curses the weeping willow, calls upon the ilex and the cypress, reverts to the river to question it, appeals to the tutelary deity whose voice had mobilized Italy's energies against Hannibal's invading army, and closes with an invocation to Italy—"Italia madre" (Mother Italy).

For Carducci the most suggestive occasions were those afforded by political and literary events. Politics held pride of place: it was the source of nearly all his greatest expectations and disappointments, though his most violent rages were sometimes due to other causes. Almost the entire sixth book of the *Juvenilia* draws its subject matter more or less directly from the political events of the years between 1859 and 1879. Both the content and the tone of the poems were closely linked with the reactions to those events in the ranks of republican, anticlerical patriots. Like so many others, Carducci was more ardent and optimistic before victory than after. He aimed his bitterest sarcasms at the city of Rome after it became the capital of Italy, whereas in previous years he had painted a tragic picture of Papal Rome.

Through the narrow paths of politics —politics in which he lived and moved and had his being, politics viewed with the impetuous spirit of a partisan— Carducci entered the broad avenues of history. In the glories of the past he sought contrasts with the present and examples for the future, and in the infamies of long ago he found additional reasons for resenting a present that repeated or perpetuated them. Nothing is more symptomatic than the evocations of ancient Rome in his poems, which are usually designed to pour abuse upon the present.

Another theme often mentioned by students of Carducci's work is "historical Nemesis"—the idea that in the long run history takes revenge on the descendants of those who commit crimes against liberty. The importance of the theme has been exaggerated. It appears rather late in Carducci's poems. And it does not necessarily mean, as some have held, that in Carducci's eyes history evolves naturally toward the sovereignty of the people. Carducci's historical nemesis reflects a nationalistic grievance rather than a democratic conviction, and it is applied exclusively to foreign dynasties and to those that opposed Italian unity and independence. (We must not forget that, in the hearts of many Italian patriots, the battle of Mentana wiped out whatever gratitude they may have felt toward Napoleon III seven or eight years before.) However staunch a republican he may have been up to 1878, Carducci never brandished the threat of historical Nemesis against the House of Savoy.

Patriotic writers of the romantic generation had found in Italy from the thirteenth to the sixteenth century an inexhaustible treasure trove. In Carducci's poems that period plays an insignificant role. Whether it was his aversion for the romantic tradition or the fact that the Italy of the communes and seigniories did not satisfy his feeling for power and grandeur, Carducci skipped the Renaissance and the Middle Ages and sought consolation and food for hope almost exclusively in ancient Rome.

Carducci's indifference to medieval Italy may have had another cause. He lived at a time when most anticlerical thinkers associated the idea of the Middle Ages with obscurantism and the supremacy of the Church. One of the poems in *New Rhymes* ("A Alessandro d'Ancona"), brilliantly expresses Carducci's love of classical, paganizing Latin. Nothing is missing: there is the man who "leaves the cloister only for the tomb," "the horrid flame of the pyre," the gothic spire that "sends life's last greeting to the desert." And the last stanza sums the contrast Carducci saw between the Dark Ages and the sunshine of Antiquity:

> Pigri terrori de l'evo medio, prole
> Negra de la barbarie e del mistero,
> Torme pallide, via! Si leva il sole,
>   E canta Omero.

(Sluggish medieval terrors, dark offspring of barbarism and mystery, pale throngs, begone! The sun rises, and Homer sings.)

In this poem contempt for the Middle Ages is founded on anticlericalism—an anticlericalism compounded of a little Voltaire and a great deal of irritation at the romanticism of the Italian Catholics. Engendered by a widely felt indignation at the Holy See's "separatist" policy, nurtured by a veneration for Graeco-Roman antiquity, and strengthened in one period of his life by an essentially Positivist scientism, Carducci's anticlericalism often developed into anti-Christianism. One example of this spirit is the famous *Inno a Satana (Hymn to Satan,* 1865) in which the locomotive, symbol of man's progress, announces the rightful victory of the fallen angel over the god of darkness. Had Carducci addressed his vehement apostrophes solely to the Pope and his Cardinals, they would not deserve any great attention—especially in view of the outbursts of patriotic irritation in

Italy against the Holy See after 1849 and still more after 1870. But the author of *The Barbarian Odes* did not limit his attacks to the Pope and church of his own day: he went back to Christ Himself, blaming Him for His race and reproaching Him almost with having perverted the very nature of Italy's soul.

Carducci's conflict with the Italian romantics and his defense of classicism supplied the inspiration for an important part of his poetic work. He wrote almost thirty poems in honor of his favorite authors—Homer, Virgil, Dante, Petrarch, Ariosto, Metastasio, Goldoni, Alfieri, Parini, Monti, Pietro Giordani, Giovanni Battista Niccolini, Terenzio Mamiani, Victor Hugo—and there are innumerable allusions to authors of the past. But Carducci would not have been Carducci had he merely sung the praises of those he venerated or admired. In the same breath, as it were, he attacked his romantic and realistic contemporaries in a language that sometimes carried vigor to the point of scurrility.

Finally, unlike many poets who either scorn technical workmanship or conceal that workmanship under a feigned carelessness, the author of *The Barbarian Odes* often took prosody as the very subject matter of his verse. When he imitated a genre he said so clearly. This is no great surprise in a man whose loyalty to the classical spirit kept him from thinking of poetry as a sudden inspiration, a gift of the gods, a fine frenzy. As he said in the *"Congedo"* ("Envoi") to his *New Rhymes,* a poet is not a "sponger," nor an "idler" or a "gardener," but a "great craftsman whose trade gives him steely muscles"; not a courtier, a dreamer, or an entertainer, but a worker who blends love and thought, past and future, and forges the alloy thus obtained into the arms and tools that make men strong and happy.

Paul Renucci is director of the Italian Institute for Higher Studies in Paris.
Translated by Robert Allen.

THE 1906 PRIZE

By GUNNAR AHLSTRÖM

WHEN Carducci won the Nobel Prize in 1906, he was universally famous although his poetic works did not consist of one of those breviaries of which one turns the pages daily. His works had grown dim, whereas the personality of the man who had held the pen had acquired the importance of a myth over the years, which is a frequent phenomenon in the world of literature. The man himself had been canonized, haloed, and metamorphosed into a venerable name, the glory of which was securely based on an impressive biography, amplified by a crop of personal anecdotes and scattered quotations. In him, burning patriotism was allied to an audacious defiance of obscurantism and the power of the Pope. Above all, he was the man who had sung the *Hymn to Satan*, and had paid homage in these words: "Hail, O Satan, O rebellion, O vengeful force of Reason! May incense and sacred vows rise up towards Thee! Thou hast vanquished the Jehovah of the priests!"

This fiery invocation gave the general public the impression that Carducci was a champion of the people and a straightforward propagandist. They did not see that his poetry was really of a highly scholarly nature. His was a poetic art which abounded in classical allusions and arose from a bookish humanism. For years his poetry had aroused the enthusi-

asm and intellectual appetites of its disciples by its impulsive interpretation of the great recognized masters of Italy.

The importance of the part played by Carducci in the intellectual life of his country justified putting forward his name as a candidate at the very start of the Nobel Prize discussions. But his candidacy was very soon faced with various obstacles. In order to simplify things, we can group them under two headings: those of age, and ideas. Both of them are characteristic of the epoch.

The discussion provoked by the first awards of the Nobel Prize revolved around the question of whether there was any justification in awarding it to old men who, in all probability, had achieved their life's work. The glitter of this enormous Prize on the literary horizon had caused a swarm among the recognized, bemedalled, and overpraised writers of Europe. But they had all, unfortunately, already inconveniently reached a much too advanced age. Were these gray- or white-bearded recluses really the laureates to whom the generous donor had meant to bequeath his money?

Carducci was without any doubt the poet laureate of Italy, and, as he was born in 1835, he already perfectly fulfilled the necessary qualification of old age. Were the gentlemen of Stockholm once more about to defy the views of youth and reward a man whose work had already been achieved, instead of encouraging some writer whose genius was just beginning to dawn? The years passed. People murmured to each other, with knitted brows, that the sage of Bologna had suffered a stroke and no longer left his chair. Anxiety deepened among his friends and compatriots. When Count Ugo Bolzani, in his capacity as a member of the Real Academia dei Lincei, proposed Carducci for the 1906 Prize, he did not fail to emphasize the risks attached to further delay: "The age and especially the state of health of the illustrious writer make it desirable not to delay too long before awarding him the Prize, if this great honor is to be the crowning achievement of his life."

He had lived so long that the obstacle of age had aggravated a situation which had already been rendered difficult by the obstacle created by his ideas. Many things had changed since the days when the *Hymn to Satan* had first appeared. Europe had entered an age of neomysticism, neo-Catholicism, neoromanticism, and other still more occult "-isms." The old guard of the defenders of liberty and radicalism felt that evolution had retrogressed. What had become of the "vengeful force of Reason?" Who talked nowadays of paganism, of anticlericalism, of rationalism, and of the republicanism of the days of Garibaldi? Where were the barricades of long ago? In these peculiar times, the laurel wreath ought to be offered to writers with idealist views, and the Swedish Academy clearly gave a precise meaning to this term.

For the supporters of Carducci, it was a question of making their old warrior acceptable, of adapting him to the standards laid down in the will of Alfred Nobel. It was hardly possible purely and simply to repudiate the ideas which had inspired the great poet: this would have

been to remove from his work that which gave it its nerves and its vital force. The solution was to bring the discussion onto a historical and human level; in this field the old professor lent himself admirably to favorable interpretation. It was easy to highlight his nobility of feeling, his self-sacrifice, and his high-mindedness in considering the trivialities and difficulties of life, without making up one's mind about his former revolutionary beliefs: he was a Cato with a generous heart and a flashing intelligence.

It was in this sense that his name had been mentioned from 1902 onwards. His candidacy was proposed by a younger colleague, Antonio Fogazzaro, who was also later to play a part in the discussions on the Nobel Prize. Strengthened by the support of the rector of Bologna University, Vittorio Puntoni, he pleaded Carducci's cause with eloquence. All reserves on the subject are transformed in this document into praise: "There are many people in Italy, including myself, who do not share all of the poet's views, but nobody would dare question the purity of a glory which has never been tarnished by a breath of vanity or cupidity. During half a century his songs have deeply stirred the soul of the nation. He has been a stout fighter and his sparkling verse, which he handles like a sword, could have inflicted many wounds: but his poetic fire has perhaps sometimes carried him away beyond his goal, and his impetuous heart has never borne a grudge."

The Prize went elsewhere in 1902, 1903, 1904, and 1905. But time was working in favor of Italian hopes. The hoary-headed professor of Bologna was beginning to find determined supporters in Sweden. Unanimity over the choice of his name was reached in 1906. The definitive decision was welcomed without any surprise or acclamation, but with the somewhat resigned satisfaction of seeing this well-deserved laurel wreath arrive in time.

Perhaps Carducci had similar feelings on receiving the letter from the Swedish Academy informing him that he had been awarded the Prize "not only in consideration of his deep learning and critical research, but above all as a tribute to the creative energy, freshness of style, and the lyrical force which characterize his poetic masterpieces." His answer bears the date of November 15, 1906. It is the letter of a weary old man who, with the help of his secretary, endeavors to carve out beautiful phrases.

The letter which you have written me in the name of the illustrious Swedish Academy, the noble language in which it is conceived, the flattering words about me which it contains, and the munificence of the Prize with which my modest works have been rewarded, have filled me with the deepest and most heartfelt gratitude and emotion, and I am writing to say that I accept the great honor which has been done to me and that I will keep it a secret until the prescribed day.

Remarkable indeed is my good fortune, in giving me the joy of obtaining, during my lifetime, one of the greatest satisfactions to which a man can aspire: it is a joy which is nevertheless overshadowed for me by the bitterness of being unable to visit that glorious capital to receive the insignia of the Prize in person, during the course of an unforgettable day, from the hands of His August Majesty the King.

My infirmities, dear Sir, at present deny me all bodily movement; there only remain the mind and the heart. With the first I would like, through your good offices, to convey my warmest thanks to the illustrious Academy of Stockholm: with the second, I send my most fervent wishes for the greatness and prosperity of the Swedish nation and its King.

The following year, Carducci was no more.

Translated by Camilla Sykes.

Grazia Deledda

1926

"For her idealistically inspired writings
which with plastic clarity picture the life
on her native island and with depth and
sympathy deal with human problems
in general"

Illustrated by BORDEAUX LE PECQ

PRESENTATION ADDRESS

By *HENRIK SCHÜCK*

PRESIDENT OF THE NOBEL FOUNDATION

―――――――

THE SWEDISH ACADEMY has awarded the Nobel Prize of 1926 to the Italian author Grazia Deledda.

Grazia Deledda was born in Nuoro, a small town in Sardinia. There she spent her childhood and her youth, and from the natural surroundings and the life of the people she drew the impressions which later became the inspiration and the soul of her literary work.

From the window of her house she could see the nearby mountains of Orthobene with their dark forests and jagged gray peaks. Farther off was a chain of limestone mountains which sometimes appeared violet, sometimes lemon-colored, sometimes dark blue, depending on the variations of the light. And in the distance, the snowy peaks to Gennargentù emerged.

Nuoro was isolated from the rest of the world. The few visitors to the town usually arrived on horseback, with the women mounted behind the men. The monotony of daily life was interrupted only by traditional religious or popular holidays and by the songs and dances in the main street at carnival time.

In this environment, Grazia Deledda's view of life developed into something uniquely ingenuous and primitive. In Nuoro it was not considered shameful to be a bandit. "Do you think," says an old peasant woman in one of Deledda's novels, "that bandits are bad people? Well, you're wrong. They are only men who need to display their skill, that's all. In the old days men went to war. Now there aren't any more wars, but men still need to fight. And so they commit their holdups, their thefts, and their cattle stealing, not to do evil but only to display somehow their ability and their strength." Thus the bandit rather enjoys the sympathy of the people. If he is caught and put in prison, the peasants have an expressive phrase which means that he has "run into trouble." And when he is freed no stigma it attached to him. In fact, when he returns to his home town, he is greeted with the words, "More such trouble a hundred years from now!"

The vendetta is still the custom in Sardinia, and a person is respected if he takes blood revenge on the killer of a kinsman. Indeed, it is considered a crime to betray the avenger. One author writes, "Even if the reward on his head were three times its size, not a single man in the whole district of Nuoro could be found to betray him. Only one law reigns there: respect for a man's strength and scorn of society's justice."

In this town, so little influenced by the Italian mainland, Grazia Deledda grew up surrounded by a savagely beautiful natural setting and by people who possessed a certain primitive grandeur, in a house that had a sort of Biblical simplicity about it. "We girls," Grazia Deledda writes, "were never allowed to go out except to go to Mass or to take an occasional walk in the countryside." She had no chance to get an advanced education, and like the other middle-class children in the area, she went only to the local school. Later she took a few private lessons in French and Italian because her family spoke only the Sardinian dialect at home. Her education, then, was not extensive. However, she was thoroughly acquainted with and delighted in the folk songs of her town with its hymns to the saints, its ballads, and its lullabies. She was also familiar with the legends and traditions of Nuoro. Furthermore, she had an opportunity at home to read a few works of Italian literature and a few novels in translation, since by Sardinian standards her family was relatively well-to-do. But this was all. Yet the young girl took a great liking to her studies, and at only thirteen she wrote a whimsical but tragic short story, "Sangue Sardo" (Sardinian Blood, 1888), which she succeeded in publishing in a Roman newspaper. The people at Nuoro did not at all like this display of audacity, since women were not supposed to concern themselves with anything but domestic duties. But Grazia Deledda did not conform; instead she devoted herself to writing novels: first *Fior di Sardegna* (Flower of Sardinia), published in 1892; then *La via del male* (The Evil Way, 1896), *Il vecchio della montagna* (The Old Man of the Mountain, 1900), *Elias Portolú* (1903), and others with which she made a name for herself. She came to be recognized as one of the best young female writers in Italy.

She had, in fact, made a great discovery—she had discovered Sardinia. In the middle of the eighteenth century a new movement had arisen in European literature. Writers at that time were tired of the models constantly drawn from Greek and Roman literature. They wanted something new. Their movement quickly joined forces with another which had begun in the same epoch with Rousseau's adoration of man in his natural state, untouched by civilization. The new school formed from these two movements advanced and gained force, particularly in the great days of romanticism. The school's most recent trophies have been won by the work of Grazia Deledda. It is true that in descriptions of local color and peasant life she had predecessors even in her own country. The so-called regionalist school in Italian literature had had such notable representatives as Verga, with his descriptions of Sicily, and Fogazzaro, with his descriptions of the Lombardo–Veneto region. But the discovery of Sardinia decidedly belongs to Grazia Deledda. She knew intimately every corner of her native land. She stayed in Nuoro until she was twenty-five; only then did she find the courage to go to Cagliari, the capital of Sardinia. Here she met Madesani, the man whom she married in 1900. After her marriage she and her husband moved to Rome, where she divided her time between her work as a writer and her family duties. In the novels written after she moved to Rome, she continued to deal with Sardinian subjects, as in the work entitled *L'Edera* (The Ivy, 1908). But in the novels written after *L'Edera,* the action frequently takes place in a less localized atmosphere, as for example, in *La Fuga in Egitto* (The Flight into Egypt, 1925), which the Academy has examined and appreciated. However, her conception of man and nature is, as always, fundamentally Sardinian in character. Although she is now artistically more mature, she remains the same serious, eloquent, but unpretentious writer who wrote *La via del male* and *Elias Portolú.*

It is rather difficult for a foreigner to judge the artistic merit of her style. I shall therefore quote one of the most famous Italian critics on this matter. "Her style," he writes, "is that of the great masters of the narrative; it has the characteristic marks of all great novelists. No one in Italy today writes novels which have the vigor of style, the power of craftsmanship, the structure, or the social relevance which is found in some, even the latest, works of Grazia Deledda such as *La Madre* (*The Mother,* 1920) and *Il Segreto dell'uomo solitario* (The Secret of the Solitary Man, 1921)." One might note only that her composition does not have the strong consistency which might be desired; unexpected passages often give the impression of hasty transitions. But this defect is more than generously compensated for by her many virtues. As a painter of nature she has few equals in European literature. She does not uselessly waste her vivid colors; but even then, the nature which she describes has the simple, broad lines of ancient landscapes, as it has their chaste purity and majesty. It is a marvelously lively nature in perfect harmony with the psychological life of her characters. Like a truly great artist, she succeeds in incorporating her representation of people's sentiments and customs into her descriptions of nature. Indeed, one need only recall the classic description of the pilgrim's sojourn on Mount Lula in *Elias Portolú.* They depart on a May morning. Family after family ascends toward the ancient votive church, some on horseback, some in old wagons. They carry along enough provisions to last a week. The wealthier families lodge in the great shelter standing next to the church. These families are descended from the church's founders, and each has a spike in the wall and a hearth to indicate the area which belongs to it. No one else can set foot in this area. Each evening the families gather in their respective areas for as long as the feast lasts. They cook their food over the fireplace and tell legends, play music, and sing during the long summer night.

In the novel *La via del male,* Grazia Deledda describes equally vividly the strange Sardinian marriage and funeral customs. When a funeral is to take place, all of the doors are shut, all of the shutters are closed, every fire is put out, no one is permitted to prepare food, and hired mourners wail their improvised dirges. The descriptions of such primitive customs are so lifelike and so simple and natural that we are almost moved to call them Homeric. In Grazia Deledda's novels more than in most other novels, man and nature form a single unity. One might almost say that the men are plants which germinate in the Sardinian soil itself. The majority of them are simple peasants with primitive sensibilities and modes of thought, but with something in them of the grandeur of the Sardinian natural setting. Some of them almost attain the stature of the monumental figures of the Old Testament. And no matter how different they may seem from the men we know, they give us the impression of being incontestably real, of belonging to real life. They in no way resemble theatrical puppets. Grazia Deledda is a master of the art of fusing realism with idealism.

She does not belong to that band of writers who work on a thesis and discuss problems. She has always kept herself far removed from the battles of the day. When Ellen Key once tried to interest her in such discussions, she answered, "I belong to the past." Perhaps this confession of attitude is not completely just. Certainly Grazia Deledda feels tied by strong bonds to the past, to the history of her people. But she also knows how to live in and respond to her own times. Although she lacks interest in theories, she has a great deal of interest in every aspect of human life. She writes in a letter, "One great anguish is life's slow death. This is why we must try to slow life down, to intensify it, thus giving it the richest possible meaning. One must try to live above one's life, as a cloud above the sea." Precisely because life seems so rich and admirable to her, she has never taken sides in the political, social, or literary controversies of the day. She has loved man more than theories and has lived her own quiet life far from the world's uproar. "Destiny," she writes in another letter, "caused me to be born in the heart of lonely Sardinia. But even if I had been born in Rome or Stockholm, I should not have been different. I should have always been what I am—a soul which becomes impassioned about life's problems and which lucidly perceives men as they are, while still believing that they could be better and that no one else but themselves prevents them from achieving God's reign on earth. Everything is hatred, blood, and pain; but, perhaps, everything will be conquered one day by means of love and good will."

These last words express her vision of life, a serious and profound vision with a religious cast. It is frequently sad, but never pessimistic. She believes that the forces of good ultimately will triumph in the life struggle. The principle which dominates all her work as a writer is represented clearly and concisely at the end of her novel *Cenere* (*Ashes,* 1904). Anania's mother is ruined. In order not to be an obstacle to her son's happiness, she has taken her own life and now lies dead before him. When he was only a baby, she had given him an amulet. He opens and and finds that it contains only ashes. "Yes, all was ashes: life, death, man; the very destiny which produced her. And still in the last hour, as he stood before the body of the most miserable of human creatures, who after doing and suffering evil in all of its manifestations had died for someone else's good, he remembered that among the ashes there often lurks the spark of a luminous and purifying flame. And he hoped. And he still loved life."

Alfred Nobel wanted the Prize for Literature to be given to someone who, in his writings, had given humanity that nectar which infuses the health and the energy of a moral life. In conformity with his wishes, the Swedish Academy has awarded the Prize to Grazia Deledda, "for her idealistically inspired writings which with plastic clarity picture the life on her native island and with depth and sympathy deal with human problems in general."

There was no formal Acceptance Speech by Deledda.

THE MOTHER

By GRAZIA DELEDDA

Translated from the Italian by Mary G. Steegmann

CHAPTER I

Tonight again Paul was preparing to go out, it seemed.

From her room adjoining his the mother could hear him moving about furtively, perhaps waiting to go out until she should have extinguished her light and got into bed.

She put out her light, but she did not get into bed.

Seated close against the door, she clasped her hands tightly together, those work-worn hands of a servant, pressing the thumbs one upon the other to give herself courage; but every moment her uneasiness increased and overcame her obstinate hope that her son would sit down quietly, as he used to do, and begin to read, or else go to bed. For a few minutes, indeed, the young priest's cautious steps were silent. She felt herself all alone. Outside, the noise of the wind mingled with the murmuring of the trees which grew on the ridge of high ground behind the little presbytery; not a high wind, but incessant, monotonous, that sounded as though it were enveloping the house in some creaking, invisible band, ever closer and closer, trying to uproot it from its foundations and drag it to the ground.

The mother had already closed the house door and barricaded it with two crossed bars, in order to prevent the devil, who on windy nights roams abroad in search of souls, from penetrating into the house. As a matter of fact, however, she put little faith in such things. And now she reflected with bitterness, and a vague contempt of herself, that the evil spirit was already inside the little presbytery, that it drank from her Paul's cup and hovered about the mirror he had hung on the wall near his window.

Just then she heard Paul moving about again. Perhaps he was actually standing in front of the mirror, although that was forbidden to priests. But what had Paul not allowed himself for some considerable time now?

The mother remembered that lately she had several times come upon him gazing at himself in the glass like any woman, cleaning and polishing his nails, or brushing his hair, which he had left to grow long and then turned back over his head, as though trying to conceal the holy mark of the tonsure. And then he made use of perfumes, he brushed his teeth with scented powder, and even combed out his eyebrows.

She seemed to see him now as plainly as though the dividing wall did not exist, a black figure against the white background of his room; a tall, thin figure, almost too tall, going to and fro with the heedless steps of a boy, often stumbling and slipping about, but always holding himself erect. His head was a little too large for the thin neck, his face pale and overshadowed by the prominent forehead that seemed to force the brows to frown and the long eyes to droop with the burden of it. But the powerful jaw, the wide, full mouth and the resolute chin seemed in their turn to revolt with scorn against this oppression, yet not be able to throw it off.

But now he halted before the mirror and his whole face lighted up, the eyelids opened to the full and the pupils of his clear brown eyes shone like diamonds.

Actually, in the depths of her maternal heart, his mother delighted to see him so handsome and strong, and then the sound of his furtive steps moving about again recalled her sharply to her anxiety.

He was going out, there could be no more doubt about that. He opened the door of his room and stood still again. Perhaps he, too, was listening to the sounds without, but there was nothing to be heard save the encircling wind beating ever against the house.

The mother made an effort to rise from her chair, to cry out "My son, Paul, child of God, stay here!" but a power stronger than her own will kept her down. Her knees trembled as though trying to rebel against that infernal power; her knees trembled, but her feet refused to move, and it was as though two compelling hands were holding her down upon her seat.

Thus Paul could steal noiselessly downstairs, open the door and go out, and the wind seemed to engulf him and bear him away in a flash.

Only then was she able to rise and light her lamp again. But even this was only achieved with difficulty, because, instead of igniting, the matches left long violet streaks on the wall wherever she struck them. But at last the little brass lamp threw a dim radiance over the small

room, bare and poor as that of a servant, and she opened the door and stood there, listening. She was still trembling, yet she moved stiffly and woodenly, and with her large head and her short, broad figure clothed in rusty black she looked as though she had been hewn with an ax, all of a piece, from the trunk of an oak.

From her threshold she looked down the slate stairs descending steeply between white-washed walls, at the bottom of which the door shook upon its hinges with the violence of the wind. And when she saw the two bars which Paul had unfastened and left leaning against the wall she was filled with sudden wild anger.

Ah no, she must defeat the devil. Then she placed her light on the floor at the top of the stairs, descended and went out, too.

The wind seized hold of her roughly, blowing out her skirts and the handkerchief over her head, as though it were trying to force her back into the house. But she knotted the handkerchief tightly under her chin and pressed forward with bent head, as though butting aside all obstacles in her path. She felt her way past the front of the presbytery, along the wall of the kitchen garden and past the front of the church, but at the corner of the church she paused. Paul had turned there, and swiftly, like some great black bird, his cloak flapping round him, he had almost flown across the field that extended in front of an old house built close against the ridge of land that shut in the horizon above the village.

The uncertain light, now blue, now yellow, as the moon's face shone clear or was traversed by big clouds, illumined the long grass of the field, the little raised piazza in front of the church and presbytery, and the two lines of cottages on either side of the steep road, which wound on and downwards till it lost itself amid the trees in the valley. And in the center of the valley, like another gray and winding road, was the river that flowed on and in its turn lost itself amid the rivers and roads of the fantastic landscape that the wind-driven clouds alternately revealed and concealed on that distant horizon that lay beyond the valley's edge.

In the village itself not a light was to be seen, nor even a thread of smoke. They were all asleep by now in the poverty-stricken cottages, which clung to the grassy hill-side like two rows of sheep, while the church with its slender tower, itself protected by the ridge of land behind it, might well represent the shepherd leaning upon his staff.

The elder trees which grew along the parapet of the piazza before the church were bending and tossing furiously in the wind, black and shapeless monsters in the gloom, and in answer to their rustling cry came the lament of the poplars and reeds in the valley. And in all this dolor of the night, the moaning wind and the moon drowning midst the angry clouds, was merged the sorrow of the mother seeking for her son.

Until that moment she had tried to deceive herself with the hope that she would see him going before her down into the village to visit some sick parishioner, but instead, she beheld him running as though spurred on by the devil towards the old house under the ridge.

And in that old house under the ridge there was no one save a woman, young, healthy and alone. . . .

Instead of approaching the principal entrance like an ordinary visitor, he went straight to the little door in the orchard wall, and immediately it opened and closed again behind him like a black mouth that had swallowed him up.

Then she too ran across the meadow, treading in the path his feet had made in the long grass; straight to the little door she ran, and she put her open hands

against it, pushing with all her strength. But the little door remained closed, it even seemed to repulse her by an active power of its own, and the woman felt she must strike it and cry aloud. She looked at the wall and touched it as though to test its solidity, and at last in despair she bent her head and listened intently. But nothing could be heard save the creaking and rustling of the trees inside the orchard, friends and accomplices of their mistress, trying to cover with their own noises all other sounds there within.

But the mother would not be beaten, she must hear and know—or rather, since in her inmost soul she already knew the truth, she wanted some excuse for still deceiving herself.

Careless now whether she were seen or not, she walked the whole length of the orchard wall, past the front of the house, and beyond it as far as the big gate of the courtyard; and as she went she touched the stones as though seeking one that would give way and leave a hole whereby she might enter in. But everything was solid, compact, fast shut—the big entrance gate, the hall door, the barred windows were like the openings in a fortress.

At that moment the moon emerged from behind the clouds and shone out clear in a lake of blue, illuminating the reddish frontage of the house, which was partly overshadowed by the deep eaves of the overhanging grass-grown roof; the inside shutters of the windows were closed and the panes of glass shone like greenish mirrors, reflecting the drifting clouds and the patches of blue sky and the tossing branches of the trees upon the ridge.

Then she turned back, striking her head against the iron rings let into the wall for tethering horses. Again she halted in front of the chief entrance, and before that big door with its three granite steps, its Gothic porch and iron gate, she felt suddenly humiliated, power-less to succeed, smaller even than when, as a little girl, she had loitered near with other poor children of the village, waiting till the master of the house should come out and fling them a few pence.

It had happened sometimes in those far-off days that the door had been left wide open and had afforded a view into a dark entrance hall, paved with stone and furnished with stone seats. The children had shouted at this and thrust themselves forward even to the threshold, their voices re-echoing in the interior of the house as in a cave. Then a servant had appeared to drive them away.

"What! You here, too, Maria Mad-dalena! Aren't you ashamed to go run-ning about with those boys, a great girl like you?"

And she, the girl, had shrunk back abashed, but nevertheless she had turned to stare curiously at the mysterious inside of the house. And just so did she shrink back now and move away, wringing her hands in despair and staring again at the little door which had swallowed up her Paul like a trap. But as she retraced her steps and walked homeward again she began to regret that she had not shouted, that she had not thrown stones at the door and compelled those inside to open it and let her try to rescue her son. She repented her weakness, stood still, irreso-lute, turned back, then homewards again, drawn this way and that by her torment-ing anxiety, uncertain what to do: until at last the instinct of self-preservation, the need of collecting her thoughts and concentrating her strength for the deci-sive battle, drove her home as a wounded animal takes refuge in its lair.

The instant she got inside the presby-tery she shut the door and sat down heavily on the bottom stair. From the top of the staircase came the dim flickering light of the lamp, and everything within the little house, up to now as steady and

quiet as a nest built in some crevice of the rocks, seemed to swing from side to side: the rock was shaken to its founda-tions and the nest was falling to the ground.

Outside the wind moaned and whistled more loudly still; the devil was destroying the presbytery, the church, the whole world of Christians.

"Oh Lord, oh Lord!" wailed the mother, and her voice sounded like the voice of some other woman speaking.

Then she looked at her own shadow on the staircase wall and nodded to it. Truly, she felt that she was not alone, and she began to talk as though another person were there with her, listening and replying.

"What can I do to save him?"

"Wait here till he comes in, and then speak to him plainly and firmly while you are still in time, Maria Maddalena."

"But he would get angry and deny it all. It would be better to go to the Bishop and beg him to send us away from this place of perdition. The Bishop is a man of God and knows the world. I will kneel at his feet; I can almost see him now, dressed all in white, sitting in his red re-ception room, with his golden cross shin-ing on his breast and two fingers raised in benediction. He looks like our Lord Himself! I shall say to him: Monsignore, you know that the parish of Aar, besides being the poorest in the kingdom, lies under a curse. For nearly a hundred years it was without a priest and the in-habitants forgot God entirely; then at last a priest came here, but Monsignore knows what manner of man he was. Good and holy till he was fifty years of age: he restored the presbytery and the church, built a bridge across the river at his own expense, and went out shooting and shared the common life of the shepherds and hunters. Then suddenly he changed and became as evil as the devil. He practiced sorcery. He began to drink

and grew overbearing and passionate. He used to smoke a pipe and swear, and he would sit on the ground playing cards with the worst ruffians of the place, who liked him and protected him, however, and for this very reason the others let him alone. Then, during his latter years, he shut himself up in the presbytery all alone without even a servant, and he never went outside the door except to say Mass, but he always said it before dawn, so that nobody ever went. And they say he used to celebrate when he was drunk. His parishioners were too frightened to bring any accusation against him, because it was said that he was protected by the devil in person. And then when he fell ill there was not a woman who would go and nurse him. Neither woman nor man, of the decent sort, went to help him through his last days, and yet at night every window in the presbytery was lighted up; and the people said that during those last nights the devil had dug an underground passage from this house to the river, through which to carry away the mortal remains of the priest. And by this passage the spirit of the priest used to come back in the years that followed his death and haunt the presbytery, so that no other priest would ever come to live here. A priest used to come from another village every Sunday to say Mass and bury the dead, but one night the spirit of the dead priest destroyed the bridge, and after that for ten years the parish was without a priest, until my Paul came. And I came with him. We found the village and its inhabitants grown quite wild and uncivilized, without faith at all, but everything revived again after my Paul came, like the earth at the return of the spring. But the superstitious were right, disaster will fall upon the new priest because the spirit of the old one still reigns in the presbytery. Some say that he is not dead and that he lives in an underground dwelling communicating with the river. I myself have never believed in such tales, nor have I ever heard any noises. For seven years we have lived here, my Paul and I, as in a little convent. Until a short time ago Paul led the life of an innocent child, he studied and prayed and lived only for the good of his parishioners. Sometimes he used to play the flute. He was not merry by nature, but he was calm and quiet. Seven years of peace and plenty have we had, like those in the Bible. My Paul never drank, he did not go out shooting, he did not smoke and he never looked at a woman. All the money he could save he put aside to rebuild the bridge below the village. He is twenty-eight years old, is my Paul, and now the curse has fallen upon him. A woman has caught him in her net. Oh, my Lord Bishop, send us away from here; save my Paul, for otherwise he will lose his soul as did the former priest! And the woman must be saved, too. After all, she is a woman living alone and she has her temptations also in that lonely house, amid the desolation of this little village where there is nobody fit to bear her company. My Lord Bishop, your Lordship knows that woman, you were her guest with all your following when you came here on your pastoral visitation. There is room and stuff to spare, in that house! And the woman is rich, independent, alone, too much alone! She has brothers and a sister, but they are all far away, married and living in other countries. She remained here alone to look after the house and the property, and she seldom goes out. And until a little while ago my Paul did not even know her. Her father was a strange sort of man, half gentleman, half peasant, a hunter and a heretic. He was a friend of the old priest, and I need say no more. He never went to church, but during his last illness he sent for my Paul, and my Paul stayed with him till he died and gave him a funeral such as had never been seen in these parts. Every single person in the village went to it, even the babies were carried in their mothers' arms. Then afterwards my Paul went on visiting the only survivor of that household. And this orphan girl lives alone with bad servants. Who directs her, who advises her? Who is there to help her if we do not?"

Then the other woman asked her:

"Are you certain of this, Maria Maddalena? Are you really sure that what you think is true? Can you actually go before the Bishop and speak thus about your son and that other person, and prove it? And suppose it should not be true?"

"Oh Lord, oh Lord!"

She buried her face in her hands, and immediately there rose before her the vision of her Paul and the woman together in a ground-floor room in the old house. It was a very large room looking out into the orchard, with a domed ceiling, and the floor was of pounded cement with which small sea-shells and pebbles had been mixed; on one side was an immense fireplace, to right and left of which stood an arm-chair and in front was an antique sofa. The whitewashed walls were adorned with arms, stags' heads and antlers, and paintings whose blackened canvases hung in tatters, little of the subjects being distinguishable in the shadows save here and there a dusky hand, some vestige of a face, of a woman's hair, or bunch of fruit.

Paul and the woman were seated in front of the fire, clasping each other's hands.

"Oh, my God!" came the mother's moaning cry.

And in order to banish that diabolic vision she evoked another. It was the same room again, but illumined now by the greenish light that came through the barred window looking out over the meadow and the door which opened direct from the room into the orchard, and through which she saw the trees and foliage gleaming, still wet with the autumn dew. Some fallen leaves were blown softly about the floor and the chains of the antique brass lamp that stood upon the mantelshelf swung to and fro in the draught. Through a half-open door on the other side she could see other rooms, all somewhat dark and with closed windows.

She stood there waiting, with a present of fruit which her Paul had sent to the mistress of the house. And then the mistress came, with a quickened step and yet a little shy; she came from the dark rooms, dressed in black, her pale face framed between two great knots of black plaits, and her thin white hands emerging from the shadows like those in the pictures on the wall.

And even when she came close and stood in the full light of the room there was about her small slender figure something evanescent, doubtful. Her large dark eyes fell instantly on the basket of fruit standing on the table, then turned with a searching look upon the woman who stood waiting, and a swift smile, half joy, half contempt, passed over the sad and sensual curves of her lips.

And in that moment, though she knew not how or why, the first suspicion stirred in the mother's heart.

She could not have explained the reason why, but her memory dwelt on the eagerness with which the girl had welcomed her, making her sit down beside her and asking for news of Paul. She called him Paul as a sister might have done, but she did not treat her as though she were their common mother, but rather as a rival who must be flattered and deceived. She ordered coffee for her, which was served on a large silver tray by a barefoot maid whose face was swathed like an Arab's. She talked of her two brothers, both influential men living far away, taking secret delight in picturing herself between these two, as between columns supporting the fabric of her solitary life. And then at last she led the visitor out to see the orchard, through the door opening straight from the room.

Big purple figs covered with a silver sheen, pears, and great bunches of golden grapes hung amid the vivid green of the trees and vines. Why should Paul send a gift of fruit to one who possessed so much already?

Even now, sitting on the stairs in the dim light of the flickering lamp, the mother could see again the look, at once ironical and tender, which the girl had turned upon her as she bade her farewell, and the manner in which she lowered her heavy eyelids as though she knew no other way of hiding the feelings her eyes betrayed too plainly. And those eyes, and that way of revealing her soul in a sudden flash of truth and then instantly drawing back into herself again, was extraordinarily like Paul. So much so that during the days following, when because of his manner and his reserve her suspicions grew and filled her heart with fear, she did not think with any hatred of the woman who was leading him into sin, but she thought only of how she might save her too, as though it had been the saving of a daughter of her own.

CHAPTER II

Autumn and winter had passed without anything happening to confirm her suspicions, but now with the return of the spring, with the blowing of the March winds, the devil took up his work again.

Paul went out at night, and he went to the old house.

"What shall I do, how can I save him?"

But the wind only mocked at her in reply, shaking the house door with its furious blasts.

She remembered their first coming to the village, immediately after Paul had been appointed parish priest here. For twenty years she had been in service and had resisted every temptation, every prompting and instinct of nature, depriving herself of love, even of bread itself, in order that she might bring up her boy rightly and set him a good example. Then they came here, and just such a furious wind as this had beset them on their journey. It had been springtime then, too, but the whole valley seemed to have slipped back into the grip of winter. Leaves were blown hither and thither, the trees bent before the blast, leaning one against another, as though gazing fearfully at the battalions of black clouds driving rapidly across the sky from all parts of the horizon, while large hailstones fell and bruised the tender green.

At the point where the road turns, overlooking the valley, and then descends towards the river, there was such a sudden onslaught of wind that the horses came to a dead stop, pricking their ears and neighing with fear. The storm shook their bridles like some bandit who had seized their heads to stop them that he might rob the travelers, and even Paul, although apparently he was enjoying the adventure, had cried out with vague superstition in his voice:

"It must be the evil spirit of the old priest trying to prevent us coming here!"

But his words were lost in the shrill whistling of the wind, and although he smiled a little ruefully, a one-sided smile that touched but one corner of his lips, his eyes were sad as they rested on the village which now came in sight, like a picture hanging on the green hill-side on the opposite slope of the valley beyond the tumbling stream.

The wind dropped a little after they

had crossed the river. The people of the village, who were as ready to welcome the new priest as though he were the Messiah, were all gathered together in the piazza before the church, and on a sudden impulse a group of the younger men among them had gone down to meet the travelers on the river bank. They descended the hill like a flight of young eagles from the mountains, and the air resounded with their merry shouts. When they reached their parish priest they gathered round him and bore him up the hill in triumph, every now and then firing their guns into the air as a mark of re-joicing. The whole valley echoed with their cheering and firing, the wind itself was pacified and the weather began to clear up.

Even in this present hour of anguish the mother's heart swelled with pride when she recalled that other hour of triumph. Again she seemed to be living in a dream, to be borne as though on a cloud by those noisy youths, while beside her walked her Paul, so boyish still, but with a look half divine upon his face as those strong men bowed before him with respect.

Up and up they climbed. Fireworks were being let off on the highest and barest point of the ridge, the flames streaming out like red banners against the background of black clouds and cast-ing their reflections on the gray village, the green hill-side and the tamarisks and elder trees that bordered the path.

Up and still up they went. Over the parapet of the piazza leaned another wall of human bodies and eager faces crowned with men's caps or framed in women's kerchiefs with long fluttering fringes. The children's eyes danced with delight at the unwonted excitement, and on the edge of the ridge the figures of the boys tending the fireworks looked like slender black demons in the distance.

Through the wide-open door of the church the flames of the lighted candles could be seen trembling like narcissi in the wind; the bells were ringing loudly, and even the clouds in the pale silvery sky seemed to have gathered round the tower to watch and wait.

Suddenly a cry rang out from the little crowd: "Here he is! Here he is! . . . And he looks like a saint!"

There was nothing of a saint about him, however, except that air of utter calm: he did not speak, he did not even acknowledge the people's greetings, he seemed in no way moved by that popular demonstration: he only pressed his lips tightly together and bent his eyes upon the ground with a slight frown, as though tired by the burden of that heavy brow. Then suddenly, when they had reached the piazza and were surrounded by the welcoming throng, the mother saw him falter as though about to fall, a man sup-ported him for an instant, then immedi-ately he recovered his balance and turn-ing swiftly into the church he fell on his knees before the altar and began to in-tone the evening prayer.

And the weeping women gave the re-sponses.

The poor women wept, but their tears were the happy tears of love and hope and the longing for a joy not of this world, and the mother felt the balm of those tears falling on her heart even in this hour of her grief. Her Paul! Her love, her hope, the embodiment of her desire for unearthly joy! And now the spirit of evil was drawing him away, and she sat there at the bottom of the stair-case as at the bottom of a well, and made no effort to rescue him.

She felt she was suffocating, her heart was heavy as a stone. She got up in order to breathe more easily, and mounting the stairs she picked up the lamp and held it aloft as she looked round her bare little room, where a wooden bedstead and a worm-eaten wardrobe kept each other company as the only furniture in the place. It was a room fit only for a servant—she had never desired to better her lot, content to find her only wealth in being the mother of her Paul.

Then she went into his room with its white walls and the narrow virginal bed. This chamber had once been kept as simple and tidy as that of a girl; he had loved quiet, silence, order, and always had flowers upon his little writing-table in front of the window. But latterly he had not cared about anything: he had left his drawers and cupboards open and his books littered about on the chairs or even on the floor.

The water in which he had washed before going out exhaled a strong scent of roses: a coat had been flung off carelessly and lay on the floor like a prostrate shadow of himself. That sight and that scent roused the mother from her preoccupation: she picked up the coat and thought scornfully that she would be strong enough even to pick up her son himself. Then she tidied the room, clattering to and fro without troubling now to deaden the sound of her heavy peasant shoes. She drew up to the table the leather chair in which he sat to read, thumping it down on the floor as though ordering it to remain in its place awaiting the speedy return of its master. Then she turned to the little mirror hanging beside the window. . . .

Mirrors are forbidden in a priest's house, he must forget that he has a body. On this point, at least, the old priest had observed the law, and from the road he could have been seen shaving himself by the open window, behind the panes of which he had hung a black cloth to show up the reflection. But Paul, on the contrary, was attracted to the mirror as to a well from whose depths a face smiled up at him, luring him down to perish. But it was the mother's own scornful face and threatening eyes that the little mirror reflected now, and with rising anger she put out her hand and tore it from its nail. Then she flung the window wide open and let the wind blow in to purify the room: the books and papers on the table seemed to come alive, twisting and circling into every corner, the fringe of the bed-cover shook and waved and the flame of the lamp flickered almost to extinction.

She gathered up the books and papers and replaced them on the table. Then she noticed an open Bible, with a colored picture that she greatly admired, and she bent down to examine it more closely. There was Jesus the Good Shepherd watering His sheep at a spring in the middle of a forest. Between the trees, against the background of blue sky, could be seen a distant city, red in the light of the setting sun, a holy city, the City of Salvation.

There had been a time when he used to study far into the night; the stars over the ridge looked in at his window and the nightingales sang him their plaintive notes. For the first year after they came to the village he often talked of leaving and going back into the world: then he settled down into a sort of waking sleep, in the shadow of the ridge and the murmur of the trees. Thus seven years passed, and his mother never suggested they should move elsewhere, for they were so happy in the little village that seemed to her the most beautiful in all the world, because her Paul was its savior and its king.

She closed the window and replaced the mirror, which showed her now her own face grown white and drawn, her eyes dim with tears. Again she asked herself if perhaps she were not mistaken. She turned towards a crucifix which hung on the wall above a kneeling-stool, raising the lamp above her head that she might see it better; and amid the shadows that her movements threw on the wall it seemed as though the Christ, thin and naked, stretched upon the Cross, bowed His head to hear her prayer. And great tears coursed down her face and fell upon her dress, heavy as tears of blood.

"Lord, save us all! Save Thou me, even me. Thou Who hang there pale and bloodless, Thou Whose Face beneath its crown of thorns is sweet as a wild rose, Thou Who art above our wretched passions, save us all!"

Then she hurried out of the room and went downstairs. She passed through the tiny dining-room, where drowsy flies, startled by the lamp, buzzed heavily round and the howling wind and swaying trees outside beat like rain upon the small, high window and thence into the kitchen, where she sat down before the fire, already banked up with cinders for the night. Even there the wind seemed to penetrate by every crack and cranny, so that instead of being in the long low kitchen, whose uneven ceiling was supported by smoke-blackened beams and rafters, she felt as if she were in a rocking boat adrift on a stormy sea. And although determined to wait up for her son and begin the battle at once, she still fought against conviction and tried to persuade herself that she was mistaken.

She felt it unjust that God should send her such sorrow, and she went back over her past life, day by day, trying to find some reason for her present unhappiness; but all her days had passed hard and clean as the beads of the rosary she held in her shaking fingers. She had done no wrong, unless perchance sometimes in her thoughts.

She saw herself again as an orphan in the house of poor relations, in that same village, ill-treated by every .one, toiling barefoot, bearing heavy burdens on her head, washing clothes in the river, or carrying corn to the mill. An elderly man, a relative of hers, was employed by the miller, and each time she went down to the mill, if there was nobody to see him, he followed her into the bushes and tufts of tamarisk and kissed her by force, pricking her face with his bristly beard and covering her with flour. When she told of this, the aunts with whom she lived would not let her go to the mill again. Then one day the man, who ordinarily never came up to the village, suddenly appeared at the house and said he wished to marry the girl. The other members of the family laughed at him, slapped him on the back and brushed the flour off his coat with a broom. But he took no notice of their jests and kept his eyes fixed on the girl. At last she consented to marry him, but she continued to live with her relations and went down each day to the mill to see her husband, who always gave her a small measure of flour unknown to his master. Then one day as she was going home with her apron full of flour she felt something move beneath it. Startled, she dropped the corners of her apron and all the flour was scattered, and she was so giddy that she had to sit down on the ground. She thought it was an earthquake, the houses rocked before her eyes, the path went up and down and she flung herself prone on the floury grass. Then she got up and ran home laughing, yet afraid, for she knew she was with child.

*   *   *

She was left a widow before her Paul was old enough to talk, but his bright baby eyes followed her everywhere, and she had mourned for her husband as for a good old man who had been kind to her, but nothing more. She was soon consoled, however, for a cousin proposed that they should go together to the town and there take service.

"In that way you will be able to support your boy, and later on you can send for him and put him to school."

And so she worked and lived only for him.

She had lacked neither the occasion nor the inclination to indulge in pleasures, if not in sin. Master of servants, peasant and townsman, all had tried to catch her as once the old kinsman had caught her among the tamarisks. Man is a hunter and woman his prey, but she had succeeded in evading all pitfalls and keeping herself pure and good, since she already looked on herself as the mother of a priest. Then wherefore now this chastisement, O Lord?

She bowed her weary head and the tears rolled down her face and fell on the rosary in her lap.

Gradually she grew drowsy, and confused memories floated through her mind. She thought she was in the big warm kitchen of the Seminary, where she had been servant for ten years and where she had succeeded in getting her Paul admitted as student. Black figures went silently to and fro, and in the passage outside she could hear the smothered laughter and larking the boys indulged in when there was nobody to reprove them. Tired to death, she sat beside a window opening on to a dark yard, a duster on her lap, but too weary to move so much as a finger towards her work. In the dream, too, she was waiting for Paul, who had slipped out of the Seminary secretly without telling her where he was going.

"If they find out they will expel him at once," she thought, and she waited anxiously till the house was quite quiet that she might let him in without being observed.

Suddenly she awoke and found herself back in the narrow presbytery kitchen, shaken by the wind like a ship at sea, but the impression of the dream was so strong that she felt on her lap for the duster and listened for the smothered laughter of the boys knocking each other

about in the passage. Then in a moment reality gripped her again, and she thought Paul must have come in while she was fast asleep and thus succeeded in escaping her notice. And actually, amid all the creakings and shaking caused by the wind, she could hear steps inside the house: some one was coming downstairs, crossing the ground-floor rooms, entering the kitchen. She thought she was still dreaming when a short, stout priest, with a week's growth of beard upon his chin, stood before her and looked her in the face with a smile. The few teeth he had left were blackened with too much smoking, his light-colored eyes pretended to be fierce, but she could tell that he was really laughing, and immediately she knew him for the former priest—but still she did not feel afraid.

"It is only a dream," she told herself, but in reality she knew she only said that to give herself courage and that it was no phantom, but a fact.

"Sit down," she said, moving her stool aside to make room for him in front of the fire. He sat down and drew up his cassock a little, exhibiting a pair of discolored and worn blue stockings.

"Since you are sitting here doing nothing, you might mend my stockings for me, Maria Maddalena: I have no woman to look after me," he said simply. And she thought to herself:

"Can this be the terrible priest? That shows I am still dreaming."

And then she tried to make him betray himself.

"If you are dead you have no need of stockings," she said.

"How do you know I am dead? I am very much alive, on the contrary, and sitting here. And before long I am going to drive both you and your son out of my parish. It was a bad thing for you, coming here, you had better have brought him up to follow his father's trade. But you are an ambitious woman, and you wanted to come back as mistress where you had lived as a servant: so now you will see what you have gained by it!"

"We will go away," she answered humbly and sadly. "Indeed, I want to go. Man or ghost, whatever you are, have patience for a few days and we shall be gone."

"And where can you go?" said the old priest. "Wherever you go it will be the same thing. Take rather the advise of one who knows what he is talking about and let your Paul follow his destiny. Let him know the woman, otherwise the same thing will befall him that befell me. When I was young I would have nothing to do with women, nor with any other kind of pleasure. I only thought of winning Paradise, and I failed to perceive that Paradise is here on earth. When I did perceive it, it was too late: my arm could no longer reach up to gather the fruit of the tree and my knees would not bend that I might quench my thirst at the spring. So then I began to drink wine, to smoke a pipe and to play cards with all the rascals of the place. You call them rascals, but I call them honest lads who enjoy life as they find it. It does one good to be in their company, it diffuses a little warmth and merriment, like the company of boys on a holiday. The only difference is that it is always holiday for them, and therefore they are even merrier and more careless than the boys, who cannot forget that they must soon go back to school."

While he was talking thus the mother thought to herself:

"He is only saying these things in order to persuade me to leave my Paul alone and let him be damned. He has been sent by his friend and master, the Devil, and I must be on my guard."

Yet, in spite of herself, she listened to him readily and found herself almost agreeing with what he said. She reflected that, in spite of all her efforts, Paul too might "take a holiday," and instinctively her mother's heart instantly sought excuses for him.

"You may be right," she said with increased sadness and humility, which now, however, was partly pretense. "I am only a poor, ignorant woman and don't understand very much: but one thing I am sure of, that God sent us into the world to suffer."

"God sent us into the world to enjoy it. He sends suffering to punish us for not having understood how to enjoy, and that is the truth, you fool of a woman! God created the world with all its beauty and gave it to man for his pleasure: so much the worse for him if he does not understand! But why should I trouble to explain this to you—all I mind about is turning you out of this place, you and your Paul, and so much the worse for you if you want to stop!"

"We are going, never fear, we are going very soon. That I can promise you, for it's my wish, too."

"You only say that because you are afraid of me. But you are wrong to be afraid. You think that it was I who prevented your feet from walking and your matches from striking: and perhaps it was I, but that is not to say that I mean any harm to you or your Paul. I only want you to go away. And mind, if you do not keep your word you will be sorry! Well, you will see me again and I shall remind you of this conversation. Meanwhile, I will leave you my stockings to mend."

"Very well; I will mend them."

"Then shut your eyes, for I don't choose that you should see my bare legs. Ha, ha!" he laughed, pulling off one shoe with the toe of the other and bending down to draw off his stockings, "no woman has ever seen my bare flesh, however much they have slandered me, and you are too old and ugly to be the first. Here is one stocking, and here is the other; I shall come and fetch them soon. . . ."

*　　　*　　　*

She opened her eyes with a start. She was alone again, in the kitchen with the wind howling round it.

"O Lord, what a dream!" she murmured with a sigh. Nevertheless, she stooped to look for the stockings, and she thought she heard the faint footfall of the ghost as it passed out of the kitchen, vanishing through the closed door.

CHAPTER III

When Paul left the woman's house and found himself out in the meadow again he too had the sensation that there was something alive, something ghostly, undefinable in the wind. It buffeted him about and chilled him through and through after his ardent dream of love, and as it twisted and flattened his coat against his body he thought with a quiver of the woman clinging to him in a passionate embrace.

When he turned the corner by the church the fury of the wind forced him to stop for a moment, with head bent before the blast, one hand holding on his hat and the other clutching his coat together. He had no breath left, and giddiness overcame him as it had overcome his young mother that far-off day on the way from the mill.

And with mingled excitement and loathing he felt that something terrible and great was born in him at that moment: for the first time he realized clearly and unmistakably that he loved Agnes with an earthly love, and that he gloried in this love.

Until a few hours ago he had been under a delusion, persuading both himself and her that his love was purely spiritual. But he had to admit that it was she who had first let her gaze linger upon him, that from their earliest meeting her eyes had sought his with a look that implored his help and his love. And little by little he had yielded to the fascination of that appeal, had been drawn to her by pity, and the solitude that surrounded her had brought them together.

And after their eyes had met their hands had sought and found each other, and that night they had kissed. And now his blood, which had flowed quietly so many years, rushed through his veins like liquid fire and the weak flesh yielded, at once the vanquished and the victor.

The woman had proposed that they two should secretly leave the village and live or die together. In the intoxication of the moment he had agreed to the proposal and they were to meet again the following night to settle their plans. But now the reality of the outside world, and that wind that seemed trying to strip him bare, tore away the veil of self-deception. Breathless, he stood before the church door; he was icy cold, and felt as though he were standing naked there in the middle of the little village, and that all his poor parishioners, sleeping the sleep of the weary, were beholding him thus in their dreams, naked, and black with sin.

Yet all the time he was thinking how best to plan his flight with the woman. She had told him that she possessed much money. . . . Then suddenly he felt impelled to go back to her that instant and dissuade her; he actually walked a few steps beside the wall where his mother had passed shortly before, then turned back in despair and fell on his knees in front of the church door and leaned his head against it, crying low, "O God, save me!" and his black cloak was blown flapping about his shoulders as he knelt there, like a vulture nailed alive upon the door.

His whole soul was fighting savagely, with a violence greater even than that of the wind on those high hills; it was the supreme struggle of the blind instinct of the flesh against the dominion of the spirit.

After a few moments he rose to his feet, uncertain still which of the two had conquered. But his mind was clearer and he recognized the real nature of his motives, confessing to himself that what swayed him most, more than the fear and the love of God, more than the desire for promotion and the hatred of sin, was his terror of the consequences of an open scandal.

The realization that he judged himself so mercilessly encouraged him to hope still for salvation. But at the bottom of his heart he knew he was henceforth bound to that woman as to life itself, that her image would be with him in his house, that he would walk at her side by day and at night sleep entangled in the inextricable meshes of her long dark hair. And beneath his sorrow and remorse, deeper and stronger still, he felt a tumult of joy glow through his inmost being as a subterranean fire burns within the earth.

Directly he opened the presbytery door he perceived the streak of light that issued from the kitchen and shone across the little dining-room into the entrance hall. Then he saw his mother sitting by the dead ashes, as though watching by a corpse, and with a pang of grief, a grief that never left him again, he instantly knew the whole truth.

He followed the streak of light through the little dining-room, faltered a second at the kitchen door, and then advanced to the hearth with hands outstretched as though to save himself from falling.

"Why have you not gone to bed?" he asked curtly.

His mother turned to look at him, her dream-haunted face still deathly pale; yet she was steady and quiet, almost stern, and while her eyes sought those of her son, his tried to evade her gaze.

"I was waiting up for you, Paul. Where have you been?"

He knew instinctively that every word that was not strictly true would be only a useless farce between them; yet he was forced to lie to her.

"I have been with a sick person," he replied quickly.

For an instant his deep voice seemed to disperse the evil dream; for an instant only, and the mother's face was transfigured with joy. Then the shadow fell again on face and heart.

"Paul," she said gently, lowering her eyes with a feeling of shame, but with no hesitation in her speech, "Paul, come nearer to me, I have something to say to you."

And although he moved no nearer to her, she went on speaking in a low voice, as though close to his ear:

"I know where you have been. For many nights now I have heard you go out, and tonight I followed you and saw where you went. Paul, think of what you are doing!"

He did not answer, made no sign that he had heard. His mother raised her eyes and beheld him standing tall and straight above her, pale as death, his shadow cast by the lamp upon the wall behind him, motionless as though transfixed upon a cross. And she longed for him to cry out and reproach her, to protest his innocence.

But he was remembering his soul's appeal as he knelt before the church door, and now God had heard his cry and had sent his own mother to him to save him. He wanted to bow before her, to fall at her knee and implore her to lead him away from the village, then and there, immediately; and at the same time he was shaking with rage and humiliation, humiliation at finding his weakness exposed, rage at having been watched and followed. Yet he grieved for the sorrow he was causing her. Then suddenly he remembered that he had not only to save himself, but to save appearances also.

"Mother," he said, going close to her and placing his hand on her head, "I tell you that I have been with someone who is ill."

"There is nobody ill in that house."

"Not all sick persons are in bed."

"Then in that case you yourself are more ill than the woman you went to see, and you must take care of yourself. Paul, I am only an ignorant woman, but I am your mother, and I tell you that sin is an illness worse than any other, because it attacks the soul. Moreover," she added, taking his hand and drawing him down towards her that he might hear her better, "it is not yourself only that you have to save, O child of God . . . remember that you must not destroy her soul . . . nor bring her to harm in this life either."

He was bending over her, but at these words he shot upright again like a steel spring. His mother had cut him to the quick. Yes, it was true; during all that hour of perturbation since he had quitted the woman he had thought only of himself.

He tried to withdraw his hand from his mother's, so hard and cold, but she grasped it so imperatively that he felt as though he had been arrested and were being led bound to prison. Then his thoughts turned again to God; it was God who had bound him, therefore he must submit to be led, but nevertheless he felt the rebellion and desperation of the guilty prisoner who sees no way of escape.

"Leave me alone," he said roughly, dragging his hand away by force, "I am no longer a boy and know myself what is good or bad for me!"

Then the mother felt as though she were turned to stone, for he had practically confessed his fault.

"No, Paul, you don't see the wrong you have done. If you did see it you would not speak like that."

"Then how should I speak?"

"You would not shout like that, but you would assure me there is nothing wrong between you and that woman. But that is just what you don't tell me, because you cannot do so conscientiously, and therefore it is better you should say nothing at all. Don't speak! I don't ask it of you now, but think well what you are about, Paul."

Paul made no reply, but moved slowly from his mother's side and stood in the middle of the kitchen waiting for her to go on speaking.

"Paul, I have nothing more to say to you, and I have no wish to say anything more. But I shall talk with God about you."

Then he sprang back to her side with blazing eyes as though he were about to strike her.

"Enough!" he cried, "you will be wise never to speak of this again, neither to me nor to anyone else; and keep your fancies to yourself!"

She rose to her feet, stern and resolute, seized him by the arms and forced him to look her straight in the eyes; then she let him go and sat down again, her hands gripping each other tightly in her lap.

Paul moved towards the door, then turned and began to walk up and down the kitchen. The moaning of the wind outside made an accompaniment to the rustle of his clothes, which was like the rustle of a woman's dress, for he wore a cassock made of silk and his cloak was of the very finest material. And in that moment of indecision, when he felt himself caught in a whirlpool of conflicting emotions, even that silken rustle seemed to speak and warn him that henceforth his life would be but a maze of errors and light things and vileness. Everything spoke to him; the wind outside, that recalled the long loneliness of his youth, and inside the house the mournful figure of his mother, the sound of his own steps, the sight of his own shadow on the floor. To and fro he walked, to and fro, treading on his shadow as he sought to overcome and stamp down his own self. He thought with pride that he had no need of any supernatural aid, such as he had invoked to save him, and then immediately this pride filled him with terror.

"Get up and go to bed," he said, coming back to his mother's side; and then, seeing that she did not move but sat with head bowed as though asleep, he bent down to look more closely in her face and perceived that she was weeping silently.

"Mother!"

"No," she said, without moving, "I shall never mention this thing to you again, neither to you nor to anyone else. But I shall not stir from this place except to leave the presbytery and the village, never to return, unless you swear to me that you will never set foot in that house again."

He raised himself from his bending position, overtaken again by that feeling of giddiness, and again superstition took hold of him, urging him to promise whatever his mother asked of him, since it was God Himself who was speaking by her mouth. And simultaneously a flood of bitter words rose to his lips, and he wanted to cry out upon his mother, to throw the blame on her and reproach her for having brought him from his native village and set his feet upon a way that was not his. But what would be the use? She would not even understand. Well, well! . . . With one hand he made a gesture as though brushing away the shadows from before his eyes, then suddenly he stretched out his hand over his

mother's head, and in his imagination saw his opened fingers extend in luminous rays above her:

"Mother, I swear to you that I will never enter that house again."

And immediately he left the kitchen, feeling that here was the end of everything. He was saved. But as he crossed the adjoining dining-room he heard his mother weeping unrestrainedly, as though she were weeping for the dead.

Back in his room, the scent of roses and the sight of the various objects strewn about which were associated with his passion, impregnated and colored by it, as it were, shook him afresh. He moved here and there without any reason, opened the window and thrust his head out into the wind, feeling as helpless as one of the million leaves whirled about in space, now in the dark shadow, now in the bright light of the moon, playthings of the winds and clouds. At last he drew himself up and closed the window, saying aloud as he did so:

"Let us be men!"

He stood erect to his full height, numb as though all his body were cold and hard and enclosed in an armor of pride. He desired no more to feel the sensations of the flesh, nor the sorrow nor the joy of sacrifice, nor the sadness of his loneliness; he had no wish even to kneel before God and receive the word of approval granted to the willing servant. He asked nothing from anyone; he wanted only to go forward in the straight way, alone and hopeless. Yet he was afraid of going to bed and putting out the light, and instead he sat down and began to read St. Paul's Epistle to the Corinthians: but the printed words fled his gaze, they swelled and shrank and danced up and down before his eyes. Why had his mother wept so bitterly, after he had sworn an oath to her? What could she have understood? Ah, yes, she understood; the mother's heart understood only too well the mortal anguish of her son, his renunciation of life itself.

Suddenly a wave of red overspread his face, and he raised his head, listening to the wind.

"There was no need to have sworn," he said to himself with a doubtful smile, "the really strong man never swears. Whoever takes an oath, as I did, is also ready to break his oath, even as I am ready."

And instantly he knew that the struggle was only really beginning, and so great was his consternation that he rose from his seat and went to look at himself in the mirror.

"Here thou standest, the man appointed by God, and if thou wilt not give thyself wholly to Him, then the spirit of evil will take possession of thee forever."

Then he staggered to his narrow bed and, dressed as he was, flung himself down upon it and burst into tears. He wept silently that his mother might not hear him, and that he might not hear his own crying, but his heart within him cried aloud and he was wrung with inward grief.

"O God, take me, bring me out of this!"

And the uttered words brought him real relief, as though he had found a plank of salvation in the midst of that sea of sorrow.

The crisis over he began to reflect. Everything seemed clear to him now, like a landscape seen from a window in the full light of the sun. He was a priest, he believed in God, he had wedded the Church and was vowed to chastity, he was like a married man and had no right to betray his wife. Why he had fallen in love with that woman and still loved her he did not exactly know. Perhaps he had reached a sort of physical crisis, when the youth and strength of his twenty-eight years awoke suddenly from its prolonged sleep and yearned towards Agnes because she had the closest affinity with him, and because she too, no longer very young, had like him been deprived of life and love, shut up in her house as in a convent.

Thus from the very first it had been love masquerading as friendship. They had been caught in a net of smiles and glances, and the very impossibility of there being any question of love between them drew them together: nobody entertained the faintest suspicion of their relationship to each other, and they met without emotion, without fear and without desire. Yet little by little, desire crept into that love of theirs, chaste and pure as a pool of still water beneath a wall that suddenly crumbles and falls in ruins.

All these things passed through his mind as he probed deep into his conscience and found the truth. He knew that from the first glance he had desired the woman, from the first glance he had possessed her in his heart, and all the rest had been only self-deception whereby he had sought to justify himself in his own eyes.

Thus it was, and he was forced to acknowledge the truth. Thus it was, because it is man's nature to suffer, to love, to find his mate and have her and to suffer again; to do good and receive it, to do evil and receive it, this is the life of man. Yet all his reflections lifted not one iota of the anguish that weighed upon his heart; and now he comprehended the true meaning of that anguish: it was the bitterness of death, for to renounce love and the possession of Agnes was to renounce life itself. Then his thoughts went further: "Was not even this vain and futile? When the momentary pleasure of love is past, the spirit resumes mastery over itself, and, with a more intense longing for solitude than before, it takes refuge again within its prison-house, the mortal body that clothes it. Why, therefore, should he be made unhappy by this loneliness? Had he not accepted and endured it for so many years, all the best years of his life? Even supposing he could really escape with Agnes and marry her, would he not always be alone within himself just the same . . . ?"

Yet the mere fact of pronouncing her name, the bare idea of the possibility of living with her, made him spring up in a fever of excitement. In imagination again he saw her stretched beside him, in imagination he held out his arms to draw her close to him, slender and supple as a reed in the stream; he whispered sweet words into the little hollow behind her ear, covered his face with her loosened hair, warm and scented like the flowers of the wild saffron. And biting hard into his pillow, he repeated to her all the Song of Songs, and when this was ended he told her he would come back to her the next day, that he was glad to grieve his mother and his God, glad that he had sworn an oath and given himself over to remorse, to superstition and to fear, for now he could break loose from everything and return to her.

CHAPTER IV

Then he grew calmer and began to reflect again.

As a sick man is relieved to know at least the nature of his malady, so Paul would have been relieved to know at least why all these things had befallen him, and like his mother, he went over all the story of his past life.

The moaning of the wind outside mingled with his earliest memories, faint and indistinct. He saw himself in a courtyard, where, he did not know, but perhaps the courtyard of the house where his mother was a servant, and he was climbing on the wall with other boys. The top of the wall was edged with pieces of glass as sharp as knives, but this did not prevent the boys from scrambling up to look over, even though they cut their hands. As a matter of fact, there was a certain daring pleasure in wounding themselves, and they showed each other their blood and then dried it beneath their armpits, under the delusion that nobody would notice their cut hands. From the top of the wall they could see nothing except the street, into which they were perfectly free to go; but they preferred climbing on to the wall because that was forbidden, and they amused themselves by throwing stones at the few people who passed and then hiding, their sensations divided between delight in their own boldness and their fear of being discovered. A deaf and dumb girl, who was also a cripple, used to sit by the wood pile at the bottom of the courtyard, and from there she used to watch them with an expression at once imploring and severe in her large dark eyes. The boys were afraid of her, but they did not dare to molest her; on the contrary, they lowered their voices as though she could hear them and sometimes they even invited her to play with them. Then the crippled child used to laugh with an almost insane delight, but she never moved from her corner.

In imagination he saw again those dark eyes, in whose depths the light of sorrow and desire already shone; he saw them far off at the bottom of his memory as at the bottom of that mysterious courtyard, and it seemed to him that they resembled the eyes of Agnes.

Then he saw himself again in that same street where he had thrown stones at the passers-by, but farther down, at the turning of a little lane shut in by a group of dilapidated old houses. His home lay just between the street and the lane, in the house of well-to-do people, all women and all fat and serious; they used to close all doors and windows at dusk and they received no visitors except other women and priests, with whom they used to joke and laugh, but always in a decorous, guarded manner.

It had been one of these priests who had caught him by the shoulders one day, and gripping him firmly between his bony knees and raising his timid face with a vigorous hand, had asked him:

"Is it true that you want to be a priest?"

The boy had nodded yes, and having been given a sacred picture and a friendly slap he had remained in a corner of the room listening to the conversation between the priests and the women. They were discussing the parish priest of Aar and describing how he went out hunting and smoked a pipe and let his beard grow, yet how nevertheless the Bishop hesitated to interdict him because he would have great difficulty in finding another priest willing to bury himself in that remote village. Moreover, the easygoing priest in possession threatened to tie up and fling into the river anyone who ventured to try and oust him from his place.

"The worst of it is that the simpletons of Aar are attached to the man, although they are frightened of him and his sorceries. Some of them actually believe he is the Antichrist, and the women all declare that they will help him to truss up his successor and throw him into the river."

"Do you hear that, Paul? If you become a priest and have any idea of going back to your mother's village, you must look out for a lively time!"

It was a woman who flung this joke at him, Marielena; she was the one who had charge of him, and when she drew him towards her to comb his hair her fat stomach and her soft breast used to make him think she was made of cushions. He was very fond of Marielena; in spite of her corpulent body she had a refined and pretty face, with cheeks softly tinted with pink and gentle brown eyes. He used to look up at her as one looks at the ripe fruit hanging on the tree, and perhaps she had been his first love.

Then came his life at the Seminary. His mother had taken him there one October morning, when the sky was blue and everything smelled of new wine. The road mounted steeply and at the top of the hill was the archway which connected the Seminary with the Bishop's house, curved like a vast frame over the sunny landscape of cottages, trees and granite steps, with the cathedral tower at the bottom of the picture. The grass was springing up between the cobblestones in front of the Bishop's house, several men road past on horseback and the horses had long legs with hairy fetlocks and were shod with gleaming iron shoes. He noticed all these things because he kept his eyes shyly on the ground, a little ashamed of himself, a little ashamed of his mother. Yes, why not confess it once for all? He had always been more or less ashamed of his mother, because she was a servant and came from that village of poor simpletons. Only later, very much later, had he overcome this ignoble feeling by sheer force of pride and will, and the more he had been unreasonably ashamed of his origin, all the more did he subsequently glory in it to himself and before God choosing voluntarily to live in this miserable hamlet, subjecting himself to his mother, and respecting her most trifling wishes and conforming to her humblest ways.

But the remembrance of his mother as a servant, aye, even less than a servant, a mere drudge in the Seminary kitchen, brought back with it the most humiliating memories of his youth. And yet she worked as a servant for his sake. On the days when he went to confession and communion his Superior obliged him to go and kiss his mother's hand and ask her pardon for the faults he had committed. The hand which she dried hurriedly with a dishcloth smelled of soapsuds and was chapped and wrinkled like an old wall, and he was filled with shame and rage at being forced to kiss it; but he asked forgiveness of God for his inability to ask forgiveness of her.

Thus God had revealed Himself to Paul, as hidden behind his mother in the damp and smoky kitchen of the Seminary: God Who is in every place, in heaven and on earth and in all things created.

And in his hours of exaltation, when he lay in his little room staring with wide-open eyes into the darkness, he had dwelt with wonder on the thought, "I shall be a priest, I shall be able to consecrate the host and change it into God." And at those times he thought also of his mother, and when he was away from her and could not see her, he loved her and realized that his own greatness was all due to her, for instead of sending him to herd goats or carry sacks of grain to the mill, as his father had done, she was making him into a priest, one who had power to consecrate the host and change it into God.

It was thus he conceived his mission in life. He knew nothing of the world; his brightest and most emotional memories were the ceremonies of the great religious festivals, and recalling these memories now, in all the bitterness of his present anguish, they awoke in him a sense of light and joy and presented themselves to his mind's eye as great living pictures. And the remembered music of the cathedral organ and the sense of mystery in the ceremonies of Holy Week became part of his present sorrow, of that anguish of life and death which seemed to weigh him down upon his bed as the burden of man's sin had lain upon Christ in the sepulcher.

It was during one of these periods of mystical agitation that for the first time he had come into intimate relations with a woman. When he thought of it now it seemed like a dream, neither good nor evil, but only strange.

Every holiday he went to visit the women with whom he had lived during his boyhood, and they welcomed him as though he were already a priest, with familiar friendliness and cheerfulness, but always with a certain dignity. When he looked at Marielena he used to blush, and then scorned himself for blushing, because though he still liked her, he now saw her in all her crude realism, fat, soft and shapeless; nevertheless her presence and her gentle eyes still roused little tremors in him.

Marielena and her sisters used often to invite him to dinner on feast days. On one occasion, Palm Sunday, he happened to arrive early, and while his hostesses were busy laying the table and awaiting their other guests, Paul went out into their little garden and began to walk up and down the path which ran beside the outer wall, beneath the aspens covered with little golden leaves. The sky was all a milky blue, the air soft and warm with the light wind from the eastern hills, and the cuckoo could already be heard calling in the distance.

Just as he was standing on tiptoe childishly to pick a drop of resin off an almond tree, he suddenly saw a pair of large greenish eyes fixed upon him from the lane on the other side of the garden wall. They looked like the eyes of a cat, and the whole personality of the woman, who was sitting crouched upon the steps of a dark doorway at the end of the lane, had something feline about it. He could conjure up her image again so clearly that he even felt as if he still held the drop of soft resin between his finger and thumb, while his fascinated eyes could not withdraw themselves from hers! And over the doorway he remembered a little window surrounded by a white line with a small cross over it. He had known that doorway and that window very well ever since he was a boy, and the cross placed there as a charm against temptation had always amused him, because the woman who lived in the cottage, Maria Paska, was a lost woman. He could see her now before him, with her fringed kerchief showing her white neck, and her long coral ear-rings, like two long drops of blood. With her elbows resting on her knees and her pale, delicate face supported between her hands, Maria Paska looked at him steadily, and at last she smiled at him, but without moving. Her white even teeth and the somewhat cruel expression of her eyes only served to accentuate the feline look about her face. Suddenly, however, she dropped her hands into her lap, raised her head and assumed a grave and sad expression. A big man, with his cap drawn down to hide his face, was coming cautiously down the lane and keeping close in the shadow of the wall.

Then Maria Paska got up quickly and went into the house, and the big man followed her and shut the door.

*   *   *

Paul never forgot his terrible agitation as he walked about in the little garden and thought of those two shut up in that squalid house in the lane. It was a sort of uneasy sadness, a sense of discomfort that made him want to be alone and to hide himself like a sick animal, and during dinner he was unusually silent amid the cheerful talk of the other guests. Directly dinner was over he returned to the garden: the woman was there, on the look-out again and in the same position as before. The sun never reached the damp corner where her door was, and she looked as if she were so white and delicate because she always lived in the shade.

When she saw the seminarist she did not move, but she smiled at him, and then her face became grave as on the arrival of the big man. She called out to Paul, speaking as one would speak to a young boy:

"I say, will you come and bless my house on Saturday? Last year the priest who was going round blessing the houses refused to come into mine. May he go to hell, he and all his bag of tricks!"

Paul made no answer, he felt inclined to throw a stone at the woman, in fact he did pick one up from the wall, but then put it back and wiped his hand on his handkerchief. But all through Holy Week, while he was hearing Mass, or taking part in the sacred function, or, taper in hand, escorting the Bishop with all the other seminarists, he always seemed to see the woman's eyes staring at him till it became a veritable obsession. He had wanted to exorcize her, as one possessed of the Devil, yet at the same time he felt somehow that the spirit of evil was within himself. During the ceremony of feet-washing, when the Bishop stooped before the twelve beggars (who looked as though they might really have been the twelve apostles), Paul's heart was moved by the thought that on the Saturday before Easter of the previous year the priest had refused to bless the house of the lost woman. And yet Christ had pardoned Mary Magdalene. Perhaps if the priest had blessed the lost woman's house she might have amended her ways. This last reflection presently began to take hold of him to the exclusion of all other thoughts, but on examining it now at this distance of time he perceived that here his instinct had played him false, for at that period he had not yet learned to know himself. And yet perhaps, even if he had known himself, he would still have gone back on the Saturday to see the lost woman in the lane.

*   *   *

[143]

When he turned the corner he saw that Maria Paska was not sitting on her doorstep, but the door was open, a sign that she had no visitor. Involuntarily he imitated the big man and went down the lane in the shadow of the wall, but he wished she had been there on the lookout and that she had risen up with a grave, sad face at his approach. When he reached the end of the lane he saw her drawing water from a well at the side of the house, and his heart gave a jump, for she looked just like the pictures of Mary Magdalene; and she turned and saw him as she was drawing up the bucket, and blushed. Never in his life had he seen a more beautiful woman. Then he was seized with a desire to run away, but he was too shy, and as she re-entered the house carrying the jug of water in her hand she said something to him which he did not understand, but he followed her inside and she shut the door. A little wooden staircase ending in a trapdoor gave access to the upper room, the one with the window over which hung a cross as a protection against temptation, and she led him up, snatching his cap from his head and tossing it aside with a laugh.

*   *   *

Paul went to see her again several times, but after he had been ordained and had taken the vow of chastity he had kept away from all women. His senses seemed to have grown petrified within the frozen armor of his vow, and when he heard scandalous tales of other priests he felt a pride in his own purity, and only thought of his adventure with the woman in the lane as an illness from which he had completely recovered.

During the first years passed in the little village he thought of himself as having already lived his life, as having known all it could offer, misery, humiliation, love, pleasure, sin and expiation; as having withdrawn from the world like some old hermit and waiting only for the Kingdom of God. And now suddenly he beheld the earthly life again in a woman's eyes, and at first he had been so deceived as to mistake it for the life eternal.

To love and be loved, is not this the Kingdom of God upon earth? And his heart swelled within him at the remembrance. O Lord, are we so blind? Where shall we find the light? Paul knew himself to be ignorant: his knowledge was made up of fragments of books of which he only imperfectly understood the meaning, but above all the Bible had impressed him with its romanticism and its realistic pictures of past ages. Wherefore he could place no reliance even on himself nor on his own inward searchings: he realized that he had no self-knowledge, that he was not master of himself and that he deceived himself ever and always.

His feet had been set upon the wrong road. He was a man of strong natural instincts, like his forbears, the millers and shepherds, and he suffered because he was not allowed to obey his instincts. Here he got back to his first simple and correct diagnosis of what ailed him: he was unhappy because he was a man and was forbidden to lead man's natural life of love and joy and the fulfillment of life's natural ends. Then he reflected that pleasure enjoyed leaves only horror and anguish behind it; therefore it could not be the flesh that cried out for its chance of life, but rather the soul imprisoned within the flesh that longed to escape from its prison. In those supreme moments of love it had been the soul which had soared upward in a rapid flight, only to fall back more swiftly into its cage; but that instant of freedom had sufficed to show it the place to which it would take its flight when its prison days were ended and the wall of flesh forever overthrown, a place of infinite joy, the Infinite itself.

[144]

He smiled at last, saddened and weary. Where had he read all these things? Certainly he must have read them somewhere, for he had no pretensions to evolve new ideas himself. But it was of no consequence, the truth is always the same, alike for all men, as all men's hearts are alike. He had thought himself different from other men, a voluntary exile and worthy of being near to God, and perhaps God was punishing him in this way, by sending him back among men, into the community of passion and of pain.

He must rise up and pursue his appointed way.

CHAPTER V

He became aware that some one was knocking at the door.

Paul started as though suddenly awakened from sleep and sprang up from his bed with the confused sensation of one who has to depart on a journey and is afraid of being too late. But directly he tried to stand up he was forced to sit down weakly on his bed again, for his limbs gave way under him and he felt as if he had been beaten all over while he lay asleep. Crouched together with his head sunk on his breast, he could only nod faintly in response to the knock. His mother had not forgotten to call him early, as he had requested her on the previous day: his mother was following her own straight path, she remembered nothing of what had happened during the night and called him as though this were just like any other morning.

Yes, it was like any other morning. Paul got up again and began to dress, and gradually he pulled himself together and stood stiff and erect in the garments of his order. He flung open the window, and his eyes were dazzled by the vivid light of the silvery sky; the thickets on the hill-side, alive with the song of birds, quivered and sparkled in the morning sun, the wind had dropped and the sound of the church bell vibrated through the pure air.

The bell called him, he lost sight of all external things, although he sought to escape from the things within him: the scent of his room caused him physical distress and the memories it evoked stung him to the quick. The bell went on calling him, but he could not make up his mind to leave his room and he wandered round it almost in a fury. He looked in the mirror and then turned away, but it was useless for him to avoid it; the image of the woman was reflected in his mind as in a mirror, he might break it in a thousand fragments, but each fragment would still retain that image entire and complete.

The second bell for Mass was ringing insistently, inviting him to come: he moved about here and there, searching for something he could not find, and finally sat down at his table and began to write. He began by copying out the verses which said, "Enter ye in by the narrow gate," etc.; then he crossed them out and on the other side of the paper he wrote:

"Please do not expect me again. We have mutually entangled each other in a net of deception and we must cut ourselves loose without delay, if we want to free ourselves and not sink to the bottom. I am coming to you no more; forget me, do not write to me, and do not try to see me again."

Then he went downstairs and called his mother, and held out the letter towards her without looking at her.

"Take this to her at once," he said hoarsely, "try and give it into her own hands and then come away immediately."

He felt the letter taken out of his hand and hurried outside, for the moment uplifted and relieved.

Now the bell was ringing the third time, pealing out over the quiet village and the valleys gray in the silvery light of the dawn. Up the hilly road, as though ascending from the depths of the valley, came figures of old men with gnarled sticks hanging from their wrists by leather straps, and women whose heads wrapped in voluminous kerchiefs looked too large for their small bodies. When they had all entered the church and the old men had taken their places in front close by the altar rails, the place was filled with the odor of earth and field, and Antiochus, the youthful sacristan, swung his censer energetically, sending out the smoke in the direction of the old men to drive away the smell. Gradually a dense cloud of incense screened the altar from the rest of the little church, and the brown-faced sacristan in his white surplice and the pale-faced priest in his vestments of red brocade moved about as in a pearly mist. Both Paul and the boy loved the smoke and the scent of the incense and used it lavishly. Turning towards the nave, the priest half closed his eyes and frowned as though the mist impeded his sight; apparently he was displeased at the small number of worshipers and was waiting for others to arrive. And in fact a few late comers did enter then, and last of all his mother, and Paul turned white to the lips.

So the letter had been delivered and the sacrifice was accomplished: a death-like sweat broke out upon his forehead, and as he raised his hands in consecration his secret prayer was that the offering of his own flesh and blood might be accepted. And he seemed to see the woman reading his letter and falling to the ground in a swoon.

When the Mass was ended he knelt down wearily and recited a Latin prayer in a monotonous voice. The congregation responded, and he felt as though he were dreaming and longed to throw himself down at the foot of the altar and fall asleep like a shepherd on the bare rocks. Dimly through the clouds of incense he saw in her glass-fronted niche the little Madonna which the people believed to be miraculous, a figure as dark and delicate as a cameo in a medallion, and he gazed at it as though he were seeing it again for the first time after a long absence. Where had he been all that time? His thoughts were confused and he could not recollect.

Then suddenly he rose to his feet and turned round and began to address the congregation, a thing he only did very occasionally. He spoke in dialect and in a harsh voice, as though he were scolding the old men, now thrusting their bearded faces between the pillars of the altar rails in order to hear better, and the women crouching on the ground, divided between curiosity and fear. The sacristan, holding the Mass-book in his arms, glanced at Paul out of his long dark eyes, then turned them on the people and shook his head, threatening them in jest if they did not attend.

"Yes," said the priest, "the number of you who come here grows ever less; when I have to face you I am almost ashamed, for I feel like a shepherd who has lost his sheep. Only on Sunday is the church a little fuller, but I fear you come because of your scruples and not because of your belief, from habit rather than from need, as you change your clothes or take your rest. Up now, it is time to awake! I do not expect mothers of families, or men who have to be at work before the dawn, to come here every morning, but young women and old men and children, such as I shall see now when I leave the church, standing at their own doors to greet the rising sun, all those should come here to begin the day with God, to praise Him in His own house and to gain strength for the path they have to tread. If you did this the poverty that afflicts you would disappear, and evil habits and temptation would no longer assail you. It is time to awake early in the morning, to wash yourselves and to change your clothing every day and not only on Sundays! So I shall expect you all, beginning from tomorrow, and we will pray together that God will not forsake us and our little village, as He will not forsake the smallest nest, and for those who are sick and cannot come here we will pray that they may recover and be able to march forward too."

He turned round swiftly and the sacristan did the same, and for a few minutes there reigned in the little church a silence so intense that the stone-breaker could be heard at his work behind the ridge. Then a woman got up and approached the priest's mother, placing a hand on her shoulder as she bent down and whispered:

"Your son must come at once to hear the confession of King Nicodemus, who is seriously ill."

Roused from her own sad thoughts, the mother raised her eyes to the speaker. She remembered that King Nicodemus was a fantastic old hunter who lived in a hut high up in the mountains, and she asked if Paul would have to climb up there to hear the confession.

"No," whispered the woman, "his relations have brought him down to the village."

So the mother went to tell Paul, who was in the little sacristy, disrobing with the help of Antiochus.

"You will come home first and drink your coffee, won't you?" she asked.

He avoided looking at her and did not even answer, but pretended to be in a great hurry to go to the old man who was ill. The thoughts of both mother and son dwelt upon the same thing, the letter which had been delivered to Agnes, but neither spoke of it. Then he hastened away, and she stood there like a block of wood while the sacristan busied himself in replacing the vestments in the black cupboard.

"It would have been better if I had not told him about Nicodemus until he had been home and had his coffee," she said.

"A priest must get accustomed to everything," replied Antiochus gravely, poking his head round the cupboard door, and then he added as though to himself as he turned back to his work inside:

"Perhaps he is angry with me, because he says I am inattentive: but it's not true, I assure you it's not true! Only when I looked at those old men I felt inclined to laugh, for they did not understand a word of the sermon. They sat there with their mouths open, but they understood nothing. I bet you that old Marco Panizza really thinks he ought to wash his face every day, he who never washes at all except at Easter and Christmas! And you'll see that from now on they will all come to church every day, because he told them that poverty would disappear if they did that."

The mother still stood there, her hands clasped beneath her apron.

"The poverty of the soul," she said, to show that she at least had understood. But Antiochus only looked at her as he had looked at the old men, with a strong desire to laugh. Because he was quite sure that nobody could understand these matters as he understood them, he who already knew the four gospels by heart and intended to be a priest himself, which fact did not prevent him from being as mischievous and inquisitive as other boys.

As soon as he had finished putting everything in order and the priest's mother had gone away, Antiochus locked the sacristy and walked across the little garden attached to the church, all overgrown with rosemary and as deserted as a cemetery. But instead of going home to where his mother kept a tavern in one corner of the village square, he ran off to the presbytery to hear the latest news of King Nicodemus, and also for another reason.

"Your son scolded me for not paying attention," he repeated uneasily, while the priest's mother was busy preparing her Paul's breakfast. "Perhaps he won't have me as sacristan any longer, perhaps he will take Ilario Panizza. But Ilario cannot read, whereas I have even learned to read Latin. Besides, Ilario is so dirty. What do you think? Will he send me away?"

"He wants you to pay attention, that is all: it is not right to laugh in church," she answered sternly and gravely.

"He is very angry. Perhaps he did not sleep last night, on account of the wind. Did you hear what an awful wind?"

The woman made no reply; she went into the dining-room and placed on the table enough bread and biscuits to satisfy the twelve apostles. Probably Paul would not touch a thing, but the mere act of moving about and making preparations for him, as though he were sure to come in as merry and hungry as a mountain shepherd, did something to assuage her trouble and perhaps quiet her conscience, which every moment stung her more and more sharply, and the boy's very remark, that "perhaps he was angry because he did not sleep last night," only increased her uneasiness. Her heavy footsteps echoed through the silent rooms as she went to and fro: she felt instinctively that although apparently *all was over,* in reality it was all only just beginning. She had well understood the words he spoke from the altar, that one must awake early and wash oneself and march forward, and she went to and fro, up and down, trying to imagine that she was marching forward in very truth. She went upstairs to put his room in order; but the mirror and the perfumes still vexed and alarmed her, in spite of the assurance that everything was

now at an end, while a vision of Paul, pale and rigid as a corpse, seemed to meet her eyes from the depths of that cursed mirror, to hang with his cassock on the wall and lie stretched lifeless upon the bed. And her heart was heavy within her, as though some inward paralysis prevented her breathing.

The pillow-slip was still damp with Paul's tears and his fevered anguish of the night, and as she drew it off to replace it with a fresh one the thought came to her, for the first time in her life:

"But why are priests forbidden to marry?"

And she thought of Agnes's wealth, and how she owned a large house with gardens and orchards and fields.

Then suddenly she felt horribly guilty in even entertaining such thoughts, and quickly drawing on the fresh pillow-slip she went away into her own room.

Marching forward? Yes, she had been marching since dawn and was yet only at the beginning of the way. And however far one went, one always came back to the same place. She went downstairs and sat by the fire beside Antiochus, who had not moved and was determined to wait there all day, if needs be, for the sake of seeing his superior and making his peace with him. He sat very still, one leg crossed over the other and his hands clasped round his knee, and presently he remarked, not without a slight accent of reproach:

"You ought to have taken him his coffee into the church, as you do when he is delayed there hearing the women's confessions. As it is, he will be famished!"

"And how was I to know he would be sent for in such a hurry? The old man is dying, it seems," retorted the mother.

"I don't think that can be true. His grandchildren want him to die because he has some money to leave. I know the old chap! I saw him once when I went up into the mountains with my father: he was sitting among the rocks in the sun, with a dog and a tame eagle beside him and all sorts of dead animals all round. That is not how God orders us to live!"

"What does He order, then?"

"He orders us to live among men, to cultivate the ground, and not to hide our money, but to give it to the poor."

The little sacristan spoke with a man's confidence, and the priest's mother was touched and smiled. After all, if Antiochus could say such sensible things it was because he had been taught by her Paul. It was her Paul who taught them all to be good, wise and prudent; and when he really wished to he succeeded in convincing even old men whose opinions were already fixed, and even thoughtless children. She sighed, and bending down to draw the coffee-pot nearer the glowing embers, she said:

"You talk like a little saint, Antiochus; but it remains to be seen if you will do as you say when you're a man, whether you really will give your money to the poor."

"Yes, I shall give everything to the poor. I shall have a great deal of money, because my mother makes a lot with her tavern, and my father is a forest keeper and earns pretty well, too. I shall give all I get to the poor: God tells us to do that, and He Himself will provide for us. And the Bible says, the ravens do not sow, neither do they reap, yet they have their food from God, and the lily of the valley is clothed more splendidly than the king."

"Yes, Antiochus, when a man is alone he can do that, but what if he has children?"

"That makes no difference. Besides, I shall never have children; priests are not allowed to have any."

She turned to look at him; his profile was towards her, against the bright background of the open doorway and the courtyard outside; it was a profile of pure, firm outline and dark skin, almost like a head of bronze, with long lashes shading the eyes with their large dark pupils. And as she gazed at the boy she could have wept, but she knew not why.

"Are you quite sure you want to be a priest?" she asked.

"Yes, if that is God's will."

"Priests are not allowed to marry, and suppose that some day you wanted to take a wife?"

"I shall not want a wife, since God has forbidden it."

"God? But it is the Pope who has forbidden it," said the mother, somewhat taken aback at the boy's answer.

"The Pope is God's representative on earth."

"But in olden times priests had wives and families, just as the Protestant clergy have now," she urged.

"That is a different thing," said the boy, growing warm over the argument: *"we* ought not to have them!"

"The priests in olden times . . ." she persisted.

But the sacristan was well-informed. "Yes, the priests in olden times," he said, "but then they themselves held a meeting and decided against it; and those who had no wives or families, the younger ones, were the very ones who opposed marriage the most strongly. That is as it should be."

"The younger ones!" repeated the mother as if to herself. "But they know nothing about it! And then they may repent, they may even go astray," she added in a low voice, "they may come to reason and argue like the old priest."

A tremor seized her and she looked swiftly round to assure herself that the ghost was not there, instantly repenting for having thus evoked it. She did not wish even to think about it, and least of all in connection with *that matter*. Was it not all ended? Moreover, Antiochus's face wore an expression of the deepest scorn.

"That man was not a priest, he was the devil's brother come to earth! God save us from him! We had best not even think about him!" and he made the sign of the cross. Then he continued, with recovered serenity:

"As for repenting! Do you suppose that *he,* your son, ever dreams of repenting?"

It hurt her to hear the boy talk like that. She longed to be able to tell him something of her trouble, to warn him for the future, yet at the same time she rejoiced at his words, as though the conscience of the innocent lad were speaking to her conscience to commend and encourage it.

"Does he, does my Paul say it is right for priests not to marry?" she asked in a low voice.

"If *he* does not say it is right, who should say so? Of course he says it is right; hasn't he said so to you? A fine thing it would be to see a priest with his wife beside him and a child in his arms! And when he ought to go and say Mass he has to nurse the baby because it's howling! What a joke! Imagine your son with one child in his arms and another hanging on to his cassock!"

The mother smiled wanly; but there passed before her eyes a fleeting vision of lovely children running about the house, and there was a pang at her heart. Antiochus laughed aloud, his dark eyes and white teeth flashing in his brown face, but there was something cruel in his laughter.

"A priest's wife would be a funny thing! When they went out for a walk together they would look from behind like two women! And would she go and confess to him, if they lived in a place where there was no other priest?"

"What does a mother do? Who do I confess to?"

"A mother is different. And who is there that your son could marry? The granddaughter of King Nicodemus, perhaps?"

He began to laugh merrily again, for the granddaughter of King Nicodemus was the most unfortunate girl in the village, a cripple and an idiot. But he instantly grew serious again when the mother, forced to speak by a will other than her own, said softly:

"For that matter, there is some one, Agnes."

But Antiochus objected jealously: "She is ugly, I don't like her, and he does not like her either."

Then the mother began to praise Agnes, but she spoke almost in a whisper as though afraid of being overheard by anyone except the boy, while Antiochus, his hands still clasped round his knee, shook his head energetically, his lower lip stuck out in disgust like a ripe cherry.

"No, no, I don't like her—can't you hear what I say! She is ugly and proud and old. And besides . . ."

A step sounded in the little hall and instantly they both were silent and stood waiting.

*   *   *

CHAPTER VI

Paul sat down at the table, which was laid ready for breakfast, and put his hat on the chair beside him, and while his mother was pouring out his coffee he asked in a calm voice:

"Did you take that letter?"

She nodded, pointing towards the kitchen for fear the boy should hear.

"Who is there?" asked Paul.

"Antiochus."

"Antiochus!" he called, and with one spring the boy was before him, cap in hand, standing to attention like a little soldier.

"Listen, Antiochus, you must go back

to the church and get everything ready for taking extreme unction to the old man later on."

The boy was speechless with joy: so *he* was no longer angry and was not going to dismiss him and take another boy in his place!

"Wait a moment, have you had anything to eat?"

"He would not have anything to eat; he never will," said the mother.

"Sit down there," ordered Paul, "you must eat. Mother, give him something."

It was not the first time that Antiochus had sat at the priest's table, so he obeyed without shyness, though his heart beat fast. He was aware somehow that his position had changed, that the priest was speaking to him in a way different from usual; he could not explain how or why, he only felt there was a difference. He looked up in Paul's face as though he saw him for the first time, with mingled fear and joy. Fear and joy and a whole throng of new emotions, gratitude, hope and pride, filled his heart as a nest full of warm fledglings ready to spread their wings and fly away.

"Then at two o'clock you must come for your lesson. It is time to set to work seriously with Latin; and I must write for a new grammar, mine is centuries old."

Antiochus had stopped eating: now he went very red and offered his services enthusiastically without inquiring the why or the wherefore. The priest looked at him with a smile, then turned his face to the window, through which the trees could be seen waving against the clear sky, and his thoughts were evidently far away. Antiochus felt again as if he had been dismissed and his spirits fell; he brushed the crumbs from the tablecloth, folded his napkin carefully and carried the cups into the kitchen. He prepared to wash up, too, and would have done it very well, for he was accustomed to washing glasses in his mother's wineshop;

but the priest's mother would not allow it.

"Go to the church and get ready," she whispered, pushing him away. He went out immediately, but before going to the church he ran round to his mother to warn her to have the house clean and tidy as the priest was coming to see her.

Meanwhile the priest's mother had gone back into the dining-room, where Paul was still idling at the table with a newspaper in front of him. Usually, when he was at home, he sat in his own room, but this morning he was afraid of going up there again. He sat reading the newspaper, but his thoughts were elsewhere. He was thinking of the old dying hunter, who had once confessed to him that he shunned the company of men because "they are evil itself," and men in mockery had called him King, as they had called Christ King of the Jews. But Paul was not interested in the old man's confession; his thoughts turned rather to Antiochus and his father and mother, for he meant to ask the latter whether they conscientiously realized what they were doing in allowing the boy to have his own way and carry out his unreasoning fancy for becoming a priest. But even this was really of little importance: what Paul actually wanted was to get away from his own thoughts, and when his mother came into the room he bowed his head over his paper, for he knew that she alone could divine what those thoughts were.

He sat there with bowed head, but he forbade his lips to frame the question he longed to ask. The letter had been delivered; what more was there for him to know? The stone of the sepulcher had been rolled into its place: but ah! how it weighed upon him, how alive he felt, buried alive beneath that great stone!

His mother began to clear the table, putting each object back in the cupboard that served as a sideboard. It was so quiet that the birds could be heard chirping in the bushes and the regular tap-tap of the stone-breaker by the roadside. It seemed like the end of the world, as though the last habitation of living men was this little white room, with its time-blackened furniture and its tiled flooring, upon which the green and gold light from the high window cast a tremulous reflection as of water and made the small place seem like some prison chamber in the dungeon of a castle.

Paul had drunk his coffee and eaten his biscuits as usual, and now he was reading the news of the great world far away. Outwardly there was nothing to show that this day was in any way differ- ent from other days, but his mother would rather he had gone up to his room as was his custom and shut the door. And why, since he was sitting there, did he not ask her more about her errand, and to whom she had given the letter? She went to the kitchen door with a cup in her hand, then carried it back to the table and stood there.

"Paul," she said, "I gave the letter into her own hand. She was already up and dressed, and in the garden."

"Very well," he answered, without raising his eyes from the newspaper.

But she could not leave him, she felt she must speak; something stronger than her will impelled her, something stronger even than the will of her son. She cleared her throat and fixed her eyes on the little Japanese landscape painted at the bottom of the cup she was holding, its colors stained and darkened with coffee. Then she went on with her tale:

"She was in the garden, for she gets up early. I went straight to her and gave her the letter: nobody saw. She took it and looked at it; then she looked at me, but still she did not open it. I said 'There is no answer,' and turned to go away, but she said, 'Wait.' Then she opened the letter as if to show me there was no

secret in it, and she turned as white as the paper itself. Then she said to me, 'Go, and God be with you!' "

"That's enough!" he cried sharply, still without looking up, but his mother saw the lashes quiver over his downcast eyes and his face turn as white as that of Agnes. For a moment she thought he was about to faint, then the blood slowly came back into his face and she breathed again with relief. Such moments as these were terrible, but they must be met bravely and overcome. She opened her lips to say something else, to murmur at least, "See what you have done, how you have hurt both yourself and her!" but at that instant he looked up, jerking his head back as though to drive the blood of evil passion from his face, and glaring angrily at his mother, he said roughly:

"Now that is enough! Do you hear? It's enough! I absolutely refuse to hear another word on this matter, otherwise I shall do what you threatened to do last night: I shall go away."

Then he got up quickly, but instead of going to his room he left the house again. His mother went into the kitchen, the cup still in her trembling hands; she put it down on the table and leaned against the corner of the fireplace, utterly broken down. She knew now he had gone away forever; even if he came back he would no longer be her Paul, but a poor wretch possessed by his evil passion, one who looked with threatening eyes at whoever crossed his path, like some thief lying in wait to commit a crime.

And Paul, indeed, was like one who had fled from home in fear. He had rushed out to avoid going up to his room, for he had an idea that Agnes might have got in secretly and be waiting for him there, with her white face and the letter in her hand. He had escaped from the house in order to escape from himself, but he was carried away by his passion more violently than by the wind on the night before. He crossed the meadow without any definite aim, feeling as though he were some inanimate thing flung bodily against the wall of Agnes's house and thrown back by the rebound as far as the square before the church, where the old men and the boys and the beggars sit on the low parapet all day long. Scarce knowing how he had come there, Paul stayed a little while talking to one or another of them without heeding their replies, and then descended the steep road that led from the village down to the valley. But he saw nothing of the road he trod nor the landscape before his eyes: his whole world had turned upside-down and was a mere chaos of rocks and ruins, upon which he looked down as boys lie flat on the ground at the cliff's edge to gaze over into the depths below.

He turned and climbed up again towards the church. The village seemed almost deserted; here and there a peach tree showed its ripe fruit over a garden wall and little white clouds floated across the clear September sky like a peaceful flock of sheep. In one house a child was crying, from another came the regular sound of the weaver at his loom. The rural *guardia,* half-keeper, half-police, who had charge of the village also, the only public functionary in the place, came strolling along the road with his great dog on a leash. He wore a mixed costume, the hunter's jacket of discolored velvet with the blue, red-striped trousers of his official uniform, and his dog was a huge black and red animal with bloodshot eyes, something between a lion and a wolf, known and feared by villagers and peasants, by shepherds and hunters, by thieves and children alike. The keeper kept his beast beside him day and night, chiefly for fear of him being poisoned. The dog growled when he saw the priest, but at a sign from his master he was quiet and hung his head.

The keeper stopped in front of the priest and gave a military salute, then said solemnly:

"I went early this morning to see the sick man. His temperature is forty, his pulse a hundred and two. In my poor opinion he has inflammation of the loins, and his granddaughter wanted me to give him quinine." (The keeper had charge of the drugs and medicines supplied for the parish and permitted himself to go round visiting the sick, which was exceeding his duty, but gave him importance in his own eyes, as he imagined he was thus taking the place of the doctor who only came to the village twice a week.) "But I said, 'Gently, my girl; in my humble opinion he does not want quinine, but another sort of medicine.' The girl began to cry, but she shed no tears; may I die if I judged wrongly! She wanted me to rush off immediately to call the doctor, but I said, 'The doctor is coming tomorrow, Sunday, but if you are in such a hurry then send a man yourself to fetch him! The sick man can well afford to pay a doctor to see him die, he has spent no money during his life.' I was quite right, wasn't I?"

The keeper waited gravely for the priest's approval, but Paul was looking at the dog, now quiet and docile at his master's bidding, and he was thinking to himself:

"If we could only thus keep our passions on a leash!" And then he said aloud, but in an absent-minded way, "Oh yes, he can wait till the doctor comes tomorrow. But he is seriously ill, all the same."

"Well then, if he is seriously ill," persisted the keeper firmly and not without contempt for the priest's apparent indifference, "a man had better go for the doctor at once. The old fellow can pay, he is not a pauper. But his granddaughter disobeyed my orders and did not give him the medicine I myself prepared and left for him."

"He should receive the Communion first of all," said Paul.

"But you have told me that a sick person may receive the Communion even if they are not fasting?"

"Well then," said the priest, losing patience at last, "the old man did not want the medicine; he clenched his teeth, and he has them all still sound, and struck out as if nothing was the matter with him."

"And then the granddaughter, in my humble opinion," continued the keeper indignantly, "has no right to order me, an official, to rush off for the doctor as though I were a servant! It was not a question of an accident or anything requiring the doctor's official presence, and I have other things to do. I must now go down to the river by the ford, because I have received information that some benefactor of his neighbors has placed dynamite in the water to destroy the trout. My respects!"

He repeated the military salute and departed, jerking his dog up by the leash. Suddenly sharing its master's repressed contempt, the animal stalked off waving its ferocious tail; it did not growl at the priest, but merely turned its head to give him a parting glance of menace out of its savage eyes.

Having completed his preparations for carrying extreme unction to the old man, Antiochus was leaning over the parapet of the piazza under the shade of the elms, waiting for the priest; and when he saw him approaching, the boy darted into the sacristy and waited with the surplice in his hands. The pair were ready in a few minutes, Paul in surplice and stole, carrying the silver amphora of oil, Antiochus robed in red from head to foot and holding a brocade umbrella with gold fringe open over Paul's head, so that he and his silver amphora were in shadow while the boy himself appeared the more brilliant in the sunshine in contrast to the black and white figure of the priest. Antiochus's face wore a look of almost tragic gravity, for he was much impressed with his own importance and imagined himself specially deputed to protect the holy oil. Nevertheless this did not prevent him from grinning with amusement at the sight of the old men hurriedly shuffling down from the parapet as the little procession passed, and the boys kneeling with their faces to the wall instead of towards the priest. The youngsters jumped up immediately, however, and followed Antiochus, who rang his bell before each door to warn the people; dogs barked, the weavers stopped their looms and the women thrust their heads out of the windows to see, and the whole village was in a tremor of mysterious excitement.

A woman who was coming from the fountain bearing a jug of water on her head set down her jug upon the ground and knelt beside it. And the priest grew pale, for he recognized one of Agnes's servants, and a nameless dread seized upon him, so that unconsciously he clasped the silver amphora tightly between his hands as though seeking their support.

The attendant crowd of boys grew larger as they approached the old hunter's dwelling. This was a two-story cottage built of rough stone and standing a little back from the road on the side towards the valley; it had a single unglazed window and in front a small yard of bare earth enclosed by a low wall. The door stood open and the priest knew that the old man was lying fully dressed on a mat in the lower room; so he entered at once, reciting the prayers for the sick, while Antiochus closed the umbrella and rang his bell loudly to drive away the children as if they were flies. But the room was empty and the mat unoccupied; perhaps the old man had at last consented to go to bed or had been carried there in a dying condition. The priest pushed open the door of an inner room, but that too was empty; so, puzzled, he returned to the door, whence he saw the old man's granddaughter limping down the road with a bottle in her hand. She had been to fetch the medicine.

"Where is your grandfather?" asked Paul, as the girl crossed herself on entering the house. She glanced at the empty mat and gave a scream, and the inquisitive boys immediately swarmed over the wall and round the door, engaging in a free fight with Antiochus, who tried to oppose their entrance, till Paul himself sternly bade them disperse.

"Where is he? Where is he?" cried the granddaughter, running from room to room, whereupon one of the boys, the last to join the crowd, sauntered up with his hands in his pockets and inquired casually, "Are you looking for the King? He went down there."

"Down where?"

"Down there," repeated the boy, pointing with his nose towards the valley.

The girl rushed down the steep path and the boys after her: the priest signed to Antiochus to reopen the umbrella and gravely and in silence the two returned to the church, while the villagers gathered together in wondering groups and the news of the sick man's flight spread from mouth to mouth.

CHAPTER VII

Paul was back again in his quiet dining-room, seated at the table and waited on by his mother. Fortunately there was now something they dare talk about and the flight of King Nicodemus was being discussed. Having hastily deposited the silver amphora and other things taken out for the rite and doffed his red cope, Antiochus had run off to collect news. The first time he came back it was with a

strange report; the old man had disappeared and his relations were said to have carried him off in order to get possession of his money.

"They say that his dog and his eagle came down and carried him off themselves!" corrected some skeptic jestingly.

"I don't believe in the dog," said one of the old men, "but the eagle is no joke. I remember that when I was a boy, one carried off a heavy sheep from our yard."

Then Antiochus came back with the further news that the sick man had been overtaken halfway up to the mountain plateau, where he wished to die. The last upflickering of his fever lent him a fictitious strength and the dying hunter walked like a somnambulist to the place where he longed to be, and in order not to worry him and make him worse, his relatives had accompanied him and seen him safely to his own hut.

"Now sit down and eat," said the priest to the boy.

Antiochus obeyed and took his place at the table, but not without first glancing inquiringly at the priest's mother. She smiled and signed to him to do as he was bidden and the boy felt that he had become one of the family. He could not know, innocent child, that the other two, having exhausted the subject of the old hunter, were afraid of being alone together. The mother would see her son's uneasy wandering eyes arrested suddenly, as though upon some unseen object, with a stony, somber gaze, o'ershadowed by the darkness of his mind, and he in turn would start from his preoccupation, aware that she was observing him and divining his inward grief. But when she had placed the meal on the table she left the room and did not return.

With the bright noonday the wind rose again, but now it was a soft west wind that scarcely stirred the trees upon the ridge; the room was flooded with sunshine checkered by the dancing of the leaves outside the window, and white clouds drifted across the sky like harp-strings whereon the wind played its gentle music.

The charm was broken suddenly by a knock at the door and Antiochus ran to open. A pale young widow with fright-ened eyes stood on the threshold and asked to see the priest. By the hand she held fast a little girl, with small, livid face and a red scarf tied over her untidy black hair; and, as the child dragged and strug-gled from side to side in her efforts to free herself, her eyes blazed like a wild-cat's. "She is ill," said the widow, "and I want the priest to read the gospel over her to drive out the evil spirit that has taken possession of her."

Puzzled and scared, Antiochus stood holding the door half open: this was not the time to worry the priest with such matters, and moreover the girl, who was twisting herself all to one side and trying to bite her mother's hand as she could not escape, was truly an object of both fear and pity.

"She is possessed, you see," said the widow, turning red with shame. So then Antiochus let her in immediately and even helped her to push in the child, who clung to the jamb of the door and re-sisted with all her might.

On hearing what was the matter and that this was already the third day on which the little victim had behaved so strangely, always trying to escape, deaf and dumb to all persuasions, the priest had her brought in to him, and taking her by the shoulders he examined her eyes and her mouth.

"Has she been much in the sun?" he inquired.

"It's not that," whispered the mother. "I think she is possessed by an evil spirit. No," she added, sobbing, "my little girl is no longer alone!"

Paul rose to fetch his Testament from his room, then stopped and sent Anti-ochus for it. The book was placed open on the table, and with his hand upon the burning head of the child, clasped tightly in the arms of her kneeling mother, he read aloud:

"And they arrived at the country of the Gadarenes; which is over against Galilee. And when he went forth to land, there met him out of the city a certain man which had devils a long time, and ware no clothes, neither abode in any house, but in the tombs. When he saw Jesus he cried out and fell down before him, and with a loud voice said, 'What have I to do with thee, Jesus, thou Son of God most high? I beseech thee, torment me not.' "

Antiochus turned over the page of the book and his eyes strayed to the priest's hand which rested on the table; at the words, "What have I to do with thee," he saw the hand tremble, and looking up quickly he perceived that Paul's eyes were full of tears. Then, overcome by an irresistible emotion, the boy knelt down beside the widow, but still keeping his arm stretched out to touch the book. And he thought to himself:

"Surely *he* is the best man in all the world, for he weeps when he reads the word of God!" And he did not venture to raise his eyes again to look at Paul, but with his free hand he pulled the little girl's skirt to keep her quiet, though not without a secret fear that the demons who were being exorcised from her body would enter into his own.

The possessed child had ceased throw-ing herself about and stood up straight and stiff, her thin brown neck stretched to its full length, her little chin stuck forward over the knot of her kerchief and her eyes fixed upon the priest's face. Gradually her expression changed, her mouth relaxed and opened, and it seemed as if the words of the Gospel, the mur-muring of the wind and the rustle of the trees on the ridge were working upon her as a charm. Suddenly she tore her skirt from Antiochus's restraining hand and fell on her knees beside him, and the priest's hand which had rested upon her head remained outstretched above it, as his tremulous voice continued reading:

"Now the man out of whom the devils were departed besought him that he might be with him: but Jesus sent him away, saying, 'Return to thine own house and show how great things God hath done unto thee. . . .' "

He ceased reading and withdrew his hand. The child was now perfectly quiet and had turned her face wonderingly towards the boy, and in the silence that succeeded the Gospel words nothing was audible save the trees rustling in the breeze and the faint tap-tap of the stone-breaker by the roadside.

Paul was suffering acutely. Not for one moment had he shared the widow's superstition that the girl was possessed by a devil and he felt, therefore, that he had been reading the Gospel without belief. The only devil which existed was the one within himself, and this one would not be driven forth. And yet there had been a moment when he had felt nearer to God: "What have I to do with thee?" And it seemed to him that those three believers in front of him, and his own mother kneeling at the kitchen door, were bowed, not before his power, but before his utter wretchedness. Yet when the widow bent low to kiss his feet he drew back sharply: he thought of his mother, *who knew all,* and feared lest she should misjudge him.

The widow was so overwhelmed with mortification when she raised her head that the two children began to laugh, and even Paul's distress relaxed a little.

"That's all right, get up now," he said, "the child is quiet."

They all rose to their feet and Antiochus ran to open the door, at which now somebody else was knocking. It was the keeper with his dog on the leash, and Antiochus burst out instantly, his face beaming with joy:

"A miracle has just happened! He has driven out the devils from the body of Nina Masia!"

But the keeper did not believe in miracles; he stood a little away from the door and said:

"Then let us make room for them to escape!"

"They will enter into the body of your dog," cried Antiochus.

"They cannot enter because they are there already," replied the keeper. He spoke in jest, but maintained his usual gravity. On the threshold of the room he drew himself up and saluted the priest without condescending even to glance at the women.

"Can I speak to you in private, sir?"

The women withdrew into the kitchen and Antiochus carried the Testament upstairs. When he came down, although still full of excitement at the miracle, he stopped to listen to what the keeper was saying:

"I beg your pardon for bringing this animal into the house, but he is quite clean and he will give no trouble because he understands where he is." (The dog, in fact, was standing motionless, with lowered eyes and hanging tail.) "I've come about the matter of old Nicodemus Pania, nicknamed King Nicodemus. He is back in his hut and has expressed the wish to see you again and to receive extreme unction. In my humble opinion . . ."

"Good heavens!" exclaimed the priest impatiently, but the next instant he was filled with childish joy at the thought of going up to the mountain plateau and by physical exertion banishing for a time the perplexities that tormented him.

"Yes, yes," he added quickly, "and I shall want a horse. What is the road like?"

"I will see about the horse and the road," said the keeper, "that is my duty."

The priest offered him a drink. On principle the keeper never accepted anything from anyone, not even a glass of wine, but on this occasion he felt that his own civil functions and the priest's religious functions were so much each a part of the other that he accepted the invitation; so he drank, and emptied the last drops of wine on the ground (since the earth claims her share of whatever man consumes), and expressed his thanks with a military salute. Then the great dog wagged his tail and looked up at Paul with an offer of friendship in his eyes.

Antiochus was ready to open the door again and then returned to the dining-room to await orders. He was sorry for his mother, waiting in vain for the priest in the little room behind the bar, which had been specially cleaned up for the occasion and the tray with glasses placed ready for the guest; but duty before all things and the visit would obviously be impossible that day.

"What must I prepare?" he asked, imitating the keeper's solemn tones. "Shall we take the umbrella?"

"What are you thinking of! I am going on horseback and you need not come at all. I could take you up behind me, however."

"No, I will walk, I am never tired," urged the boy, and in a few minutes he was ready, with a little box in his hand and his red cope folded over his arm. As far as he was concerned, he would have liked to take the umbrella too, but he was obliged to obey superior orders.

While he was waiting for the priest in front of the church all the ragged urchins who made of the square their regular playground and battlefield gathered round him curiously without venturing too near, and regarded the box with respect not unmixed with terror.

"Let's go nearer," said one.

"You keep your distance, or I'll let loose the keeper's dog at you!" shouted Antiochus.

"The keeper's dog? Why, you daren't go within ten miles of him!" jeered the urchins.

"Daren't I?" said Antiochus with magnificent scorn.

"No, you daren't! And you think you're as good as the Lord Himself because you're carrying the holy oil!"

"If I were you," advised one open-minded youth, "I should make off with that box and perform all kinds of sorceries with the holy oil."

"Be off, you horse-fly! The devil that came out of Nina Masia's body has entered into yours!"

"What's that? The devil?" cried the boys in chorus.

"Yes," said Antiochus solemnly, "this very afternoon *he* drove out a devil from the body of Nina Masia. Here she comes."

The widow, leading the little girl by the hand, was just coming out of the presbytery; the boys all rushed to meet her and in one moment the news of the miracle spread through the village. Then occurred a scene which recalled that which had taken place on the first arrival of the priest. The whole population assembled together in the square and Nina Masia was placed by her mother on the top step before the church door, where she sat, thin and brown-skinned, with her green eyes and the red kerchief over her head, looking like some primitive idol set up to be worshiped by those simple and credulous country folk.

The women began to weep and all wanted to touch the girl. Meanwhile the keeper had arrived on the scene with his dog, and then the priest crossed the square on horseback. The crowd immediately collected around him and made a procession to follow him, but while he waved his hand to them and turned from side to side acknowledging their greetings, his annoyance at what had happened was even greater than his distress. When he reached the top of the hill he reined in his horse and seemed about to speak, then suddenly put spurs to the animal and rode rapidly down the road. He had a desperate craving to gallop furiously away, to escape through the valley and lose himself and his whole being somewhere in that wide horizon spread out before his gaze.

The wind was freshening: the afternoon sun shone warmly on the thickets and bushes, the river reflected the blue sky and the spray thrown up by the mill-wheel sparkled like diamonds. The keeper with his dog and Antiochus with his box descended the hill soberly, fully conscious of their office, and presently Paul drew rein and rode along quietly. After crossing the river the road became a mere path and wound upwards towards the plateau, bordered by stones and low walls, rocks and stunted trees, and the west wind blew sweet and warm, heavy-laden with perfume, as though it had gathered all the thyme flowers and wild roses it had found upon its way and was now strewing them again upon the earth.

The path wound ever upwards: when they turned round the side of the hill and lost sight of the village, the world seemed nothing but wind and stones, and white vapors that on the horizon linked earth and sky in one. From time to time the dog barked, and the echo in the hills seemed to bring him answers from other dogs all around.

When they were half-way to their destination the priest offered to take Antiochus up behind him on the horse, but the boy refused, and only very unwillingly yielded up the box. And only then did he permit himself to open a conversa-

tion with the keeper; a vain attempt, however, for the keeper never forgot his own imaginary importance for one moment. Every now and then he would stop, with a portentous frown, and drawing the peak of his cap low over his eyes he would inspect the landscape on every side, as though the whole world belonged to him and were threatened with some imminent peril. Then the dog would stop too, rigid on his four paws, snuffing the wind and quivering from ears to tail. Luckily all was serene on that windy afternoon, the only moving things in sight being the agile goats climbing on distant rocks, black silhouettes against the blue sky and rosy clouds.

At last they came to a sort of declivity covered with masses of granite, a regular waterfall of rocks balanced one upon another with marvelous precision. Antiochus recognized the place, as he had once been there with his father, and while the priest kept to the path, which wound some considerable way round, and the keeper followed him as in duty bound, the boy scrambled down from rock to rock and was the first to reach the hut of the old hunter.

The hut was a ramshackle erection of logs and boughs surrounded by a partly natural enclosure of great boulders, against which the old man, in order to complete this sort of prehistoric fortress, had piled other stones in large numbers. The sun slanted down into this enclosure as into a well: the view was completely shut in on three sides, and only on the right, between two rocks, a silver streak in the blue distance, might be discerned the sea.

On hearing steps the old man's grandson thrust his curly black head out of the hut door. "They are coming," announced Antiochus.

"Who are coming?"

"The priest and the keeper."

The man sprang out, as agile and hairy as his own goats, and swore roundly at the keeper for always interfering in other people's business.

"I'll break all his bones for him!" he growled threateningly, but when he saw the dog he drew back, while the old man's dog ran forward to sniff at and greet the visitor.

Antiochus took charge of the box again and sat down on a stone facing the opening in the rocks. All around were an immense number of wild-boar-skins, striped black and gray, and of marten skins flecked with gold, spread out on the rocks to dry. Inside the hut he could see the form of the old man lying on a heap of other skins, his dark face, framed in the white hair and beard, already set in the composure of approaching death. The priest was bending down to interrogate him, but the dying man made no reply, and lay with closed eyes and a drop of blood trembling on his violet lips. A little way off, on another stone, sat the keeper with his dog stretched at his feet and his eyes also fixed on the interior of the hut. He was indignant because the dying man was disobeying the law in not declaring what was his last will and testament, and as Antiochus turned his mischievous eyes in that direction he thought somewhat maliciously that the keeper would have liked to set his dog on the stubborn old hunter as on a thief.

CHAPTER VIII

Inside the hut the priest bent still lower, his hands clasped between his knees, his face heavy with weariness and displeasure. He too was silent now: he almost seemed to have forgotten why he was there and sat listening to the wind as if it were the distant murmur of the sea. Suddenly the keeper's dog sprang up barking, and Antiochus heard the rustle of wings over his head: he looked up and saw the old hunter's tame eagle alighting on a rock, with its great wings outspread and slowly beating the air like an immense black fan.

Inside the hut Paul was thinking to himself:

"And this is death. This man fled from other men because he was afraid of committing murder or some other great crime. And here he lies now, a stone among stones. So shall I lie in thirty, forty years, after an exile that has lasted through eternity. And perhaps she will still be expecting me tonight . . ."

He started up. Ah, no, he was not dead as he had thought: life was beating within him, surging up strong and tenacious like the eagle among the stones.

"I must remain up here all night," he told himself. "If I can get through this night without seeing her I shall be saved."

He went outside and sat down beside Antiochus. The sun was sinking in a crimson sky, the shadows of the high rocks were lengthening over the enclosure and the wind-tossed bushes, and in the same way as he could not distinguish objects clearly in the uncertain light without, so Paul could not tell which of the two desires within him was the strongest. Presently he said:

"The old man cannot speak now, he is dying. It is time to administer extreme unction, and if he dies we must arrange for the body to be moved. It will be necessary . . ." he added as though to himself, but did not dare to complete the sentence, "it will be necessary to spend the night here."

Antiochus got up and began to make preparations for the ceremony. He opened the box, pressing the silver fasteners with enjoyment, and drew out the white cloth and the amphora of oil: then he unfolded his red cope and put it on— he might have been himself the priest!

When everything was ready they went back into the hut, where the grandson, on his knees, was supporting the dying man's head. Antiochus knelt down on the other side, with the folds of his cope spread out on the ground. He laid the white cloth over the stone that served as a table, and the scarlet of his cope was reflected in the silver amphora. The keeper, too, knelt down outside the hut, with his dog beside him.

Then the priest anointed the old man's forehead, and the palms of his hands which had never sought to do violence to anyone, and his feet which had borne him far from men as from evil itself.

The setting sun shone direct into the hut with a last dazzling splendor, lighting up Antiochus in his scarlet cope, so that between the old man and the priest he looked like a live coal among dead cinders.

"I shall have to go back," thought Paul. "I have no excuse for remaining here." Presently he went outside the hut and said: "There is no hope, he is quite unconscious."

"Comatose," said the keeper with precision.

"He cannot live more than a few hours and arrangements must be made for transporting the body down to the village," continued Paul; and he longed to add, "And I must stay here all night," but he was ashamed of his untruth.

Moreover he was beginning now to feel the need of walking and a craving to get back to the village. As night fell the thought of sin began subtly to attract him again and drew him in with the invisible net of darkness. He felt it and was afraid; but he kept guard over himself, and he knew his conscience was awake and ready to uphold him.

"If only I could get through this one night without seeing her I should be saved!" was his silent cry. If only some one would detain him by force! If the old

man would revive and hold him fast by the hem of his robe!

He sat down again and cast about for some excuse for delaying his departure. The sun had now sunk below the edge of the high plateau, and the trunks of the oaks stood out boldly against the red glow of the sky like the pillars of some gigantic portico, surmounted by an immense black roof. Not even the presence of death could mar the peace of that majestic solitude. Paul was weary and, as in the morning at the foot of the altar, he would have liked to lie down upon the stones and fall asleep.

Meanwhile the keeper had come to a decision on his own account. He entered the hut and, kneeling down beside the dying man, whispered something into his ear. The grandson looked on with suspicion and contempt, then approached the priest and said:

"Now that you have done your duty, depart in peace. I know what has to be done now."

At that moment the keeper came outside again.

"He is past speaking," he said, "but he gave me to understand by a sign that he has put all his affairs in order. Nicodemus Pania," he added, turning towards the grandson, "can you assure us on your conscience that we may leave here with quiet minds?"

"Except for the holy sacrament of extreme unction, you need not have come at all. What business have you to meddle in my affairs?" answered the grandson truculently.

"We must carry out the law! And don't raise your voice like that, Nicodemus Pania!" retorted the keeper.

"Enough, enough, no shouting," said the priest, pointing to the hut.

"You are always teaching that there is only one duty in life, and that is to do one's own duty," said the keeper sententiously.

Paul sprang to his feet, struck by those words. Everything he heard now seemed meant specially for him, and he thought God was making known His will through the mouths of men. He mounted his horse and said to the old man's grandson:

"Stay with your grandfather until he is dead. God is great and we never know what may happen."

The man accompanied him part of the way, and when they were out of earshot of the keeper he said:

"Listen, sir. My grandfather did give his money into my charge; it's here, inside my coat. It is not much, but whatever it is, it belongs to me, doesn't it?"

"If your grandfather gave it to you for yourself alone, then it is yours," replied Paul, turning round to see if the others were following.

They were following. Antiochus was leaning on a stick he had fashioned for himself out of the branch of a tree, and the keeper, the glazed peak of his cap and the buttons of his tunic reflecting the last rays of the evening light, had halted at the corner of the path and was giving the military salute in the direction of the hut. He was saluting death. And from his rocky perch the eagle answered the salute with a last flap of his great wings before he too went to sleep.

*   *   *

The shades of night crept rapidly up from the valley and soon enveloped the three wayfarers. When they had crossed the river, however, and had turned into the path that led up towards home, their road was lit up by a distant glare that came from the village itself. It looked as if the whole place were on fire; huge flames were leaping on the summit of the ridge, and the keepers' keen sight distinguished numerous figures moving about in the square in front of the church. It was a Saturday, and nearly all the men would have returned to their homes for the Sunday rest, but this did not explain the reason for the bonfires and the unusual excitement in the village.

"I know what it is!" called Antiochus joyfully. "They are waiting for us to come back, and they are going to celebrate the miracle of Nina Masia!"

"Good heavens! Are you quite mad, Antiochus?" cried the priest, with something akin to terror as he gazed at the hillside below the village, over which the bonfires were casting their lurid glare.

The keeper made no remark, but in contemptuous silence he rattled the dog's chain and the animal barked loudly. Whereupon hoarse shouts and yells echoed through the valley, and to the priest in his misery it seemed as though some mysterious voice were protesting against the way in which he had imposed on the simplicity of his parishioners.

"What have I done to them?" he asked himself. "I have made fools of them just as I have made a fool of myself. May God save us all!"

Suggestions for heroic action rushed into his mind. When he reached the village he would stop in the middle of his people and confess his sin; he would tear open his breast before them all and show them his wretched heart, consumed with grief, but burning more fiercely with the flame of his anguish than the fires of brushwood upon the ridge.

But here the voice of his conscience spoke:

"It is their faith that they are celebrating. They are glorifying God in thee and thou hast no right to thrust thyself and thy wretchedness between them and God."

But from deeper still within him another voice made itself heard:

"It is not that. It is because thou art base and vile and art afraid of suffering, of burning in very truth."

And the nearer they came to the vil-

[162]

lage and the men, the more abased did Paul feel. As the leaping flames fought with the shadows on the hill-side so light and darkness seemed to fight in his conscience, and he did not know what to do. He remembered his first arrival in the village years ago, with his mother following him anxiously as she had followed the first steps of his infancy.

"And I have fallen in her sight," he groaned. "She thinks she has raised me up again, but I am wounded to death."

Then suddenly he bethought him, with a sense of relief, that this improvised festival would help him out of his difficulty and avert the danger he feared.

"I will invite some of them to the presbytery to spend the evening, and they are sure to stay late. If I can get through this night I shall be safe."

The black figures of the men leaning over the parapet of the square could now be distinguished, and higher up, behind the church, the flames of the bonfires were waving in the air like long red flags. The bells were not ringing as on that former occasion, but the melancholy sound of a concertina accompanied the general uproar.

All at once from the top of the church tower there shot up a silver star, which instantly broke into a thousand sparks with an explosion that echoed through the valley. A shout of delight went up from the crowd, followed by another brilliant shower of sparks and the noise of shots being fired. They were letting off their guns in sign of rejoicing, as they did on the nights of the great feasts.

"They have gone mad," said the keeper, and he ran off at full speed in advance, the dog barking fiercely as though there were some revolt to be quelled up there.

Antiochus, on the other hand, felt inclined to weep. He looked at the priest sitting straight upright on his horse and thought he resembled some saint carried in procession. Nevertheless, his reflections took a practical turn:

"My mother will do good business tonight with all these merry folk!"

And he felt so happy that he unfolded the cope and threw it over his shoulders. Then he wanted to carry the box again, though he would not give up his new stick, and thus he entered the village looking like one of the Three Kings.

The old hunter's granddaughter called to the priest from her door and asked for news of her grandfather.

"All is well," said Paul.

"Then grandfather is better, is he?"

"Your grandfather is dead by this time."

She gave a scream, and that was the only discordant note of the festival.

The boys had already gone down the hill to meet the priest; they swarmed round his horse like a cloud of flies, and all went up together to the church square. The people there were not so numerous as they had looked from a distance, and the presence of the keeper with his dog had infused some sort of order into the proceedings. The men were ranged round the parapet underneath the trees and some were drinking in front of the little wineshop kept by the mother of Antiochus: the women, their sleeping infants in their arms, were sitting on the church steps, and in the middle of them sat Nina Masia, as quiet now as a drowsy cat.

In the center of the square stood the keeper with his dog, as stiff as a statue.

On the arrival of the priest they all got up and gathered round him; but the horse, secretly spurred by its rider, started forward towards a street on the opposite side from the church, where was the house of its master. Whereupon the master, who happened to be one of the men drinking in front of the wineshop, came forward glass in hand and caught the animal by the bridle.

"Heh, nag, what are you thinking of? Here I am!"

The horse stopped immediately, nuzzling towards its master as if it wanted to drink the wine in his glass. The priest made a movement to dismount, but the man held him fast by one leg, while he led horse and rider in front of the wineshop, where he stretched out his glass to a companion who was holding the bottle.

The whole crowd, men and women, now formed a circle round the priest. In the lighted doorway of the wineshop, smiling at the scene, stood the tall, gipsy-like figure of Antiochus's mother, her face almost bronze-colored in the reflection of the bonfires. The babies had wakened up startled and were struggling in their mothers' arms, the gold and coral amulets with which all, even the poorest, was adorned, gleaming as they moved. And in the center of this restless throng, confused gray figures in the darkness, sat the priest high upon his horse, in very truth like a shepherd in the midst of his flock.

A white-bearded old man placed his hand on Paul's knee and turned towards the people.

"Good folk," he said in a voice shaking with emotion, "this is truly a man of God!"

"Then drink to a good vintage!" cried the owner of the horse offering the glass, which Paul accepted and immediately put to his lips; but his teeth shook against the edge of the glass as though the red wine glowing in the light of the fires were not wine, but blood.

CHAPTER IX

Paul was seated again at his own table in the little dining-room, lighted by an oil lamp. Behind the ridge, which looked a mountain as seen from the presbytery window, the full moon was rising in the pale sky.

He had invited several of the villagers to come in and keep him company, among them the old man with the white beard and the owner of the horse, and they were still sitting there drinking and joking, and telling hunting stories. The old man with the white beard, a hunter himself, was criticizing King Nicodemus because, in his opinion, the old recluse did not conduct his hunting according to the law of God.

"I don't want to speak ill of him in his last hour," he was saying; "but to tell the truth, he went out hunting simply as a speculation. Now last winter he must have made thousands of lire by marten skins alone. God allows us to shoot animals, but not to exterminate them! And he used to snare them, too, and that is forbidden, because animals feel pain just as we do, and the hours they lie caught in the snares must be terrible. Once I myself, with these very eyes, I saw a snare where a hare had left her foot. Do you understand what that means? The hare had been caught in the snare and had gnawed the flesh away all round her foot, and had broken her leg off to get free. And what did Nicodemus do with his money, after all? He hid it, and now his grandson will drink it all in a few days."

"Money is made to be spent," said the owner of the horse, a man much given to boasting; "I myself, for instance, I have always spent freely and enjoyed myself, without hurting anyone. Once at our festival, having nothing else to do, I stopped a man who sold silk reels and happened to be passing with a load of his goods; I bought the whole lot, then I set them rolling about on the piazza and ran after them, kicking them here and there and everywhere! In one instant the whole crowd was after me, laughing and yelling, and the boys and young men, and even some of the older men began to imitate me. That was a game that's not forgotten yet! Every time the old priest saw me he used to shout from ever so far: 'Hallo, Pasquale Masia, haven't you any reels to set rolling today?' "

All the guests laughed at the tale, only Paul seemed absent-minded and looked pale and tired. The old man with the white beard, who was observing him with reverent affection, winked at his companions to suggest an immediate departure. It was time to leave the servant of God to his holy solitude and well-merited repose.

The guests rose from their seats all together and took respectful leave of their host; and Paul found himself alone, between the flickering flame of the oil lamp and the calm splendor of the moon that shone in through the high window, while the sound of the heavy iron-shod shoes of his departing guests echoed down the deserted street.

It was yet early to go to bed, and although he was utterly worn out and his shoulders ached with fatigue, as though he had been bearing a heavy yoke all the day, he had no thought of going up to his own room. His mother was still in the kitchen: he could not see her from where he sat, but he knew that she was watching as on *the previous night*.

The previous night! He felt as if he had been suddenly awakened out of a long sleep, and the distress of his return home from the house of Agnes, and his thoughts in the night, the letter, the Mass, the journey up the mountain, the villagers' demonstration, had all been only a dream. His real life was beginning again now: he had but to take a step, a dozen steps, to open the door . . . and go back to her. . . . His real life was beginning again.

"But perhaps she is not expecting me any longer. Perhaps she will never expect me again!"

Then he felt his knees trembling and terror took hold of him again, not at the thought of going back to her, but at the thought that she might have accepted her fate and be already beginning to forget him.

Then he realized that in the depths of his heart the hardest thing to bear since he came down from the mountain had been this—not knowing anything about her, her silence, her vanishing out of his life.

This was the veritable death, that she should cease to love him.

He buried his face in his hands and tried to bring her image before his mind's eye, then he began to reproach her for those things for which she might justly have reproached him.

"Agnes, you cannot forget your promises! How can you forget them? You held my wrists in your two strong hands and said to me: 'We are bound to each other forever, in life and in death.' Is it possible that you can forget? You said, you know . . ."

His fingers gripped at his collar, for he was suffocating with his distress.

"The devil has caught me in his snare," he thought, and remembered the hare who had gnawed off her own foot.

He drew a deep breath, rose from his chair, and took up the lamp. He determined to conquer his will, to gnaw his own flesh also if thereby he could only free himself. Now he decided to go up to his room, but as he moved towards the hall he saw his mother sitting in her accustomed place in the silent kitchen, and beside her was Antiochus fast asleep. He went to the door.

"Why is that boy still here?" he asked.

His mother looked at him hesitatingly: she would have preferred not to answer, but to have hidden Antiochus behind her wide skirts in order that Paul should not wait up any longer, but go to his room and to bed. Her faith in him was now completely restored, but she too thought of the devil and his snares. At this moment, however, Antiochus woke up and remembered very well why he was still waiting there, in spite of the fact that the woman had several times asked him to go.

"I was waiting here because my mother is expecting a visit from you," he explained.

"But is this a time of night to go paying visits?" protested the priest's mother. "Come now, be off with you, and tell her that Paul is tired and will go and see her tomorrow."

She spoke to the boy, but she was looking at her son: she saw his glassy eyes fixed upon the lamp, but his eyelids quivered like the wings of a moth in a candle.

Antiochus got up with an expression of deep disappointment.

"But my mother is expecting him; she thinks it's something important."

"If it was anything important he would go and tell her at once. Come, be off with you!"

She spoke sharply, and as Paul looked at her his eyes lit up again with quick resentment: he saw that his mother was afraid lest he should go out again, and the knowledge filled him with unreasoning anger. He banged the lamp down on the table again and called to Antiochus:

"We will go and see your mother."

In the hall, however, he turned and added:

"I shall be back directly, mother; don't fasten the door."

She had not moved from where she sat, but when the two had left the house she went to peep through the half-open door and saw them cross the moonlit square and enter the wineshop, which was still lighted up. Then she went back to the kitchen and began her vigil as on the previous night.

She marveled at herself to find that she was no longer afraid of the old priest reappearing; it had all been a dream. At the bottom of her heart, however, she did not feel at all certain that the ghost would not come back and demand his mended socks.

"I have mended them all right," she said aloud, thinking of those she had mended for her son. And she felt that even if the ghost did come back she would be able to hold her own with him and keep on friendly terms.

Complete silence reigned all round. Outside the window the trees shone silver in the bright moonlight, the sky was like a milky sea, and the perfume of the aromatic shrubs penetrated even into the house. And the mother herself was tranquil now, though she hardly knew why, seeing that Paul might yet fall again into sin; but she no longer felt the same terror of it. She saw again in her mind's eye the lashes trembling on his cheeks, like those of a child about to cry, and her mother's heart melted with tenderness and pity.

"And why, oh Lord, why, why?"

She dared not complete her question, but it remained at the bottom of her heart like a stone at the bottom of a well. Why, oh Lord, was Paul forbidden to love a woman? Love was lawful for all, even for servants and herdsmen, even for the blind and for convicts in prison; so why should Paul, her child, be the only one to whom love was forbidden?

Then again the consciousness of reality forced itself on her. She remembered the words of Antiochus, and was ashamed of being less wise than a boy.

"They themselves, the youngest among the priests, asked permission to live chaste and free, apart from women."

Moreover, her Paul was a strong man, in no wise inferior to his ancient predecessors. He would never give way to tears; his eyelids would close over eyes dry as those of the dead, for he was a strong man.

"I am growing childish!" she sobbed.

She felt as if she had grown twenty years older in that one long day of wearing emotions: each hour that passed had added to the burden she bore, each minute had struck a blow upon her soul as the hammer of the stone-breaker struck upon the heaps of broken rock there behind the ridge. So many things now seemed clear to her, different from on the previous day. The figure of Agnes came before her, with the proud look that concealed all she really felt.

"She is strong too," thought the mother; "she will hide everything."

Then slowly she rose from her chair and began to cover the fire with ashes, banking it up carefully so that no sparks could fly out and set fire to anything near: then she shut the house door, for she knew Paul always carried a key with him. She stamped about loudly, as though he could hear her across the square, and believe her firm footsteps to be an outward sign of her inward assurance.

She felt, however, that this assurance was not so very firm after all. But then what is really firm in this life? Neither the base of the mountains nor the foundations of the churches, for an earthquake may overthrow them both. Thus she felt sure of Paul for the future, and sure of herself, but always with an underlying dread of the unknown which might chance to supervene. And when she reached her bedroom she dropped warily into a chair, wondering whether it would not have been better after all to leave the front door open.

Then she got up and began to untie her apron string; but it had twisted into a knot over which she lost patience at last, and went to fetch a pair of scissors from her work-basket. She found the kitten curled up asleep inside the basket, and the scissors and reels were all warm from contact with its tiny body; and somehow the touch of the living thing made her repent of her impatience, and she went back to the lamp, and drawing the knot in front of her she succeeded at last in untying it. With a sigh of relief she slowly undressed, carefully folding her garments one by one on the chair, first, however, taking the keys out of her apron pocket and laying them in a row on the table like a respectable family all asleep. Thus her masters had taught her in her youth to cultivate order and tidiness, and she still obeyed the old instructions.

She sat down again, half undressed, her short chemise displaying thin brown legs that might have been made of wood, and she yawned with weariness and resignation. No, she would not go downstairs again; her son should come home and find the door closed, and see from that fact that his mother had full confidence in him. That was the right way to manage him, show that you trusted him absolutely. Nevertheless, she was on the alert, and listened for the least sound; not in the same way as on the previous night, but still she listened. She drew off her shoes and placed them side by side, like two sisters who must keep each other company even during the night, and went on murmuring her prayers and yawning, yawning with weariness and resignation, and with sheer nervousness, too.

Whatever could Paul have to say to Antiochus's mother? The woman had by no means a good reputation, she lent money on usury and was commonly supposed to be a procuress too. No, Paul's mother could not understand it. Then she blew out the candle, snuffed the smoking wick with her fingers and got into bed, but could not bring herself to lie down.

Presently she thought she heard a step in her room. Was it the ghost come back? She was filled with a horrible fear lest he should come up to the bed and take hold of her; for a moment her blood froze in her veins, then surged to her heart as a people in tumult rushes through the streets of its city to the principal square. Then she recovered herself and was ashamed of her fear, only caused, she was sure, by the wicked doubts she had entertained of her Paul.

No, those doubts were all ended: never again would she inquire into the very smallest of his actions; it was her place to keep quietly in the background, as she was now, in her little room fit only for a servant. She lay down and drew the bedclothes over her, covering her ears, too, so that she might not hear whether Paul came home or not; but in her inner consciousness she *felt* all the same, she felt that he was not coming home, that he had been carried off by some one against his will, as one drawn reluctantly into a dance.

Nevertheless she felt quite sure of him; sooner or later he would manage to escape and come home. Anyhow, she was resting quietly under the bedclothes, though not yet asleep, and she had a confused impression that she was still trying to undo the knot in her apron string. Then the faint buzzing in her ears beneath the coverlet turned gradually into the murmuring of the crowd in the square beneath her window, and farther off still the murmuring of a people who lamented, and yet while lamenting laughed and danced and sang. Her Paul was there in the middle of them, and above them all in some high, far place, a lute was being softly played. Perhaps it was God Himself playing to the dance of men.

CHAPTER X

All day long Antiochus's mother had been speculating as to what could be the object of the priest's visit, for which her boy had prepared her, but she took good care not to betray by her manner that she was expecting him. Perhaps he intended making a few remarks on the subject of usury, and certain other trades which she practiced; or because she was in the habit of lending out—for purely medical purposes, but always for a small fee—certain very ancient relics which she had inherited from her husband's family. Or perhaps he wanted to borrow money, either for himself or some one else. Whatever it might prove to be, as soon as the last customer had departed she went to the door and stood there with her hands in her pockets, heavy with copper coins, looking out to see whether Antiochus at least were not in sight.

Then immediately she pretended to be busied with shutting the door, and in fact she did shut the lower half, bending down to fasten the bolt. She was active in her movements, although tall and stout; but, contrary to the other women of the place, she had a small head, which only looked large because of the great mass of black plaits that encircled it.

As the priest approached she drew herself up and bade him good evening with much dignity, though her black eyes looked straight into his with an ardent, langorous gaze. Then she invited him to take a seat in the room behind the wineshop, and Antiochus's wistful eyes begged her to press the invitation. But the priest said good-humoredly:

"No, let us stay here," and he sat down at one of the long, wine-stained tables that furnished the little tavern, while Antiochus, resigned to the inevitable, stood beside him, casting anxious glances round, however, to see if everything was in order and fearful lest any belated customer should come in to disturb the conference.

Nobody came and everything was in order. The big petroleum lamp threw an immense shadow of his mother on the wall behind the little bar, covered with shelves filled with bottles of red, yellow and green liqueurs, the light falling crudely on the small black casks ranged along the opposite side of the shop. There was no other furniture except the long table at which sat the priest, and another smaller one, and over the door hung a bunch of broom which served the double purpose of informing passers-by that this was the door of a wineshop and of attracting flies away from the glasses.

Antiochus had been waiting for this moment during the whole of the day, with the feeling that some mystery would then be revealed. He was afraid of some intruder coming in, or that his mother would not behave as she should. He would have liked her to be more humble, more docile in the presence of the priest; but instead of that she had taken her seat again behind the bar, and sat there as composedly as a queen on her throne. She did not even appear to realize that the man seated at the tavern table like an ordinary customer was a saint who worked miracles, and she was not even grateful for the large quantity of wine which he had been the indirect means of her selling that day!

At last, however, Paul opened the conversation.

"I should have liked to see your husband as well," he began, resting his elbows on the table and placing his finger-tips together, "but Antiochus tells me that he will not be back until Sunday week."

The woman merely nodded in assent.

"Yes, on Sunday week, but I can go and fetch him, if you like," broke in Antiochus, with an eagerness of which neither of the others took the least notice.

"It is about the boy," continued Paul. "The time has come when you must really consider in earnest what you are going to do with him. He is growing big

now and you must either teach him a trade or, if you want to make a priest of him, you must think very seriously of the responsibility you are undertaking."

Antiochus opened his lips, but as his mother began to speak he listened to her silently, though with a shade of disapproval on his anxious young face.

The woman seized the occasion, as she always did, to sound the praises of her husband, also to excuse herself for having married a man much older than herself:

"My Martin, as your Reverence knows, is the most conscientious man in the world; he is a good husband and a good father and a better workman than anyone else. Who is there in the whole village who works as hard as he does? Tell me that, your Reverence, you who know what sort of a character the village has got through the idleness of its inhabitants! I say, then, that if Antiochus wants to choose a trade, he has only to follow his father's; that is the best trade for him. The boy is free to do as he likes, and even if he wants to do nothing (I don't say it for vanity), he will be able to live without turning thief, thank God! But if he wants a trade different from his father's, then he must choose for himself. If he wants to be a charcoal-burner, let him be a charcoal-burner; if he wants to be a carpenter, let him be a carpenter; if he wants to be a laborer, let him be a laborer."

"I want to be a priest!" said the boy with quivering lips and eager eyes.

"Very well then, be a priest," replied his mother.

And thus his fate was decided.

Paul let his hands fall upon the table and gazed slowly round him. Quite suddenly he felt it was ridiculous that he should thus interest himself in other people's business. How could he possibly solve the problem of the future for Antiochus when he could not succeed in solving it for himself? The boy stood before him in ardent expectation, like a piece of red-hot iron awaiting the stroke of the hammer to mold it into shape, and every word had the power to either make or mar him. Paul's gaze rested on him with something akin to envy, and in the depths of his conscience he applauded the mother's action in leaving her son free to follow his own instincts.

"Instinct never leads us wrong," he said aloud, following his own train of thought. "But now, Antiochus, tell me in your mother's presence the reason why you wish to be a priest. Being a priest is not a trade, you know; it is not like being a charcoal-burner or a carpenter. You think now that it is a very easy, comfortable kind of life, but later on you will find that it is very difficult. The joys and pleasures allowed to all other men are forbidden to us, and if we truly desire to serve the Lord our life is one continuous sacrifice."

"I know that," replied the boy very simply. "I desire to serve the Lord."

He looked at his mother then, because he was a little ashamed of betraying all his enthusiasm before her, but she sat behind the bar as calmly and coldly as when she was merely serving customers. So Antiochus went on:

"Both my father and mother are willing for me to become a priest; why should they object? I am very careless sometimes, but that is because I am still only a boy, and in future I mean to be much more serious and attentive."

"That is not the question, Antiochus; you are too serious and attentive already!" said Paul. "At your age you should be heedless and merry. Learn and prepare yourself for life, certainly, but be a boy too."

"And am I not a boy?" protested Antiochus; "I do play, only you don't happen to see me just when I am playing! Besides, why should I play if I don't feel

inclined? I have lots of amusements: I enjoy ringing the church bells and I feel as if I was a bird up in the tower. And haven't I had an amusing time today? I enjoyed carrying the box and climbing up ever so high among the rocks, and I got there before you, although you were riding! I enjoyed coming home again . . . and today I enjoyed . . . I was happy," and the boy's eyes sought the ground as he added, "when you drove the devils out of the body of Nina Masia."

"You believed in that?" asked the priest in a low voice, and immediately he saw the boy's eyes look upward, so glorious with the light of faith and wonder that instinctively he lowered his own to hide the dark shadow that rested on his soul.

"Only, when we are children we think in one way and everything looks great and beautiful to us," continued Paul, much disturbed, "but when we are grown up things look different. One must reflect very carefully before undertaking anything important so that one may not come to repent afterwards."

"I shall not repent, I'm sure," said the boy with decision. "Have you repented? No, and neither shall I repent."

Paul lifted up his eyes: again he felt that he held in his hands the soul of this child, to mold it like wax, and that a few careless touches might deform it forever. And again he feared and was silent.

All this time the woman behind the bar had listened quietly, but now the priest's words began to cause her a certain uneasiness. She opened a drawer in front of her, wherein she kept her money, and the cornelian rings and the brooches and mother-of-pearl ornaments pledged by the village women in return for small loans; and evil thoughts flashed through the darkest recesses of her mind, like those forlorn trinkets at the bottom of her drawer.

"The priest is afraid that Antiochus

will turn him out of his parish some time or other," she was thinking, "or else he is in need of money and is working off his bad temper first. Now he'll be asking for a loan."

She closed the drawer softly and resumed her tranquil demeanor. She always sat there in silence and never took part in the discussions between her customers, even though invited to give her opinion, especially if they were playing cards. Thus she left her little Antiochus to face his adversary by himself.

"How is it possible not to believe?" said the boy, between awe and excitement. "Nina Masia was possessed, wasn't she? Why, I myself felt the devil inside her shaking her like a wolf in a cage. And it was nothing but the words of the Gospel spoken by you that set her free!"

"That is true, the Word of God can achieve all things," admitted the priest. Then suddenly he rose from his seat.

Was he going? Antiochus gazed at him in consternation.

"Are you going?" he murmured.

Was this the famous visit? He ran to the bar and made a desperate sign to his mother, who turned round and took down a bottle from the shelves. She was disappointed too, for she had hoped for a chance of lending money to the parish priest, even at a very low interest, thereby in some way legitimizing her usury in the sight of God. But instead of that, he had simply come to inform Antiochus that being a priest was not the same thing as being a carpenter! However, she must do him honor, in any case.

"But your Reverence is not going away like that! Accept something to drink, at least; this wine is very old."

Antiochus was already holding the tray with a glass goblet upon it.

"Then only a little," said Paul.

Leaning across the bar, the woman poured out the wine, careful not to spill a drop. Paul raised his glass, within which the ruby liquid exhaled a perfume like a dusky rose, and after first making Antiochus taste it, he put it to his own lips.

"Then let us drink to the future parish priest of Aar!" he said.

Antiochus was obliged to lean against the bar, for his knees gave way under him; that was the happiest moment of his life. The woman had turned round to replace the precious bottle on the shelf, and, absorbed in his joy, the lad did not notice that the priest had gone deathly pale and was staring out of the doorway as though he beheld a ghost.

A dark figure was running silently across the square, came to the wineshop door, looked round the interior with wide-open black eyes, and then entered, panting.

It was one of Agnes's servants.

The priest instinctively withdrew to the far end of the tavern, trying to hide himself, then came forward again on a sudden impulse. He felt as if he were revolving round and round like a top, then pulled himself together and remembered that he was not alone and must be careful not to excite remark. So he stood still. But he had no desire to hear what the servant was telling the woman, listening eagerly behind the bar, his only desire was flight and safety; his heart had stopped beating, and all the blood in his body had rushed to his head and was roaring in his ears. Nevertheless the servant's words penetrated to the utmost depths of his soul.

"She fell down," said the girl breathlessly, "and the blood poured from her nose in a stream, such a stream that we thought she had broken something inside her head! And she's bleeding still! Give me the keys of St. Mary of Egypt, for that is the only thing that can stop it."

Antiochus, who stood listening with the tray and glass still in his hands, ran to fetch the keys of an old church, now demolished, which keys when actually laid on the shoulders of anyone suffering from hemorrhage of the nose did to some extent arrest the flow of blood.

"All this is just pretense," thought Paul, "there is no truth whatever in the tale. She sent her servant to spy on me and endeavor to lure me to her house, and they are probably in league with this worthless woman here."

And yet deep, deep within him the agitation grew till all his being was in a tumult. Ah, no, the servant was not lying; Agnes was too proud to confide in anyone, and least of all in her servants. Agnes was really ill, and with his inward eye he saw her sweet face all stained with blood. And it was he himself who had struck her the blow. "We thought she had broken something inside her head."

He saw the shifty eyes of the woman behind the bar glance swiftly in his direction, with obvious surprise at his apparent indifference.

"But how did it happen?" he then asked the servant, but coolly and calmly, as though seeking to conceal his anxiety even from himself.

The girl turned and confronted him, her dark, hard, pointed face thrust out towards him like a rock against which he feared to strike.

"I was not at home when she fell. It happened this morning while I was at the fountain, and when I got back I found her very ill. She had fallen over the doorstep and blood was flowing from her nose, but I think she was more frightened than hurt. Then the blood stopped, but she was very pale all day and refused to eat. Then this evening her nose began to bleed again, and not only that, but she had a sort of convulsion, and when I left her just now she was lying cold and stiff, with blood still flowing. I am very nervous," added the girl, taking the keys which Antiochus handed to her and

wrapping them in her apron, "and we are only women in the house."

She moved towards the door, but kept her black eyes on Paul as though seeking to draw him after her by the sheer power of her gaze, and the woman seated behind the bar said in her cold voice:

"Why does not your Reverence go and see her?"

He wrung his hands unconsciously and stammered: "I hardly know . . . it is too late. . . ."

"Yes, come, come!" urged the servant. "My little mistress will be very glad, and it will give her courage to see you."

"It is the devil speaking by your mouth," thought Paul, but unconsciously he followed the girl. He had gripped Antiochus by the shoulder and was drawing him along as a support, and the boy went with him like a plank of safety upon the waves. So they crossed the square and went as far as the presbytery, the servant running on ahead, but turning every few steps to look back at them, the whites of her eyes gleaming in the moonlight. Seen thus at night, the black figure with the dark and mask-like face had truly something diabolical about it, and Paul followed it with a vague sense of fear, leaning on Antiochus's shoulder as he walked and feeling like Tobit in his blindness.

On passing the presbytery door the boy tried to open it, and then Paul perceived that his mother had locked it. He stopped short and disengaged himself from his companion.

"My mother has locked up because she knew in advance that I should not keep my word," he thought to himself; then said to the boy: "Antiochus, you must go home at once."

The servant had stopped also, then went on a few steps, then stopped again and saw the boy returning towards his own home and the priest inserting his key in his door; then she went back to him.

"I am not coming," he said, turning almost threateningly to confront her, and looking her straight in the face as though trying to recognize her true nature through her outward mask; "if you should absolutely need me, you understand—only if you do absolutely need me—you can come back and fetch me."

She went away without another word, and he stood there before his own door, with his hand on the key as though it had refused to turn in the lock. He could not bring himself to enter, it was beyond his power; neither could he go forward in that other path he had begun to tread. He felt as if he were doomed to stand there for all eternity, before a closed door of which he held the key.

Meanwhile Antiochus had reached home. His mother locked the door and he went to wash up the glasses and put them away; and the first glass he washed in the clean water was the one from which *he* had drunk. The boy dried it carefully with a white cloth, which he passed round and round inside with his thumb; then he held it up to the flame of the lamp and examined it with one eye, keeping the other screwed up, which had the effect of making the glass shine like a big diamond. Then he hid it away in a secret cupboard of his own with as much reverence as if it had been the chalice of the Mass.

CHAPTER XI

Paul had gone home too, and was feeling his way upstairs in the dark: he dimly remembered going up some stairs in the dark like this when he was a boy, but he could not remember where it had been. Now, as then, he had the feeling that there was some danger near him which he could only escape by strict attention to what he was doing. He reached the landing, he stood before his own door, he was safe. But he hesitated an instant before opening it, then crossed over and tapped lightly with the knuckle of his forefinger at his mother's door and entered without waiting for a reply.

"It is I," he said brusquely; "don't light the candle, I have something to tell you."

He heard her turning round in her bed, the straw mattress creaking under her: but he could not see her, he did not want to see her; their two souls must speak together in the darkness as though they had already passed to the world beyond.

"Is it you, Paul? I was dreaming," she said in a sleepy yet frightened voice; "I thought I heard dancing, some one playing on the flute."

"Mother, listen," he said, paying no attention to her words. "That woman, Agnes, is ill. She has been ill since this morning. She had a fall; it seems she hurt her head and is bleeding from her nose."

"You don't mean it, Paul? Is she in danger?"

In the darkness her voice sounded alarmed, yet at the same time incredulous. He went on, repeating the breathless words of the servant:

"It happened this morning, after she got the letter. All day long she was pale and refused to eat, and this evening she grew worse and fell into convulsions."

He knew that he was exaggerating, and stopped: his mother did not speak. For a moment in the silence and the night there was a deathlike tension, as though two enemies were seeking each other in the darkness and seeking in vain. Then the straw mattress creaked again; his mother must have raised herself to a sitting position in the high bed, because her clear voice now seemed to come from above.

"Paul, who told you all this? Perhaps it is not true."

Again he felt that it was his conscience speaking to him through her, but he answered at once:

"It may be true. But that is not the question, mother. It is that I fear she may commit some folly. She is alone in the hands of servants, and I must see her."

"Paul!"

"I must," he repeated, raising his voice almost to a shout; but it was himself he was trying to convince, not his mother.

"Paul, you promised!"

"I know I promised, and for that very reason I have come to tell you before I go. I tell you that it is necessary that I should go to her; my conscience bids me go."

"Tell me one thing, Paul: are you sure you saw the servant? Temptation plays evil tricks on us and the devil has many disguises."

He did not quite understand her.

"You think I am telling a lie? I saw the servant."

"Listen—last night I saw the old priest, and I thought I heard his footsteps again just now. Last night." she went on in a low voice, "he sat beside me before the fire. I actually saw him, I tell you: he had not shaved, and the few teeth he had left were black from too much smoking. And he had holes in his stockings. And he said, 'I am alive and I am here, and very soon I shall turn you and your son out of the presbytery.' And he said I ought to have taught you your father's trade if I did not wish you to fall into sin. He so upset my mind, Paul, that I don't know whether I have acted rightly or wrongly! But I am absolutely sure that it was the devil sitting beside me last night, the spirit of evil. The servant you saw might have been temptation in another shape."

He smiled in the darkness. Nevertheless, when he thought of the fantastic figure of the servant running across the meadow, he felt a vague sense of terror in spite of himself.

"If you go there," continued his mother's voice, "are you certain you will not fall again? Even if you really saw the servant and if that woman is really ill, are you sure not to fall?"

She broke off suddenly; she seemed to see his pale face through the darkness, and she was filled with pity for him. Why should she forbid him to go to the woman? Supposing Agnes really died of grief? Supposing Paul died of grief? And she was as wracked with uncertainty as he had been in the case of Antiochus.

"Lord," she sighed; then she remembered that she had already placed herself in the hands of God, Who alone can solve all our difficulties. She felt a sort of relief, as if she had really settled the problem. And had she not settled it by entrusting it in the hands of God?

She lay back on her pillow and her voice came again nearer to her son.

"If your conscience bids you go, why did you not go at once instead of coming in here?"

"Because I promised. And you threatened to leave me if I went back to that house. I swore . . ." he said with infinite sadness. And he longed to cry out, "Mother, force me to keep my oath!" but the words would not come. And then she spoke again:

"Then go: do whatever your conscience bids you."

"Do not be anxious," he said, coming close up to the bed; and he stood there motionless for a few minutes and both were silent. He had a confused impression that he was standing before an altar with his mother lying upon it like some mysterious idol, and he remembered how, when he was a boy in the Seminary, he was always obliged to go and kiss her hand after he had been to confession. And something of the same repugnance and the same exaltation moved him now. He felt that if he had been alone, without her, he would have gone back to Agnes long since, worn out by that endless day of flight and strife; but his mother held

[174]

him in check, and he did not know whether he was grateful to her or not.

"Do not be anxious!" Yet all the time he longed and feared that she would say more to him, or that she would light the lamp and, looking into his eyes, read all his thoughts and forbid him to go. But she said nothing. Then the mattress creaked again as she stretched herself in the bed.

And he went out.

He reflected that after all he was not a scoundrel: he was not going with any bad motive or moved by passion, but because he honestly thought that there might be some danger he could avert, and the responsibility for this danger rested upon him. He recalled the fantastic figure of the servant running across the moonlit grass, and turning back to look at him with bright eyes as she said:

"My little mistress will take courage if only you will come."

And all his efforts to break away from her appeared now base and stupid: his duty was to have gone to her at once and given her courage. And as he crossed the meadow, silvery in the moonlight, he felt relieved, almost happy, he was like a moth attracted by the light. And he mistook the joy he felt at the prospect of seeing Agnes again in a few moments for the satisfaction of doing his duty in going to save her. All the sweet scent of the grass, all the tender radiance of the moon bathed and purified his soul, and the healing dew fell upon it even through his clothes of death-like black.

Agnes, little mistress! In truth, she was little, weak as a child, and she was all alone, without father or mother, living in that labyrinth of stone, her dark house under the ridge. And he had taken advantage of her, had caught her in his hand like a bird from the nest, gripping her till the blood seemed driven from her body.

He hurried on. No, he was not a bad man, but as he reached the bottom of the steps that led up to the door he stumbled, and it was sharply borne in upon him that even the stones of her threshold repulsed him. Then he mounted softly, hesitatingly, raised the knocker and let it fall. They were a long time coming to answer the door, and he felt humiliated standing there, but for nothing in the world would he have knocked a second time. At last the fanlight over the door was lit up and the dark-faced maid let him in, showing him at once into the room he knew so well.

Everything was just as it had been on other nights, when Agnes had admitted him secretly by way of the orchard; the little door stood ajar, and through the narrow opening he could smell the fragrance of the bushes in the night air. The glass eyes in the stuffed heads of stags and deer on the walls shone in the steady glow of the big lamp, as though taking careful note of all that happened in the room. Contrary to custom, the door leading to the inner rooms stood wide open; the servant had gone through there and the board flooring could be heard creaking under her heavy step. After a moment a door banged violently as though blown by a gust of wind, making the whole house shake, and he started involuntarily when immediately afterwards he beheld Agnes emerge from the darkness of the inner rooms, with white face and distorted hair floating in black wisps across it, like the phantom of a drowned woman. Then the little figure came forward into the lamplight and he almost sobbed with relief.

She closed the door behind her and leaned against it with bowed head. She faltered as though about to fall, and Paul ran to her, holding out his hands, but not daring to touch her.

"How are you?" he asked in a low voice, as he had asked at former meetings. But she did not answer, only stood trembling all over her body, her hands pressed against the door behind her for support. "Agnes," he continued after a moment's tense silence, "we must be brave."

But as on that day when he had read the Gospel words over the frenzied girl, he knew that his voice rang false, and his eyes sought the ground as Agnes raised hers, bewildered, yes, but full of mingled scorn and joy.

"Then why have you come?"

"I heard that you were ill."

She drew herself up proudly and pushed back the hair from her face.

"I am quite well and I did not send for you."

"I know that, but I came all the same—there was no reason why I should not come. I am glad to find that your maid exaggerated, and that you are all right."

"No," she repeated, interrupting him, "I did not send for you and you ought not to have come. But since you are here, since you are here, I want to ask you— why you did it . . . why?—why?"

Her words were broken by sobs and her hands sought blindly for support, so that Paul was afraid, and repented that he had come. He took her hands and led her to the couch where they had sat together on other evenings, placing her in the corner where the weight of other women of the family had worn a sort of niche, and seated himself beside her, but he let go her hands.

He was afraid of touching her; she was like a statue which he had broken and put together again, and which sat there apparently whole but ready to fall in pieces again at the slightest movement. So he was afraid of touching her, and he thought to himself:

"It is better so, I shall be safe," but in his heart he knew that at any moment he might be lost again, and for that reason he was afraid of touching her. Looking

closely at her beneath the lamplight, he perceived that she was changed. Her mouth was half-open, her lips discolored and grayish like faded rose-leaves; the oval of her face seemed to have grown longer and her cheekbones stood out sharply beneath eyes sunk deep in their livid sockets. Grief had aged her by twenty years in a single day, yet there was something childlike still in the expression of her trembling lips, drawn tightly over her teeth to check her weeping, and in the little hands, one of which, lying nerveless on the dark stuff of the couch, invited his own towards it. And he was filled with anger because he dared not take that little hand in his and link up again the broken chain of their two lives. He remembered the words of the man possessed with a devil, "What have I to do with Thee?" and he began to speak again, clasping his hands together to prevent himself taking one of hers. But still he heard his voice ring false, and as on that morning in church when he read the Gospel, and when he carried the sacrament to the old hunter, he knew himself to be lying.

"Agnes, listen to me. Last night we were both on the brink of destruction— God had left us to ourselves and we were slipping over the edge of the abyss. But now God has taken us by the hand again and is guiding us. We must not fall, Agnes, Agnes," and his voice shook with emotion as he spoke her name. "You think I don't suffer? I feel as if I were buried alive and that my torments would last through all eternity. But we must endure for your good, for your salvation. Listen, Agnes, be brave, for the sake of the love which united us, for God's goodwill toward us in putting us through this trial. You will forget me. You will recover; you are young, with all your life still before you. When you think of me it will be like a bad dream, as though you had lost your way in the valley and met

some evil creature who had tried to do you harm; but God has saved you, as you deserved to be saved. Everything looks black at present, but it will clear up soon and you will realize that I am only acting for your good in causing you a little momentary pain now, just as we are sometimes obliged to seem cruel to those who are ill. . . ."

He stopped, the words froze in his throat.

Agnes had roused herself and was sitting upright in her corner, gazing at him with eyes as glassy as those in the stags' heads on the walls. They reminded him of the women's eyes in church, fixed on him as he preached. She waited for his words, patient and gentle in every line of her fragile form, yet ready to break down at a touch. Then speechless himself, he heard her low voice as she shook her head slowly.

"No, no, that is not the truth," she said.

"Then what is the truth?" he asked, bending his troubled face towards her.

"Why did you not speak like that last night? And the other nights? Because it was a different kind of truth then. Now somebody has found you out, perhaps your mother herself, and you are afraid of the world. It is not the fear of God which is driving you away from me!"

He wanted to cry out, to strike her; he seized her hand and twisted the slender wrist as he would have liked to twist and stifle the words she spoke. Then he drew himself up stiffly.

"What then? You think it does not matter? Yes, my mother has discovered everything and she talked to me like my conscience itself. And have you no conscience? Do you think it right that we should injure those who depend on us? You wanted us to go away and live together, and that would have been the right thing to do if we had not been able to overcome our love; but since there are beings who would have been cut off from life by our flight and our sin, we had to sacrifice ourselves for them."

But she seemed not to understand, caught only one word, and shook her head as before.

"Conscience? Of course I have a conscience, I am no longer a child! And my conscience tells me that I did wrong in listening to you and letting you come here. What is to be done? It is too late now; why did not God make you see things clearly at first? I did not go to your home, but you came to mine and played with me as if I had been a child's toy. And what must I do now? Tell me that. I cannot forget you, I cannot change as you change. I shall go away, even if you will not come with me—I want to try and forget you. I must go right away, or else . . ."

"Or else?"

Agnes did not reply; she leaned back in her corner and shivered. Something ominous, like the dark wing of madness, must have touched her, for her eyes grew dim and she raised her hand with an instinctive movement as though to brush away a shadow from before her face. He bent again towards her, stretching across the couch and his fingers gripping and breaking through the old material as though it were a wall that rose between them and threatened to stifle him.

He could not speak. Yes, she was right; the explanation he had been trying to make her believe was not the truth—it was the truth that was rising like a wall and stifling him, and which he did not know how to break down. And he sat up, battling with a real sense of suffocation. Now it was she who caught his hand and held it as though her fingers had been grappling-hooks.

"O God," she whispered, covering her eyes with her free hand, "if there be a God, He should not have let us meet each other if we must part again. And you came tonight because you love me still. You think I don't know that? I do know, I do know, and that is the truth!"

She raised her face to his, her trembling lips, her lashes wet with tears. And his eyes were dazzled as by the glitter of deep waters, a glitter that blinds and beckons, and the face he gazed into was not the face of Agnes, nor the face of any woman on this earth,—it was the face of Love itself. And he fell forward into her arms and kissed her upon the mouth.

CHAPTER XII

The world had ceased for Paul. He felt himself sinking slowly, swept down by a whirlpool through luminous depths to some dazzling iridescent place beneath the sea. Then he came to himself again and drew his lips away from hers, and found himself, like a shipwrecked man upon the sand, safe though maimed, and shaking with fear and joy, but more with fear than joy. And the enchantment that he thought had been broken forever, and for this very reason had seemed more beautiful and dear, wove its spell over him afresh and held him again in thrall. And again he heard the whisper of her voice:

"I knew you would come back to me. . . ."

He wanted to hear no more, just as he had tried not to hear the servant's tale in the house of Antiochus. He put his hand over Agnes's mouth as she leaned her head upon his shoulder and then gently caressed her hair, on which the lamplight threw golden gleams. She was so small, so helpless in his grasp, and therein lay her terrible power to drag him down to the bottom of the sea, to raise him to the highest heights of heaven, to make of him a thing without will or desire of his

own. While he had fled through the valleys and the hills she had remained shut up within her prison-house, waiting in the certainty that he would come back to her, and he came.

"You know, you know . . ." She tried to tell him more; her soft breath touched his neck like a caress, he placed his hand on her mouth again and with her own she pressed it close. And so they remained in silence for a while; then he pulled himself together and tried to regain the mastery over his fate. He had come back to her, yes, but not the same man she had expected. And his gaze still rested on her gleaming hair, but as on something far away, as on the bright sparkle of the sea from which he had escaped.

"Now you are happy," he whispered. "I am here, I have come back and I am yours for life. But you must be calm, you have given me a great fright. You must not excite yourself, nor wander on any account from the straight path of your life. I shall cause you no more trouble, but you must promise me to be calm and good, as you are now."

He felt her hands tremble and struggle between his own; he divined that she was already beginning to rebel and he held them tightly, as he would have liked to hold her soul imprisoned.

"Dear Agnes, listen! You will never know all I have suffered today, but it was necessary. I stripped off all the outward shell of me, all that was impure, and I scourged myself until I bled. But now here I am, yours, yours, but as God wills that I should be yours, in spirit. . . . You see," he went on, speaking slowly and laboriously, as though dragging his words up painfully from his inmost depths and offering them to her, "it seems to me that we have loved each other for years and years, that we have rejoiced and suffered the one for the other, even unto hatred, even unto death

And all the tempests of the sea and all its implacable life are within us. Agnes, soul of my soul, what would you have of me greater than that which I can give you, my soul itself?"

He stopped short. He felt that she did not understand, she could not understand. And he beheld her ever more detached from him, as life from death; but for this very reason he loved her still, yea, more than ever, as one loves life that is dying.

She slowly raised her head from his shoulder and looked him in the face with eyes grown hostile again.

"Now you listen to me," she said, "and tell me no more lies. Are we or are we not going away together as we settled last night? We cannot go on living here, in this way. That is certain! . . . That is certain!" she repeated with rising anger, after a moment of painful silence. "If we are to live together we must go away at once, this very night. I have money, you know, it is my own. And your mother and my brothers and everyone else will excuse us afterwards when they see that we only wanted to live according to the truth. We cannot go on living like this, no, we cannot!"

"Agnes!"

"Answer me quick! Yes or no?"

"I cannot go away with you."

"Ah—then why have you come back? . . . Leave me! Get away, leave me!"

He did not leave her. He felt her whole body shaking and he was afraid of her; and as she bowed herself over their united hands he expected to feel her teeth fasten in his flesh.

"Go, go!" she insisted. "I did not send for you! Since we must be brave, why did you come back? Why have you kissed me again? Ah, if you think you can play with me like this you are mistaken! If you think you can come here at night and write me humiliating letters in the way you are mistaken again! You came

back tonight and you will come back tomorrow night and every night after that, until at last you drive me mad. But I won't have it, I won't have it!"

"We must be pure and brave, you say," she continued, and her face, grown old and tragic, became now pale as death; "but you never said that before tonight. You fill me with horror! Go away, far away, and go at once, so that tomorrow I can wake up without the terror of expecting you and being humiliated like this again."

"O God, O God!" he groaned, bending over her, but she repulsed him sharply.

"Do you think you are speaking to a child?" she burst out now: "I am old, and it is you who have made me grow old in a few hours. The straight path of life! Oh, yes, it would be going straight if we continued this secret intrigue, wouldn't it? I should find myself a husband and you should marry me to him, and then we could go on seeing each other, you and I, and deceiving everyone for the rest of our lives. Oh, you don't know me if that is your idea! Last night you said, 'Let us go away, we will get married and I will work.' Didn't you say that? Didn't you? But tonight you come and talk to me instead about God and sacrifice. So now there is an end of it all: we will part. But you, I say it again, you must leave the village this very night, I never wish to see you again. If tomorrow morning you go once more into our church to say Mass I shall go there too, and from the altar steps I shall say to the people: 'This is your saint, who works miracles by day and by night goes to unprotected girls to seduce them!' "

He tried in vain to shut her mouth with his hand, and as she kept on crying aloud, "Go, go!" he seized her head and pressed it to his breast, glancing with alarm at the closed doors. And he remembered his mother's words and her voice, mysterious in the darkness: "The old priest sat beside me and said, I will soon turn both you and your son out of the parish."

"Agnes, Agnes, you are mad!" he groaned, his lips close to her ear, while she struggled fiercely to escape from him: "Be calm, listen to me. Nothing is lost; don't you feel how I love you? A thousand times more than before! And I am not going away, I am going to stay near you, to save you, to offer up my soul to you as I shall offer it up to God in the hour of death. How can you know all that I have suffered between last night and now? I fled and I bore you with me: I fled like one who is on fire and who thinks by fleeing to escape the flames which only envelop him the more. Where have I not been today, what have I not done to keep myself from coming back to you? Yet here I am, Agnes, and how could I not be here? . . . Do you hear me? I shall not betray you, I shall not forget you, I do not wish to forget you! But, Agnes, we must keep ourselves unsoiled, we must keep our love for all eternity, we must unite it with all that is best in life, with renunciation, with death itself, that is to say, with God. Do you understand, Agnes? Yes, tell me that you understand!"

She fought him back, as though she wanted to break in his breast with her head, till at last she freed herself from his embrace and sat rigid and upright, her beautiful hair twisted like ribbons round her stony face. With tight-shut lips and closed eyes, she seemed to have suddenly fallen into a deep sleep, wherein she dreamed of vengeance. And he was more afraid of her silence and immobility than of her frenzied words and excited gestures. He took her hands again in his, but now all four hands were dead to joy and to the clasp of love.

"Agnes, can't you see that I am right? Come, be good; go to bed now and tomorrow a new life will begin for us all.

We shall see each other just the same, always supposing you desire it: I will be your friend, your brother, and we shall be a mutual help and support. My life is yours, dispose of me as you wish. I shall be with you till the hour of death, and beyond death, for all eternity."

This tone of prayer irritated her afresh. She twisted her hands slightly within his and opened her lips to speak. Then, as he set her free, she folded her hands in her lap and bowed her head and her face took on an expression of the deepest grief, but now a grief that was desperate and determined.

He continued to gaze steadfastly at her, as one gazes at the dying, and his fear increased. He slid to his knees before her, he laid his head in her lap and kissed her hands; he cared nothing now if he were seen or heard, he knelt there at the feet of the woman and her sorrow as at the feet of the Mother of Sorrows herself. Never before had he felt so pure of evil thought, so dead to this earthly life; and yet he was afraid.

Agnes sat motionless, with icy hands, insensible to those kisses of death. Then he got up and began to speak lies again.

"Thank you, Agnes—that is right and I am very pleased. The trial has been won and you can rest in peace. I am going now, and tomorrow," he added in a whisper, bending nervously towards her, "tomorrow morning you will come to Mass and together we will offer our sacrifice to God."

She opened her eyes and looked at him, then closed them again. She was as one wounded to death, whose eyes had opened wide with a last menace and appeal before they closed for ever.

"You will go away tonight, quite away, so that I shall never see you again," she said, pronouncing each word distinctly and decisively, and he realized that for the moment at least it was useless to oppose that blind force.

"I cannot go like that," he murmured: "I must say Mass tomorrow morning and you will come and hear it, and afterwards I will go away, if necessary."

"Then I shall come tomorrow morning and denounce you before all the congregation."

"If you do that it will be a sign that it is God's will. But you won't do it, Agnes! You may hate me, but I leave you in peace. Goodbye."

Even yet he did not go. He stood quite still, looking down at her, at her soft and gleaming hair, the sweet hair he loved and through which so often his hands had strayed, and it awoke in him an infinite pity, for it seemed like the black bandage round a wounded head.

For the last time he called her by her name:

"Agnes! Is it possible that we part like this? . . . Come," he added after a moment, "give me your hand, get up and open the door for me."

She got up obediently, but she did not give him her hand; she went direct to the door through which she had entered the room, and there she stood still, waiting.

"What can I do?" he asked himself. And he knew very well that there was only one thing he could do to appease her: to fall at her feet again, to sin and be lost with her forever.

And that he would not do, never never more. He remained firm, there where he stood, and lowered his eyes that he might not meet her look, and when he raised them again she was no longer there; she had disappeared, swallowed up in the darkness of her silent house.

The glass eyes of the stags' and deer's heads upon the walls looked down at him with mingled sadness and derision. And in that moment of suspense, alone in the big melancholy room, he realized the whole immensity of his wretchedness and

his humiliation. He felt himself a thief, and worse than a thief, a guest who takes advantage of the solitude of the house that shelters him to rob it basely. He averted his eyes, for he could not meet even the glassy stare of the heads upon the wall: but he did not waver in his purpose for one moment, and even if the death-cry of the woman had suddenly filled the house with horror, he would not have repented having rejected her.

He waited a few minutes longer, but nobody appeared. He had a confused idea that he was standing in the middle of a dead world of all his dreams and his mistakes, waiting till someone came and helped him to get away. But nobody came. So at last he pushed open the door that led into the orchard, traversed the path that ran beside the wall and went out by the little gate he knew so well.

CHAPTER XIII

Once more Paul found himself ascending his own staircase; but now the danger was past, or at least the fear of danger.

Nevertheless he halted before his mother's door, deeming that it would be advisable to tell her the result of his interview with Agnes and of her threat to denounce him. But he heard the sound of regular breathing and passed on; his mother had quietly fallen asleep, for henceforth she was sure of him and felt that he was safe.

Safe! He looked round his room as though he had just returned from a long and disastrous journey. Everything was peaceful and tidy, and he moved about on tiptoe as he began to undress, for the sake of not disturbing that orderliness and silence. His clothes hanging from their hooks, blacker than their shadows on the wall, his hat above them, stuck forward on a wooden peg, the sleeves of his cassock falling limply as though tired out, all had the vague appearance of some dark and empty phantom, some fleshless and bloodless vampire that inspired a nameless dread. It was like the shadow of that sin from which he had cut himself free, but which was waiting to follow him again tomorrow on his way through the world.

An instant more, and he perceived with terror that the nightmare obsessed him still. He was not safe yet, there was another night to be got through, as the voyager crosses a last stretch of turbulent sea. He was very weary and his heavy eyelids drooped with fatigue, but an intolerable anxiety prevented him from throwing himself on his bed, or even sitting down on a chair or resting in any way whatever; he wandered here and there, doing small, unusual, useless things, softly opening drawer after drawer and inspecting what there was inside.

As he passed before the mirror he looked at his own reflection and beheld himself gray of face, with purple lips and hollow eyes. "Look well at yourself, Paul," he said to his image, and he stepped back a little so that the lamplight might fall better on the glass. The figure in the mirror stepped back also, as though seeking to escape him, and as he stared into its eyes and noted the dilated pupils he had a strange impression that the real Paul was the one in the glass, a Paul who never lied and who betrayed by the pallor of his face all his awful fear of the morrow.

"Why do I pretend even to myself a security which I do not feel?" was his silent question. "I must go away this very night as she bade me."

And somewhat calmer for the resolve he threw himself on his bed. And thus, with closed eyes and face pressed into the pillow, he believed he could search more deeply into his conscience.

"Yes, I must leave tonight. Christ Himself commands us to avoid creating scandals. I had better wake my mother and tell her, and perhaps we can leave together; she can take me away with her again as she did when I was a child and I can begin a new life in another place."

But he felt that all this was mere exaltation and that he had not the courage to do as he proposed. And why should he? He really felt quite sure that Agnes would not carry out her threat, so why should he go away? He was not even confronted with the danger of going back to her and falling into sin again, for he had now been tried and had overcome temptation.

But the exaltation took hold of him again.

"Nevertheless, Paul, you will have to go. Awaken your mother and depart together. Don't you know who it is speaking to you? It is I, Agnes. You really believe that I shall not carry out my threat? Perhaps I shall not, but I advise you to go, all the same. You think you have got rid of me? And yet I am within you, I am the evil genius of your life. If you remain here I shall never leave you alone for one single instant; I shall be the shadow beneath your feet, the barrier between you and your mother, between you and your own self. Go."

Then he tried to pacify her, in order to pacify his own conscience.

"Yes, I am going, I tell you! I am going—we will go together, you within me, more alive than I myself. Be content, torment me no more! We are together, journeying together, borne on the wings of time towards eternity. Divided and distant we were when our eyes first met and our lips kissed; divided were we then and enemies; only now begins our real union, in your hatred, in my patience, in my renunciation."

*   *   *

Then weariness slowly overcame him. He heard a subdued, continuous moaning outside his window, like a dove seeking her mate: and that mournful cry was like the lament of the night itself, a night pale with moonlight, a soft, veiled light, with the sky all flecked with little white clouds like feathers. Then he became aware that it was he himself who was moaning; but sleep was already stealing over him, calming his senses, and fear and sorrow and remembrance faded away. He dreamed he was really on a journey, riding up the mountain paths towards the plateau. Everything was peaceful and clear; between the big yellow elder trees he could see stretches of grass, of a soft green that gave rest to the eyes, and motionless upon the rocks the eagles blinked at the sun.

Suddenly the keeper stood before him, saluted, and placed an open book on his saddle-bow. And he began to read St. Paul's Epistle to the Corinthians, taking it up at the precise point where he had left off the previous night: "The Lord knows the thoughts of the wise and that they are vain."

On Sundays Mass was later than on other days, but Paul always went early to the church to hear the confessions of those women who wished to attend Communion later. So his mother called him at the usual time.

He had slept for some hours, a heavy dreamless sleep, and when he woke his memory was a complete blank, he only had a supreme desire to go to sleep again immediately. But the knocks on his door persisted, and then he remembered. Instantly he was on his feet, numb with dread.

"Agnes will come to church and denounce me before all the people," was his one thought.

He did not know why, but somehow

while he slept the certainty that she would carry out her threat had taken firm root in his consciousness.

He dropped down in his chair with trembling knees and a sense of complete helplessness. His mind was clouded and confused: he wondered vaguely if it would not be possible even now to avert the scandal—he might feign illness and not say Mass at all, and thus gain time in which he might endeavor to pacify Agnes. But the very idea of beginning the whole thing over again, of suffering a second time all his misery of the previous day, only increased his mental torment.

He got up, and his head seemed to hit the sky through the glass of his window, and he stamped his feet on the floor to dispel the numbness that was paralyzing his very blood. Then he dressed, drawing his leather belt tightly round his waist and folding his mantle round him as he had seen the hunters buckle on their cartridge-belts and wrap themselves up in their cloaks before starting out for the mountains. When at last he flung open his window and leaned out he felt that only then were his eyes awaking to the light of day after the nightmare of the dark hours, only then had he escaped from the prison of his own self to make his peace with external things. But it was a forced peace, full of secret rancor, and it sufficed for him to draw in his head from the cool fresh air outside to the warm and perfumed atmosphere of his room for him to fall back into himself, a prey again to his gnawing dread.

So he fled downstairs, wondering what he had better tell his mother.

He heard her somewhat harsh voice driving off the chickens who were trying to invade the dining-room, and the fluttering of their wings as they scattered before her, and he smelled the fragrance of hot coffee and the clean sweet scents from the garden. In the lane under the ridge there was a tinkle of bells as the goats were driven to their pasture, little bells that sounded like childish echoes of the cheerful if monotonous chime wherewith Antiochus, up in the church tower, summoned the people to wake from sleep and come to hear Mass.

Everything around was sweet and peaceful, bathed in the rosy light of early morning. And Paul remembered his dream.

There was nothing to hinder him from going out, from going to church and taking up his ordinary life again. Yet all his fear returned upon him; he was afraid alike of going forward or of turning back. As he stood on the step of the open door he felt as if he were on the summit of some precipitous mountain, it was impossible to get any higher and below him yawned the abyss. So he stood there for unspeakable moments, during which his heart beat furiously and he had the physical sensation of falling, of struggling at the bottom of a gulf, in a swirl of foaming waters, a wheel that turned helplessly, vainly beating the stream that swept on its relentless course.

It was his own heart that turned and turned helplessly in the whirlpool of life. He closed the door and went back into the house, and sat down on the stairs as his mother had done the previous night. He gave up trying to solve the problem that tortured him and simply waited for someone to come and help him.

And there his mother found him. When he saw her he got up immediately, feeling somehow comforted at once, yet humiliated, too, in the very depths of his being, so sure was he of the advice she would give him to proceed upon his chosen way.

But at the first sight of him her worn face grew pale, as though refined through grief.

"Paul!" she cried, "what are you doing there? Are you ill?"

"Mother," he said, walking to the front door without turning into the dining-room, "I did not want to wake you last night, it was so late. Well, I went to see her. I went to see her. . . ."

His mother had already recovered her composure and stood looking fixedly at him. In the brief silence that followed his words they could hear the church bell ringing quickly and insistently as though it were right over the house.

"She is quite well," continued Paul, "but she is very excited and insists that I shall leave the place at once: otherwise she threatens to come to church and create a scandal by denouncing me before the congregation."

His mother kept silence, but he felt her at his side, stern and steadfast, upholding him, supporting him as she had supported his earliest steps.

"She wanted me to go away this very night. And she said that . . . if I did not go, she would come to church this morning. . . . I am not afraid of her: besides, I don't believe she will come."

He opened the front door and a flood of golden light poured into the dark little passage, as though trying to entice him and his mother out into the sunshine. Paul walked towards the church without turning round, and his mother stood at the door looking after him.

She had not opened her lips, but a slight trembling seized her again, and only with an effort could she maintain her outward composure. All at once she went up to her bedroom and hurriedly dressed for church: she was going too and she, too, drew in her belt and walked with firm steps. And before she left the house she remembered to drive out the intruding chickens again, and to draw the coffee-pot to the side of the fire; then she twisted the long end of her scarf over her mouth and chin to hide the obstinate trembling that would persist in spite of all her efforts to overcome it.

So it was only with a glance of the

eyes that she could return the greetings of the women who were coming up from the village, and of the old men already seated on the low parapet round the square before the church, their black pointed caps standing out in sharp relief against the background of rosy morning sky.

CHAPTER XIV

Meanwhile Paul had gone into the church.

A few eager penitents were waiting for him, gathered round the confessional; the woman who had arrived first was already kneeling at the little grating, while the others waited their turn in the benches close by.

Nina Masia was kneeling on the floor under the holy-water stoup, which looked as though it were resting on her wicked little head, while several boys who were early astir were gathered in a circle round her. Hurrying in with his thoughts elsewhere the priest knocked up against them, and his anger rose instantly as he recognized the girl, who had been placed there by her mother on purpose that she might attract attention. She seemed to be always in his way, at once a hindrance and a reproach.

"Clear out of this instantly!" he bade them, in a voice so loud that it was heard all over the church; and immediately the circle of boys spread itself out and moved a little farther off, with Nina still in the middle, but they grouped themselves round her in such a way that she could be seen by everyone. The women all turned their heads to look at her, though without interrupting their prayers for an instant: she really looked as if she were the idol of the barbaric little church, redolent of the smell of the fields brought in by the peasants and flooded

with the rosy haze of a country morning.

Paul walked straight up the nave, but his secret anguish grew ever greater. As he passed, his cassock brushed against the seat where Agnes usually sat; it was the old family pew, the kneeling-stool in front of it richly carved, and with his eyes and measured paces he calculated the distance between it and the altar.

"If I watch for the moment when she rises to carry out her fatal threat I shall have time to get into the sacristy," was his conclusion, and he shivered now as he entered.

Antiochus had hurried down from the belfry to help Paul robe himself, and was waiting for him beside the open cupboard where his vestments hung. He had a pale and serious, almost tragic air, as though already overshadowed by the future career which had been settled for him the previous evening. But the gravity was transient and a smile flickered over the boy's face, just fresh from the wind-swept belfry; his eyes sparkled with joy beneath their decorously lowered lids, and he had to bite his lips to check the ready laugh; his young heart responded to all the radiance, the inspirations, the joyousness of that festal morning. Then his eyes clouded suddenly as he was arranging the lace of the alb over the priest's wrist and he shot a quick look at his master, for he had perceived that the hand beneath the lace was trembling and he saw that the beloved face was pallid and distraught.

"Do you feel ill, sir?"

Paul did feel ill, although he shook his head in denial. He felt as though his mouth were full of blood, yet a tiny germ of hope was springing up in the middle of his distress.

"I shall fall down dead, my heart will break; and then, at least, there will be an end of everything."

He went down into the church again to hear the confessions of the women, and saw his mother at the bottom of the nave near the door. Stern and motionless she knelt there, keeping watch over all who entered the church, over the whole church itself, ready, apparently, to support and hold it up were it even to collapse upon her head.

But he had no more courage left: only that tiny germ of hope within his heart, the hope of death, grew and grew till the breath in him stifled and failed.

When he was seated inside the confessional he felt somewhat calmer; it was like being in a grave, but at least he was hidden from view and could look his horror in the face. The subdued whispering of the women behind the gratings, broken by their little sighs and their warm breath, was like the rustling of lizards in the long grass on the ridge. And Agnes was there too, safe in the secret retreat where he had so often taken her in his thoughts. And the soft breathing of the young women, the scent of their hair and their gala dress, all perfumed with lavender, mingled with his distress and further inflamed his passion.

And he gave them all absolution, absolved them from all their sins, thinking that perhaps before many days had passed he himself would be a suppliant to them for their compassion.

*   *   *

Then he was seized with the craving to get out, to see whether Agnes had arrived. But her seat was empty.

Perhaps she was not coming after all. Yet sometimes she remained at the bottom of the church, kneeling on a chair which her servant brought for her. He turned to look, but saw only his mother's rigid figure, and as he knelt before the altar and began the Mass, he felt that her soul was bending before God, clothed in her grief as he was clothed in his alb and stole.

Then he determined not to look behind him again, to close his eyes each time he had to turn round to give the blessing. He felt as if he were climbing ever higher up some steep and stony Calvary, and a sensation of giddiness seized him whenever the ritual obliged him to face the congregation. Then he closed his eyes to shut out the sight of the abyss that yawned at his feet; but even through his closed eyelids he saw the carven bench and the figure of Agnes, her black dress standing out in relief against the gray wall of the church.

And Agnes was really there, dressed in black with a black veil round her ivory-white face; her eyes were fixed on her prayer-book, the gilt clasp of which glittered in her black-gloved hands, but she never turned a page. The servant with the head of a slave was kneeling on the floor of the aisle beside the bench, and every now and then she raised her eyes, like a faithful dog, to her mistress's face, as though in silent sympathy with the sad thoughts that possessed her.

And he beheld everything from his place at the altar and hope died within him; only from the bottom of his heart he told himself it was impossible that Agnes would carry out her insane threat. He turned the pages of the Gospel, but his faltering voice could scarcely pronounce the words; he broke into a sweat of apprehension, and caught hold of the book as he felt himself fainting.

In a moment he pulled himself together. Antiochus was looking at him, watching the awful change that came over his face as over the face of a corpse, keeping close beside him to support him if he fell, and glancing at the old men by the altar rails to see if they had noticed the priest's distress. But nobody noticed it—even his mother remained in her place, praying and waiting without seeing anything amiss with her son. Then Antiochus drew still closer to him with a protecting movement, so that Paul looked round startled, but the boy gave him a reassuring glance out of his bright eyes, as much as to say:

"I am here, it's all right, go on——"

And he went on, climbing that steep Calvary till the blood flowed back into his heart and the tension of his nerves relaxed. But it was the relaxation of despair, the abandonment to danger, the quiet of the drowning man who has no more strength to battle with the waves. When he turned again to the congregation he did not close his eyes.

"The Lord be with you."

Agnes was there in her place, bent over the page she never turned, the gilt clasp of the book shining in the dim light. The servant was crouching at her feet and all the other women, including his mother at the bottom of the church, were sitting back on their heels on the bare floor, ready to resume their kneeling position immediately the priest should move the book.

And he moved the book and went on with the prayers and the slow gestures of the ritual. And a feeling of tenderness crept into his despair at the thought that Agnes was bearing him company on his road to Calvary, as Mary had followed too, that in another moment she would mount the altar steps and stand beside him once again, having overcome their transgression, to expiate together as together they had sinned. How could he hate her if she brought his punishment with her, if her hatred was only love disguised?

Then came the Communion, and the few drops of wine went down into his breast like quickening blood; he felt strong, revived, his heart filled with the presence of God.

And as he descended the steps towards the women the figure of Agnes in her seat stood out prominent amid the crowd of bowed heads. She, too, had bowed her head upon her hands; perhaps she was summoning her courage before she moved. And suddenly he felt infinite pity for her; he would have liked to go down to her and give her absolution, and administer the Communion as to a dying woman. He, too, had summoned his courage, but his hands shook as he held the wafer to the women's lips.

*   *   *

Immediately the Communion was ended an old peasant began to intone a hymn. The congregation sang the verses after him in subdued voices, and repeated the antiphons twice out loud. The hymn was primitive and monotonous, old as the earliest prayers of man uttered in forests where as yet scarcely man dwelt, old and monotonous as the breaking of waves on a solitary shore; yet that low singing around her sufficed to bring Agnes's thoughts back, as though she had been rushing breathless by night through some primeval forest and had suddenly emerged upon the seashore, amid sand-hills covered with sweet flowers and golden in the light of dawn.

Something stirred in the very depths of her being, a strange emotion gripped her throat; she felt the world turning round with her as though she had been walking head downwards and now resumed her natural position.

It was her past and the past of all her race that surged up and took hold of her, with the singing of the women and the old men, with the voices of her nurse and her servants, the men and women who had built and furnished her house, and ploughed her fields and woven the linen for her swaddling clothes.

How could she denounce herself before all these people who looked up to her as their mistress and held her even purer than the priest at the altar? And then she, too, felt the presence of God around her and within her, even in her passion itself.

She knew very well that the punishment she meant to inflict upon the man with whom she had sinned was her own punishment too; but now a merciful God spoke to her with the voices of the old men and women and the innocent children, and bade her beware of her own self, counseled her to seek salvation.

As her people round her sang the verses of the hymn, all the days of her solitary life unrolled themselves before her inward vision. She saw herself again a little child, then a young girl, then a grown woman in this same church, on this same seat blackened and worn by the elbows and knees of her forefathers. In a sense the church belonged to her family; it had been built by one of her ancestors, and tradition said that the image of the Madonna had been captured from Barbary pirates and brought back to the village by a far-away grandfather of hers.

She had been born and brought up amid these traditions, in an atmosphere of simple grandeur that kept her aloof from the smaller people of Aar, yet still in the middle of them, shut in among them like a pearl in its rough shell.

How could she denounce herself before her people? But this very feeling of being mistress even of the sacred building rendered more insufferable still the presence of the man who had been her companion in sin, and who appeared at the altar wearing a mask of saintliness and bearing the holy vessels in his hands— tall and splendid he stood above her as she knelt at his feet, guilty in that she had loved him.

Her heart swelled anew with rage and grief as the hymn rose and fell around her, like a supplication rising from out some abyss, imploring help and justice, and she heard the voice of God, dark and

stern, bidding her drive His unworthy servant out of His temple.

She grew pale as death and broke into a cold sweat; her knees shook against the seat, but she bowed no more and with head erect she watched the movements of the priest at the altar. And it was as though some evil breath went out from her to him, paralyzing him, enveloping him in the same icy grip that held her fast.

*   *   *

And he felt that mortal breath that emanated from her will, and just as on bitter winter mornings, his fingers were frozen and uncontrollable shivers ran down his spine. When he turned to give the benediction he saw Agnes gazing at him. Their eyes met as in a flash, and like a drowning man he remembered in that instant all the joy of his life, joy sprung wholly and solely from love of her, from the first look of her eyes, the first kiss of her lips.

Then he saw her rise from her seat, book in hand.

"Oh God, Thy will be done," he stammered, kneeling—and he seemed to be actually in the Garden of Olives, watching the shadow of an inexorable fate.

He prayed aloud and waited, and amid the confused sound of the people's prayers he thought he could distinguish Agnes's step as she moved toward the altar.

"She is coming—she has left her seat, she is between her seat and the altar. She is coming . . . she is here—everyone is staring at her. She is at my side!"

The obsession was so strong that the words failed on his lips. He saw Antiochus, who had already begun to extinguish the candles, suddenly turn and look round, and he knew for certain that she was there, close to him, on the chancel steps.

He rose to his feet, the roof seemed to fall down upon his head and fracture it; his knees scarcely upheld him, but with a sudden effort he managed to get up to the altar again and take the pyx. And as he turned to enter the sacristy he saw that Agnes had advanced from her seat to the railing and was about to mount the steps.

"Oh, Lord, why not let me die?" and he bowed his head over the pyx as though baring his neck to the sword that was about to strike it. But as he entered the sacristy door he looked again and perceived Agnes bowed at the altar railing as she knelt on the lowest step.

*   *   *

She had stumbled at the lowest step outside the railing, and as though a wall had suddenly risen up before her, she had dropped on her knees. A thick mist dimmed her sight and she could go no further.

Presently the dimness cleared and she could see the steps again, the yellow carpet before the altar, flowers upon the table and the burning lamp. But the priest had disappeared, and in his place a ray of sunlight smote obliquely through the dusk and made a golden patch upon the carpet.

She crossed herself, rose to her feet and moved towards the door. The servant followed her and the old men, the women and the children turned to smile at her and bless her with their eyes; she was their mistress, their symbol of beauty and of faith, so far removed from them and yet in the middle of them and all their misery, like a wild rose among the brambles.

At the church door the servant offered her holy water on the tips of her fingers, and then stooped to brush off the dust of the altar steps which still clung to her dress. As the girl raised herself again she saw the ashen face of Agnes turned towards the corner where the priest's mother had knelt through all ther service. Then she saw the mother sitting motionless on the ground, her head sunk forward on her breast, her shoulders leaning against the wall as though she had made a supreme effort to uphold it in a great collapse. Noticing the fixed gaze of Agnes and the servant, a woman also turned to look, then sprang quickly to the side of the priest's mother, spoke to her in a whisper and raised her face in her hand.

The mother's eyes were half-closed, glassy, the pupils upturned; the rosary had dropped from her hand and her head fell sideways on to the shoulder of the woman who held her.

"She is dead!" shrieked the woman.

And instantly the whole congregation was on its feet and crowding to the bottom of the church.

Meanwhile Paul had gone back into the sacristy with Antiochus, who was carrying the book of the Gospel. He was trembling with cold and with relief; he actually felt as though he had just escaped from a shipwreck, and he wanted to energize and walk about to warm himself and convince himself that it had all been a bad dream.

Then a confused murmur of voices was heard in the church, at first low, then growing quickly louder and louder. Antiochus put his head out of the sacristy door and saw all the people collected together at the bottom of the nave, as though there were some obstruction at the entrance, but an old man was already hastening up the chancel steps and making mysterious signs.

"His mother is taken ill," he said.

Paul, still robed in his alb, was down there at one bound and threw himself on his knees that he might look more closely into his mother's face as she lay stretched on the ground, with her head in a woman's lap and hemmed in by the pressing crowd.

"Mother, mother!"

The face was still and rigid, the eyes half-closed, the teeth clenched in the effort not to cry aloud.

And he knew instantly that she had died of the shock of that same grief, that same terror which he had been enabled to overcome.

And he, too, clenched his teeth that he might not cry aloud when he raised his head; and across the confused mass of the people surging round, his eyes met the eyes of Agnes fixed upon him.

THE LIFE AND WORKS OF
GRAZIA DELEDDA

By *GIUSEPPE RAVEGNANI*

"Petite, with a large head and tiny hands and feet, she had all the physical characteristics peculiar to the women of her race, which may be of Libyan origin; a rather snub-nosed profile, unruly teeth, and an overlong upper lip; but she had a white, velvety complexion, very beautiful black hair with a slight wave to it, large, almond-shaped eyes of a golden black which sometimes took on greenish gleams, and the large pupil of Hamitic women which a Latin poet called a 'double pupil' and whose passionate glow is irresistible." Thus Grazia Deledda describes herself in *Cosima*, an autobiographical novel published in 1937, shortly after her death. Cosima was in fact the second Christian name of the novelist herself.

Various problems are raised by the art of Grazia Deledda, and they are complicated by the fact that it is so thoroughly imbued with the spirit of her native island—rude and ardent Sardinia, with its hardened, cheerless men, its stoic women whose minds feed on superstition. Francesco Flora has rightly cautioned us against the tendency to set too much store by local color and atmosphere: "True, the landscape of these books is compounded of the very substance in which the sensibilities of Grazia

Deledda were steeped in the heroic days of childhood, when youngsters learn to see, hear and talk, and take upon their frail shoulders the weight of the air and the heavens. Here was the source of all her memories and so of all her writings. But what she has written is not a more or less local document, it is an unlocking of the storehouse of memory, a theme of universal art, a stuff of poetry which is entirely her own."

This poetic material, drawn from the folk life and color of Sardinia, was shaped by the hand of a literary artist who learned her art at home, alone, unconscious of wider horizons and unschooled in any genuine literary tradition. For she hardly attended school at all; she read at random and observed the folk ways around her; hers was a purely local culture which, even in her day, was equated with lack of culture.

She was born in the small town of Nuoro in the center of Sardinia, at the foot of Mount Orthobene, a rocky peak almost overhanging the town. Many reference books give 1875 as the year of her birth, but this is demonstrably wrong: her birth certificate is dated September 27, 1871. She herself was responsible for the error. As the Italian critic Eurialo De Michelis has aptly commented: "How human, and how very feminine, of Grazia Deledda to take four years off her age. In so tough and virile a character, it is an amiable and endearing weakness."

Her father was a person of note in Nuoro and mayor of the town for several years. A man of warm feelings and strict principles, he was also a poet, not only writing but improvising poetry in the local dialect. Her mother was of a gentle and retiring disposition, "impassive and almost enigmatic," as her daughter describes her in *Cosima*. It was a well-to-do family with connections in various walks of life: landowners, farmers, priests, and peasants.

Remote and lonely though the place was, art and culture existed in Nuoro, and Grazia Deledda breathed them in from her earliest childhood, not only through her father's poetry but from the local folk songs and ballads as well. She educated herself by reading the collection of books bequeathed to her by an uncle who had been a priest. She lived an intense life of her own in the world of her imagination, nourished by the sight of the mountains and the road, by the people who came by. Reading *Cosima*, one realizes how precocious an observer she was, how keenly her curiosity was aroused by the people she saw at home or met outside. When she began to write she was a teenage girl with plaited hair hanging over her shoulders: she could move only within the restricted circle of family and provincial life. Tinged with unconscious realism and naïve exemplars of Italian regionalism, her first sketches and stories were written (so she says in a letter) at the age of thirteen and published in the *Star of Sardinia*. One story was so realistic that it is said to have aroused the anger of a hunchback grocer who recognized himself in one of the characters. There may be an element of legend in this, but it is certain that in 1888–1889, when she was only seventeen

or eighteen, her stories were being published in a fashion magazine called *Ultima Moda,* while others were collected and published in Milan by Trevisini under the title *Nell'Azzurro.*

These early stories clearly show the impress of the whimsical, highly colored books she had read and admired; De Amicis, Dumas, Ponson du Terrail, Heine, and Bourget were prominent among them. By the time she came to write *Fior di Sardegna* (Flower of Sardinia), published in 1892, she was further indebted to such various sources of influence as Byron, Sue, Hugo, George Sand, and even Cavallotti. Later she read and studied, almost haphazardly, Balzac and Guerrini, Manzoni and Scott, D'Annunzio and Costanzo, Carmen Sylva, Gogol, Tolstoy, and, lastly, Verga and Dostoevsky.

The course of her development was complex, and it is sometimes difficult to tell how much she owed to her unusual background and how much to imagination. It is safe to say, however, that the latter gradually absorbed the former, with the result that art acted as a catalytic agent, prompting Grazia Deledda to strike out on a path of her own and to assert her personality, first in *Elias Portolú,* then in other novels which paint a picture of Sardinia that transcends documentary realism. Even so, while it is difficult to estimate the impact of realism on the novels of her second period, from 1903 to 1920 (that is, from *Elias Portolú* to *La Madre* [*The Mother,* 1920]), it cannot be denied that realism was in the air in Italy; it was very much in evidence in Matilda Serao, Verga, certain books by Fogazzaro, and in the early work of D'Annunzio. So it was only natural that Grazia Deledda, seeking her way forward and testing her powers, should have turned first of all to the things she knew best, the things she had grown up with, and to the memories that transfigured those things; but, except in *Cosima,* the autobiographical background is always veiled and objective, merging into the autonomous world of the novel.

Secretive, taciturn, introspective, she was nevertheless frank enough to indicate the channels and literary sympathies by which her art arrived at that remarkable equilibrium between psychology and dream which illuminates her greatest books, beginning with *Elias Portolú, The Mother, Cenere* (Ashes), and *Colombi e sparvieri* (Doves and Falcons, 1912). Her reserve, one might almost say her inscrutability, has been discussed by several writers who were on more familiar terms with Grazia Deledda than I. True, in the letters I occasionally received from her, written in a free-flowing hand, light and delicate as a cobweb, she referred again and again to herself and her books. Of one letter, among the last she wrote to me from Rome, I remember the opening words as well as if I had received it yesterday: "Why speak of myself? To speak of that . . . what does it matter after all? It is better to close the books and speak of the snow whitening my hair, a sign of the approaching day when only one book will count: the ledger reckoning up the assets and liabilities of our life, if we have ever really done anything . . ."

She was, then, before all else, an unrhetorical woman, an unliterary writer. Her letters, like her dedications, were sober, down to earth, with no flourishes. In her correspondence, as in her life, she instinctively avoided display, lyricism, phrase-making, or anything in the way of self-confession. A strong, forthright personality, she stamped her words with a trim, serene simplicity, sometimes verging on severity. But she was a woman of feeling, sensitive to human suffering, to the evils and sorrows of life, and she seemed at times to check the cry of protest rising to her lips, to suppress it and to reformulate her vehement feelings in words of a clear, resolute equanimity.

"The house was plain but comfortable: two rooms, large and rather low, on each floor, with wooden ceilings and flooring and whitewashed walls. The entrance was divided as follows: on the right, the staircase whose first flight was made of granite, the rest of slate; on the left, a few steps going down to the cellar. The stout front door, bolted with a thick iron bar, had a knocker that struck like a hammer, a heavy chain and a lock with a key as big as that of a castle door." Thus begins the opening chapter of *Cosima,* with recollections of the house in Nuoro, at No. 28 of what is now via Grazia Deledda, where she spent her childhood and youth.

At the old wooden door opening on the courtyard appears the worthy caretaker, Elía Sanna: from the moment he answers the bell and meets the interested visitor on the doorstep he becomes the officiating priest of this house, to him a sanctuary. Short and stocky, sallow complexioned, with dark, restless eyes and thick lips, Elía Sanna worships the memory of Grazia Deledda. On a set of shelves in the room where he sleeps, all her novels and stories are ranged in good order, well bound, read and reread; many volumes are inscribed with the author's dedications which he proudly shows with slightly trembling hands. He knows everything about Grazia Deledda and is glad of every opportunity to talk about her. As he talks he draws a parallel between the descriptions of things in her books and the things themselves in the house and outside it—people, places, landscapes, mountains—in a word, Sardinia. He talks of far-off days, long ago, when Grazia, as a girl, used to spend the summer months on the top of Mount Orthobene, in a kind of convent cell backed against the Madonna of the

Mountain, in the stillness of these dense woods of evergreen oak; or when she walked almost daily up to the Chapel of the Wilderness, the lonely shrine standing out white and sharp against the shadowy slopes of Orthobene, among the crags and woodlands, where it seems to watch over the low houses of Nuoro scattered below like a grazing flock.

So much of Nuoro and the surrounding country went into the books: her father's house in *Cosima,* in *Il paese del vento* (Land of the Wind, 1931), and *Sino al confine* (Up to the Limit, 1910); the olive press in *Cenere;* the vineyard in *La via del male* (The Evil Way, 1896); familiar woods and fields, roads, villages, and mountains, people and faces. But it is precisely in moving among these things and taking them in, that one is made to realize how much they were recast and transfigured in the prose art of Grazia Deledda: from the scenery and folkways of her native place, she distilled poetry. It is at Nuoro that one discovers the imaginative side of Grazia Deledda, an imaginativeness which does not gloss over the truth or misrepresent the people and the Sardinia that she knew, but which, by the expansive power of art, transcends the geographical limits of Sardinia and creates a self-contained world of poetry. This is an essential point to be borne in mind if we are to understand the true character of her narrative art which, on the strength of its imaginative and poetic resources, rises to a level of extreme romanticism.

These somewhat lengthy remarks, given by way of introduction, are necessary for an understanding of Grazia Deledda's character as a woman and for an insight into her individual qualities as a writer. It is important next to point out that many critics, both Italian and foreign, while having nothing but praise for her narrative skill, have seen fit to limit the scope of her complex moral world, to

narrow it down to the ethnically well-defined island race whose outlook and way of life she has so vividly described. The characters in her many novels must therefore be recognizably and indeed unmistakably local; and they must, in this view, move and have their being in an atmosphere of folklore. They do, up to a point. But we must beware of going too far in this direction.

However generous critics may be with praise, it is evident that those who see the characters in her novels as almost purely the product of a local setting, are prone to overestimate outside influences, which of course are present and readily discernible. The result is that the art of Grazia Deledda ends up being consigned to the category of regionalism and accordingly thought of as limited in scope and invention. The truth is that the types, the landscapes, the colors, the atmosphere of her novels, and all those local touches which the narrowness of provincial life thrusts into the foreground with seemingly willful insistence, all this is but means to an end: the depiction of life. And life, in the art of Grazia Deledda, is searchingly explored, with an intensely feminine insight and sensitivity. Not only is the life she depicts considered *sub specie aeternitatis,* but it is rich in overtones of an almost biblical flavor, something of the primitive grandeur of the Old Testament.

"Man sins and in sin itself he finds his punishment," we read in *Anime oneste, romanzo famigliare* (Honest Souls, 1895). "Evil must be overcome in ourselves, by our own strength," says Uncle Martinu in *Elias Portolú.* And again Uncle Martinu: "Dream is one thing, reality another, Elias Portolú. I don't advise you against it if you have the vocation [for the priesthood], but I tell you that even that will not save you. We are men, men weak as reeds, bear that in mind. Above us is a force that we cannot overcome. But if there is anything you can do, Elias Portolú, try to do it!" Taking over the words of St. Mark ("He is not the God of the dead, but the God of the living"), Grazia Deledda confessed in *Il Dio dei viventi* (The God of the Living, 1922) to her moral conviction that the only salvation lies in making atonement on earth for every evil deed committed in this life: "God judges us every day," she wrote, "because He is not the God of the dead, but the God of the living."

There is a connection between these Biblical overtones and the race from which Grazia Deledda sprang, and it helps to explain why she preferred to use her native Sardinia as a setting rather than other places. For there she found that atmosphere, at once fatalistic and superstitious, which she felt to be the inalienable moral climate of her art. Or so it seems to the present writer, and this view finds confirmation in the very qualities and resources of her style. First of all, even in the novels now considered the finest and most significant, *Elias Portolú, Colombi e sparvieri* (Doves and Falcons), and *Canes in the Wind,* it is clear that she dwells with a certain complacency on themes and colors that are specifically Sardinian. Then, little by little, from *Il Segreto dell'uomo solitario* (The Secret of the Solitary Man, 1921), which marks her departure from regionalism, to *Annalena Bilsini* (1927), the moral imperative of her art became more and more inward and compelling, finding its justification in itself, independently of local atmosphere.

Yet, throughout this period of change and development, there is never a hint in her work of sensationalism, of any straining after novelty or fashionable appeal, nor is there any resort to the new veins of expression then being opened up in Italian and European literature. Her nature remained, as always, elemental and primitive, one might almost say archaic. At the same time, her gift of invention, her power of evoking the marvelous, which in some novels—*La via del male* (The Evil Way, 1896), *Il nostro padrone* (Our Master, 1910), *Nel deserto* (In the Desert, 1911)—had flowed so easily, even dashingly, subsided to a calmer, steadier note, gaining in persuasiveness and compulsiveness what it lost in decorative value, a decorative value which might have been thought (unjustifiably, however) to constitute its most natural appeal. As I see it, therefore, in view of the intimate quality of her evocations of the marvelous, the narrative content of her writings was already implicit in her mind, instinct and nature before finding expression in her accomplished prose— so accomplished as to give the illusion not so much of a well-contrived story as of a life experience spontaneously embodied in words and reflecting some facet of human truth.

It is worthwhile pursuing this approach and studying the folklore background from different angles. Then it will not seem unreasonable to consider the Sardinia of Grazia Deledda as a Sardinia of the imagination—which does not mean that it is fanciful or unreal.

As early as 1900, when she published *Il vecchio della montagna* (The Old Man of the Mountain), her regionalism achieved an epic quality. By the time her art reached its maturity, there may have seemed some danger of repetition and flagging inspiration, considering the limited extent of her subject matter. But her long fidelity to a single source of inspiration was justified by the wider significance she imparted to it, and what is more, she proved herself a first-rate storyteller even when she turned for subject matter to the Italian world outside Sardinia. Indeed, it is only fair to emphasize the fact that her insistence on the themes and colors of a particular setting stemmed not so much from a personal preference as from a determined desire to grasp and render the truth of a local world whose essential features transcend its narrow bounds and prove to be universally applicable.

I should not like to conclude from this that the later novels are superior to those whose subject matter is Sardinia, its people and its landscape. But there is no escaping the fact that in time her characters became more autonomous, more individually alive; and that her world ceased to depend for its convincingness on the authenticity of a local setting, on familiar landmarks to which the characters were related beforehand. On the contrary, her art gained an impressive breadth and range, embracing universal values, those common to men everywhere: an art whose implications extended beyond the details evoking a particular background, an art that found fulfillment in action—in other words, in life.

Such, to my mind, is the most conspicuous side of Grazia Deledda's work considered as a whole, even while admitting that the greatest novels, or at least the most significant, are those of the early period. For her power of realism does not stop at the surface of things or at the description of emotions, but confers on them a glimmer of fatalism, a religious and indeed a Biblical implication. The very construction of her novels and stories seems to be governed by an inflexible will, a harsh and superhuman law. It follows perforce that the art of Grazia Deledda must be seen, in its total signification, as the representation of a world in which God is an active presence. Evil must be paid for on earth, in ourselves first of all, against and despite our own will.

To a greater or a lesser degree, then, all the novels of Grazia Deledda, including those most thoroughly steeped in the secluded life of Sardinia, reveal a strange,

immanent sense of existence, on which weighs, like a mysterious willpower, that "God of the living" invoked by St. Mark, which may be understood as a warning of earthly justice aimed at the sinner—an oversimplification perhaps, but an instinctive and wholly natural one, and no less moral for that. But equally searching and accurate seems to me Grazia Deledda's exploration of the human consciousness of matter and the world, an exploration begun in the earliest novels, consistently pursued and effectively invalidating the assumption that matter and world consist exclusively of a local setting and color, even though there exists a correlation with the religious and ethnic instinct that reveals itself in the origins and modulations of her writings. However, if there had only been this ethnic strand of thought, the dramatic pathos of her art would have taken the pattern of its rhythm not from the inside, but from the outside.

Having said so much, it is not for me to reject the "two periods" of her work, particularly if due regard is paid to values of style. True, in the earlier period, the novels are full of characters, the plots are intricate and spirited, the descriptions are perhaps indulged in a little too much for their own sake, and the secondary figures are not always necessary, being added as a means of heightening the colors that set off the essential theme. Later her art became sparer, more concentrated, stressing the gist of the matter and throwing it into relief. All her novels offer a wealth of fresh and crystalline notations, but until then that wealth had overflowed with an exuberance and abundance hardly justified by the requirements of the narrative, and issuing rather from a desire to surround the figures and background with plenty of color and contrasting incident. In the later period she plied her brush with growing restraint and sobriety, perhaps because by then she was drawing on memories unconnected with her native Sardinia.

Let us pause, for example, over *Annalena Bilsini*, a novel whose action is set in the Po Valley of northern Italy. Here then we have an atmosphere, a landscape, and a cast of characters quite different from those of her Sardinian novels. And yet how firmly, how accurately and sharply she brushes in this unfamiliar background. Here is a glimpse of winter coming to an end: "Already the first faint shadows of the trees flickered over the earth, still heavy-clodded and darkly sodden. The sky lifted and cleared a little more each day." And here is a jotting as good as a portrait: "When she spoke, the white of her teeth gleamed, with a bluish tinge like the white of her eyes, but she spoke little and her eyelids were always lowered." And Dionisio on his death bed: "The sick man seemed to recover consciousness, to rise again to the surface. His heavy, greenish eyelids were raised and the eyes appeared, set like crystals and but faintly reflecting the flicker of the lamp, then suddenly closed again. It seemed to Pietro that this was done to avoid the sight of him, and as if paralyzed himself he fell back, clammy and stiff, on to the chair where the old man's clothes were lying." And this limpid view of the countryside in the Po Valley: "A sudden shiver swept over the next field of uncut corn, as if fox cubs were frolicking across it. The shallow ditchwater, coated with a green film of moss, trembled every now and then and

seemed to stare with wide black eyes that reflected the blue eyes of the sky between the trees: it was the frogs jumping into the water. And the heavy fragrance of the grass, of clover above all, seemed to give a green tint to the air.'"

Such passages as these lend support to what has been said above. For they show that in her novels Grazia Deledda remains faithful rather to herself and to the inward mood of her art than to Sardinia and the themes and characters with which it provided her. They show too that this art, so justly honored by the Nobel Prize award, goes far beyond the picturesque appeal of regionalism and folklore to attain a wider, more universal resonance, worthy in every way of a Verga, a De Roberto, or an Alvaro. It is true that many of her novels attracted readers and aroused interest because of what they had to tell about Sardinia, its people, scenery, and way of life. It would, however, be a mistake to suppose that Grazia Deledda's highly personal art —which cannot be categorized by any such labels as romantic, realist, or decadent—achieves its power and fascination solely by virtue of its regional themes. I repeat, with renewed emphasis, that the imaginativeness of Grazia Deledda "transcends the geographical limits of Sardinia and creates a self-contained world of poetry." It is this country of the mind, mapped out by her art and truly expressing her soul, that remains her most important legacy, and it will occupy an enduring place in world culture.

Giuseppe Ravegnani is an Italian literary critic.
Translated by James Emmons.

THE 1926 PRIZE

By KJELL STRÖMBERG

THE NOBEL PRIZE for 1926 was withheld, and awarded in the following year to Grazia Deledda. Twenty years after Carducci, the first poet of the united Italy which arose from the wars of liberation, this Sardinian novelist became the second Italian writer to win this high distinction. She was also the second woman writer to reach the summit of literary glory, Selma Lagerlöf having been the first in 1909.

As far back as 1913 Grazia Deledda, who was then forty-one, had been proposed as candidate, mainly by a small group of writers and scientists who were members of an academy *dei Lincei e de la Crusca,* the origins of which go back to Queen Christina's conclaves in Rome toward the end of the seventeenth century. They returned to the nomination several times, strongly supported by Sweden's Minister to the Quirinal, Charles de Bildt, who was himself a great writer and a member of the Swedish Academy. Selma Lagerlöf, who must have recognized a twin soul in the Italian novelist, certainly did not withhold her support, although at heart she would have preferred the great Norwegian novelist, Sigrid Undset, to receive the award. But it was not until 1927 that the combined Italo-Swedish efforts were at last crowned with success, under the powerful impetus of old Professor

Schück, the president of the Nobel Foundation.

Among the new candidates for 1926 were the French writer Edouard Estaunié, at that time the very distinguished president of the *Société des Gens de Lettres,* and of the American novelist Edith Wharton, who already had a vast public in Sweden. As usual, German and Scandinavian candidates were in the majority, but one must admit that Grazia Deledda was lucky: that year neither Thomas Mann nor Sigrid Undset had been proposed in due form and within the allotted time limit. They were dangerous competitors who both carried off the Prize during the next few years.

But the main threat to Grazia Deledda's victory came from Italy, for no less than three compatriots, whose claims were carefully examined and discussed, were in competition with her. First of all, there was the excellent novelist and fiery poet Ada Negri, whose seventy years and more had not softened her Neapolitan *passionalità.* Unfortunately, it was whispered that she was Mr. Mussolini's favorite laureate, which must have made the members of the Swedish jury ponder a little: they were not very inclined to give in to arguments unconnected with the art of the writer. There was also the famous poet, Cesare Pascarella, who wrote in Roman dialect and sang of the charms of Trastevere and other populous parts of the Italian capital. He also wrote of the grandeur of eternal Rome *ab urbe condita,* expressing himself in poetic language which kept all the flavor of the daily speech of humble folk. He was praised by old Carducci ("Pascarella," he said, "has raised popular poetry to the summits of the epic poem"), translated into German by Paul Heyse, another Nobel Prizewinner, and finally, warmly recommended by Benedetto Croce, the most influential critic in Italy, who himself became a candidate for the Prize.

The third Italian candidate to compete with Grazia Deledda was Guglielmo Ferrero. His historical work, *Rome, Its Greatness and Its Decadence,* of which the sixth and last volume had just appeared, was judged as being comparable with the great German historian Theodor Mommsen's *Römische Geschichte:* Mommsen had been awarded one of the very first Nobel Prizes—in 1902.

The welcome given to the new laureate was somewhat tepid in Sweden and elsewhere, except obviously in Italy, where the Italians did their best to interpret this personal distinction as exceptional homage paid to the rebirth of Italian letters under the enlightened rule of the Duce. Grazia Deledda herself had always kept out of politics: in 1900, after her marriage to a highly placed official in the Ministry of War, she had abandoned her native island of Sardinia to take up residence in Rome. She had never shown any particularly favorable feelings toward the Fascist regime: nevertheless, she accepted it with a good grace as a citizen who was loyal to all established authority, without any fuss, like most of her compatriots.

Grazia Deledda went to Stockholm to receive the Prize but made no formal acceptance speech.

Translated by Camilla Sykes.

José Echegaray

1904

"In recognition of the numerous and
brilliant compositions which, in an
individual and original manner, have
revived the great traditions of the
Spanish drama"

PRESENTATION ADDRESS

By C. D. AF WIRSÉN

PERMANENT SECRETARY
OF THE SWEDISH ACADEMY

AFTER THE SPLENDOR of the Greek theater, it is principally among
the English and the Spanish that a national dramatic art has developed.
To understand modern Spanish drama, it is necessary to know what
conditions in the life of past periods lie behind it. For a long time
Spanish drama has displayed sharp contrasts. On the one hand, there
is the most luxurious flowering of fantasy; on the other, an extremely
subtle and at times conventional casuistry. In one place, there is brilliant
coloring, and in another, a great affection for rhetorical antithesis.
Emphatic language is coupled with tangled intrigue. Striking effects
are violent, the lyric order intense. Disharmonies are sharp, and conflicts
almost always have a tragic resolution. Dialectic is vigorous. However,
interior life is very rich, and the severe, inflexibly applied dictates of
honor do not exclude the luxury of sudden expressions of fantasy. In
Spanish drama the artificial has managed to become fused with a
genuine originality.

The heir and continuator of these glorious and characteristic traditions
is the writer who has been awarded half of the Nobel Prize this year.
A son of the modern age and perfectly independent in his judgments,
he has not the same conception of the world Calderón had. Loving
liberty and having fought often for tolerance, he is no friend of despotism
or of hierarchy, but still there is in him the same exotic ardor and the
same dignity which from oldest times have been the distinctive marks
of Spanish dramatists. This writer is José Echegaray. Like his forebears,
he knows how to present conflict, is extremely moving and vitally interested in different temperaments and ideals, and like them he enjoys

studying the most complicated cases of conscience. He is complete master of the art of producing in the audience pity and fear, the well-known fundamental effects of tragedy. Just as in the masters of the old Spanish drama, there is in him a striking union of the most lively imagination and the most refined artistic sense. For this it can be said of him—as a critic otherwise unsympathetic to him declared—"that he is of pure Spanish breed." However, his conception of the world is vast. His sense of duty has been purified, his fundamental conceptions are benevolent, and his moral heroism, while retaining a peculiar national character, has the features of a universal humanity.

José Echegaray was born in Madrid in 1833 but spent his childhood years in Murcia, where his father held the chair of Greek Studies at the Institute. Receiving his bachelor's degree at fourteen, he soon entered the School of Civil Engineering, where he distinguished himself by his zealous application and his penetrating skill. Five years later, in 1853, he completed his engineering career after having compiled a most brilliant record. Mathematics and mechanics had been his favorite studies, and his singular understanding of these branches of learning enabled him, after one year, to be appointed a professor in the very school which he had so recently attended as a student. It appears that for some years his struggle for existence was quite hard, and he had to give private lessons in order to sustain the most modest way of life. In spite of everything, he soon became an eminent professor, distinguishing himself both in pure and applied mathematics, and he became an outstanding engineer. At the same time he energetically studied political economy, embracing the ideas of free trade. Soon, that great talent, that vivacious engineer, was called to the highest and greatest tasks. Three times he has been a minister of his country's government. According to those who know him, whether they were adversaries or friends, he has always shown a singular skill in the administration of public finance and public works.

We can easily understand the general astonishment when this scholar, who had published treatises on analytic geometry, physics, and electricity, dedicated his indefatigable energy to writing for the theater. It has been said that his creations for the stage had the form of equations and problems. If the new manifestation of his genius was enthusiastically acclaimed by numerous admirers, it also found severe critics. Nevertheless, no one could deny that his works were distinguished by a deep moral sense. In a way, the critics were not mistaken who maintained that in his dramas, following the example of some surgeons, he rarely used any other method than that of *urere et secare;* still, however, there is something to admire in this muse of romantic exaltation and austere severity which condemns any compromise with duty.

Despising the transient approval of fashion and listening only to the inspirations of his genius, Echegaray pursued his triumphal career, demonstrating a dramatic fecundity which makes us think of Lope de Vega and Calderón.

Even in his youth, when he was attending the School of Civil Engineering, he was enthusiastic about drama and used his savings to obtain theater tickets. In 1865 he wrote a play entitled *La hija natural* (The Illegitimate Daughter), which was followed by *El libro talonario* (Book of Accounts) in 1874. The playbill carried a pseudonym instead of the author's name, but it did not take the public long to guess that the acclaimed dramatist was Echegaray, then Spain's Minister of Finance. Some months later *La última noche* (The Last Night) was staged, and since then his fertile imagination has not stopped engendering ever-new creations. He works with such speed that in one year he has published three or four works. Since lack of time prohibits a complete review here of all of his productions, suffice it to make brief mention of some which have won general attention. Echegaray scored his first triumph in November, 1874, with the drama *La esposa del vengador* (The Avenger's Wife), in which his true genius was revealed and in which, side by side with certain exaggerations, the greatest beauties can be admired. The public could imagine that it had been taken back to the Golden Age of Spanish drama, and it saluted Echegaray as the regenerator of the most brilliant era of the nation's dramatic poetry.

En el puño de la espada (The Sword's Handle), presented the following year, was received with the same applause. The sublime power that is manifest in this noble conception so moved the many spectators that the applause did not stop with the performance, and, after the last act, Echegaray had to appear on stage seven times to receive the acclaim of the audience. But great controversies arose in 1878 when, in *En el pilar y en la cruz* (The Stake and the Cross), the poet showed himself the defender of free thought against intolerance, of humanity against fanaticism. Typical of Echegaray, as he himself has observed, is his *Conflicto entre dos deberes* (Conflict of Duties), which was presented in 1882. A conflict of duties is found in almost all of his dramas, but rarely has the conflict been pushed to such an extreme as in this piece.

Two other dramas have made his name famous. These two inspired, excellent plays are *O locura ó santidad* (*Madman or Saint*) and *El gran Galeoto* (*The Great Galeoto*), the former presented in January, 1877, and the latter in March, 1881. In *O locura ó santidad* there is a great wealth of ideas and profound genius. It shows a man who, moved by his righteousness to sacrifice his prosperity and worldly goods, is considered crazy and treated as such by his friends and by the world at large. Lorenzo de Avendano renounces a name and a fortune when he learns unexpectedly but undeniably that they do not legally belong to him, and he persists in his resolution when the one indisputable proof of his illegitimacy has disappeared. Such idealism is judged madness by his family, and Lorenzo is looked upon by everybody as a Don Quixote, stubborn and simple-minded. The structure of the drama is firm and solid, demonstrating that it is the work of an engineer who calculates precisely all the elements that have gone into it, but it shows us to a still greater degree the poet of mature creative genius. More than an external collision, it treats the internal conflict of an extremely sad figure. It consists of a struggle between duty and opportunism, and Lorenzo in following the dictate of his conscience reaches martyrdom. Experience has always shown that very frequently he who faithfully obeys his conscience must be prepared to bear the fate of a martyr.

El gran Galeoto made an even greater impression. In the first month after it opened, it went through no fewer than five editions and inspired a national subscription to honor its author. Because of the masterful portrayal of the psychology of the characters the play has a lasting value. It shows the power of slander. The most innocent trait is disfigured and scandalously deformed by the gossip of people. Ernesto and Teodora have nothing for which to reproach themselves, but the world believes them guilty, and at last, abandoned by everyone, they end by throwing themselves into one another's arms. Subtlety of psychological analysis is revealed with such masterly detail of observation that those two noble spirits, in no way desirous of stealing the right of their neighbor, become mutually enamored without suspecting it. They discover the fact of their love only by means of the persecution to which they see themselves exposed. Romanticism triumphs in this drama whose poetic beauty is clearly perceptible, whose lyric details possess a dazzling coloring, and whose structure is without a flaw.

Echegaray goes on working as a dramatist. This year (1904) he has published a new play, *La desequilibrada* (The Disturbed Woman), whose first act is a genuine masterpiece of exposition and individualization, and which in its entirety reveals no weakening of poetic inspiration. In this play, we are shown Don Mauricio de Vargas, a clear type of that chivalry so dear to Echegaray, that chivalry which does not want to buy even its own happiness at the cost of compromising duty.

Thus it is just that the Nobel Prize be awarded to this great poet, whose production is distinguished by its virile energy and whose mode of seeing is impregnated with such high ideals that with abundant reason an eminent German critic has been able to say of him: *"Er verlangt Recht und Pflichterfüllung unter allen Umständen."*

Echegaray has put in the mouth of one of the characters of *El gran Galeoto* the most pessimistic words about the world, which "never recognizes the subtleties of the genius until three centuries after his death."

No doubt this can happen. But against the general application of the above thesis we can offer the justified admiration which the work of Echegaray has aroused. To those tributes of appreciation the Swedish Academy has agreed to add still one more, awarding the Nobel Prize in homage to the celebrated poet, the honor and glory of the Spanish Academy, José Echegaray.

There was no formal Acceptance Speech by Echegaray.

THE GREAT GALEOTO

A PLAY IN THREE ACTS WITH A PROLOGUE

By JOSÉ ECHEGARAY

Translated by Hanna Lynch

PERSONS OF THE DRAMA

TEODORA, *wife of*

DON JULIAN

DONA MERCEDES, *wife of*

DON SEVERO

PEPITO, *their son*

ERNEST

RUEDA

A WITNESS

TWO SERVANTS

SCENE—*Madrid of our day.*

THE GREAT GALEOTO

PROLOGUE

A study; to the left a balcony, on right a door; in the middle a table strewn with papers and books, and a lighted lamp upon it. Towards the right a sofa. Night.

SCENE I

ERNEST (*Seated at table and preparing to write*). Nothing—impossible! It is striving with the impossible. The idea is there; my head is fevered with it; I feel it. At moments an inward light illuminates it, and I see it. I see it in its floating form, vaguely outlined, and suddenly a secret voice seems to animate it, and I hear sounds of sorrow, sonorous sighs, shouts of sardonic laughter . . . a whole world of passions alive and struggling . . . They burst forth from me, extend around me, and the air is full of them. Then, then I say to myself: " 'Tis now the moment." I take up my pen, stare into space, listen attentively, restraining my very heart-beats, and bend over the paper. . . . Ah, but the irony of impotency! The outlines become blurred, the vision fades, the cries and sighs faint away . . . and nothingness, nothingness encircles me. . . . The monotony of empty space, of inert thought, of dreamy lassitude! and more than all the monotony of an idle pen and lifeless paper that lacks the life of thought! Ah! How varied are the shapes of nothingness, and how, in its dark and silent way, it mocks creatures of my stamp! So many, many forms! Canvas without color, bits of marble without shape, confused noise of chaotic vibrations. But nothing more irritating, more insolent, meaner than this insolent pen of mine (*throws it away*), nothing worse than this white sheet of paper. Oh, if I cannot fill it, at least I may destroy it—vile accomplice of my ambition and my eternal humiliation. Thus, thus . . . smaller and still smaller. (*Tears up paper. Pauses.*) And then! How lucky that nobody saw me! For in truth such fury is absurd and unjust. No, I will not yield. I will think and think, until either I have conquered or am crushed. No, I will not give up. Let me see, let me see . . . if in that way——

SCENE II

ERNEST, DON JULIAN *on the right, in evening-dress, with overcoat upon his arm.*

D. JULIAN (*At the door, without entering*). I say, Ernest!

ERNEST. Don Julian!

D. JULIAN. Still working? Do I disturb you?

ERNEST (*Rising*). Disturb me! What a question, Don Julian! Come in, come in. And Teodora?

(DON JULIAN *enters.*)

D. JULIAN. We have just come from the Opera. She has gone upstairs with my brother, to see something or other that Mercedes has bought, and I was on my way to my room when I saw your light, so I stopped to say good night.

ERNEST. Was there a good house?

D. JULIAN. As usual. All our friends inquired after you. They wondered you were not there too.

ERNEST. That was kind of them.

D. JULIAN. Not more than you deserve. And how have you improved the shining hours of solitude and inspiration?

ERNEST. Solitude, yes; inspiration, no. It shuns me though I call on it ever so humbly and fondly.

D. JULIAN. It has failed at the rendezvous?

ERNEST. And not for the first time, either. But if I have done nothing else, at least I have made a happy discovery.

D. JULIAN. What?

ERNEST. That I am a poor devil.

D. JULIAN. The deuce! That's a famous discovery.

ERNEST. Nothing less.

D. JULIAN. But why are you so out of sorts with yourself? Is the play you talked of the other day not going on?

ERNEST. How can it? The going on is done by me going out of my wits.

D. JULIAN. How is this? Both the drama and inspiration are faithless to my poor friend.

ERNEST. This is how I stand. When I first conceived the idea, I imagined it full of promise, but when I attempt to give it form, and vest it in an appropriate stage garb, the result shows something extraordinary, difficult, undramatic and impossible.

D. JULIAN. How is it impossible? Come, tell me. You've excited my curiosity. (*Sits down on the sofa.*)

ERNEST. Imagine the principal personage, one who creates the drama and develops it, who gives it life and provokes the catastrophe, who, broadly, fills and possesses it, and yet who cannot make his way to the stage.

D. JULIAN. Is he so ugly, then? So repugnant or bad?

ERNEST. Not so. Bad as you or I may be—not worse. Neither good nor bad, and truly not repugnant. I am not such a cynic—neither a misanthrope, nor one so out of love with life as to fall into such unfairness.

D. JULIAN. What, then, is the reason?

ERNEST. The reason, Don Julian, is that there is no material room in the scenario for this personage.

D. JULIAN. Holy Virgin! What do you mean? Is it by chance a mythological drama with Titans in it?

ERNEST. Titans, yes, but in the modern sense of the word.

D. JULIAN. That is to say——?

ERNEST. That is to say, this person is . . . *everybody*.

D. JULIAN. *Everybody!* You are right. There is no room for everybody on the stage. It is an incontrovertible truth that has more than once been demonstrated.

ERNEST. Then you agree with me?

D. JULIAN. Not entirely. Everybody may be condensed in a few types and characters. This is matter beyond my depth, but I have always understood that the masters have more than once accomplished it.

ERNEST. Yes, but in my case it is to condemn me, not to write my drama.

D. JULIAN. Why?

ERNEST. For many reasons it would be difficult to explain,—above all, at this late hour.

D. JULIAN. Never mind. Give me a few.

ERNEST. Look! Each individual of this entire mass, each head of this monster of a thousand heads, of this Titan of the century, whom I call *everybody,* takes part in my play for a flying moment, to utter but one word, fling a single glance. Perhaps his action in the tale consists of a smile, he appears but to vanish. Listless and absentminded, he acts without passion, without anger, without guile, often for mere distraction's sake.

D. JULIAN. What then?

ERNEST. These light words, these fugitive glances, these indifferent smiles, all these evanescent sounds and this trivial evil, which may be called the insignificant rays of the dramatic light, condensed to one focus, to one group, result in conflagration or explosion, in strife and in victims. If I represent the whole by a few types or symbolical personages, I bestow upon each one that which is really dispersed among many, and such a result distorts my idea. I must bring types on the stage whose guile repels and is the less natural because evil in them has no object. This exposes me to a worse consequence, to the accusation of meaning to paint a cruel, corrupted, and debased society, when my sole pretension is to prove that not even the most insignificant actions are in themselves insignificant or lost for good or evil. For, concentrated by the mysterious influences of modern life, they may reach to immense effects.

D. JULIAN. Say no more, my friend. All this is metaphysics. A glimmer of light, perhaps, but through an infinitude of cloud. However, you understand these things better than I do. Letters of exchange, shares, stock, and discount, now —that's another matter.

ERNEST. No, no; you've common sense, and that's the chief thing.

D. JULIAN. You flatter me, Ernest.

ERNEST. But you follow me?

D. JULIAN. Not in the least. There ought to be a way out of the difficulty.

ERNEST. If that were all!

D. JULIAN. What! More?

ERNEST. Tell me what is the great dramatic spring?

D. JULIAN. My dear fellow, I don't exactly know what you mean by a dramatic spring. All I can tell you is that I have not the slightest interest in plays where love does not preponderate— above all unfortunate love, for I have enough of happy love at home.

ERNEST. Good, very good! Then in my play there can be little or no love.

D. JULIAN. Ah, so much the worse. Though I know nothing of your play, I suspect it will interest nobody.

ERNEST. So I have been telling you. Nevertheless, it is possible to put in a little love,—and jealousy too.

D. JULIAN. Ah, then, with an interesting intrigue skillfully developed, and some effective situations——

ERNEST. No, nothing of the sort. It will be all simple, ordinary, almost vulgar . . . so that the drama will not have any external action. The drama evolves within the personages: it advances slowly: today takes hold of a thought,

tomorrow of a heart-beat, little by little, undermines the will.

D. JULIAN. But who understands all this? How are these interior ravages manifested? Who recounts them to the audience? In what way are they evident? Must we spend a whole evening hunting for a glance, a sigh, a gesture, a single word? My dear boy, this is not amusement. To cast us into such depths is to hurl us upon philosophy.

ERNEST. You but echo my own thought.

D. JULIAN. I have no wish to discourage you. You best know what you are about—there. Though the play seems rather colorless, heavy, uninteresting, perhaps if the *dénouement* is sensational —and the explosion—eh?

ERNEST. Sensation! Explosion! Hardly, and that only just upon the fall of the curtain.

D. JULIAN. Which means that the play begins when the curtain falls?

ERNEST. I am inclined to admit it. But I will endeavor to give it a little warmth.

D. JULIAN. My dear lad, what you have to do is to write the *second* play, the one that begins where the first ends. For the other, according to your description, would be difficult to write, and is not worth the trouble.

ERNEST. 'Tis the conclusion I have come to myself.

D. JULIAN. Then we agree, thanks to your skill and logic. And what is the name?

ERNEST. That's another difficulty. I can find none.

D. JULIAN. What do you say? No name either?

ERNEST. No, unless, as Don Hermogenes [1] says, we could put it into Greek for greater clarity.

---

[1] A pendant in Moratin's *Comedia Nueva*, who quotes Greek incessantly to make himself better understood.—*Tran.*

D. JULIAN. Of a surety, Ernest, you were dozing when I came in. You have been dreaming nonsense.

ERNEST. Dreaming! yes. Nonsense! perhaps. I talk both dreams and nonsense. But you are sensible and always right.

D. JULIAN. In this case it does not require much penetration. A drama in which the chief personage cannot appear; in which there is hardly any love; in which nothing happens but what happens every day; that begins with the fall of the curtain upon the last act, and which has no name. I don't know how it is to be written, still less how it is to be acted, how it is to find an audience, nor how it can be called a drama.

ERNEST. Nevertheless, it is a drama, if I could only give it proper form, and that I can't do.

D. JULIAN. Do you wish to follow my advice?

ERNEST. Can you doubt it?—you, my friend, my benefactor, my second father! Don Julian!

D. JULIAN. Come, come, Ernest, don't let us drop into a sentimental drama on our own account instead of yours, which we have declared impossible. I asked you if you would take my advice.

ERNEST. And I said yes.

D. JULIAN. Then leave aside your plays. Go to bed, rest yourself, and come out shooting with me tomorrow. Kill a few partridges, and that will be an excuse for your not killing one or two characters, and not exposing yourself to the same fate at the hands of the public. After all, you may thank me for it.

ERNEST. I'll do no such thing. I mean to write that play.

D. JULIAN. But, my poor fellow, you've conceived it in mortal sin.

ERNEST. I don't know, but it is conceived. I feel it stir in my brain. It clamors for life, and I must give it to the world.

D. JULIAN. Can't you find another plot?

ERNEST. But this idea?

D. JULIAN. Send it to the devil.

ERNEST. Ah, Don Julian, you believe that an idea which has gripped the mind can be effaced and destroyed at our pleasure. I wanted to think out another play, but this accursed idea won't give it room, until it itself has seen the light.

D. JULIAN. God grant you a happy delivery.

ERNEST. That's the question, as Hamlet says.

D. JULIAN. Couldn't you cast it into the literary foundling hospital of anonymity? (*In a low voice with an air of comical mystery.*)

ERNEST. Don Julian, I am a man of conscience. Good or bad, my children are legitimate. They bear my name.

D. JULIAN (*Preparing to go*). I have nothing more to say. What must be done will be done.

ERNEST. I wish it were so. Unfortunately, it is not done. But no matter; if I don't do it, somebody else will.

D. JULIAN. Then to work, and good luck, and may nobody rob you of your laurels.

SCENE III

ERNEST, DON JULIAN, *and* TEODORA.

TEODORA (*Outside*). Julian, Julian!

D. JULIAN. It's Teodora.

TEODORA. Are you there, Julian?

D. JULIAN (*Going to the door*). Yes, I'm here. Come in.

TEODORA (*Entering*). Good evening, Ernest.

ERNEST. Good evening, Teodora. Was the singing good?

TEODORA. As usual; and have you been working much?

ERNEST. As usual; nothing.

TEODORA. Then you'd have done better to come with us. They all asked after you.

ERNEST. It seems that everybody is interested in me.

D. JULIAN. I should think so, since *everybody* is to be the principal personage of your play. You may imagine if they are anxious to be on good terms with you.

TEODORA. A play?

D. JULIAN. Hush! 'Tis a mystery. Ask no questions. Neither title, nor characters, nor action, nor catastrophe—the sublime! Good night, Ernest. Come, Teodora.

ERNEST. Adieu, Don Julian.

TEODORA. Till tomorrow.

ERNEST. Good night.

TEODORA (*To Don Julian*). How preoccupied Mercedes was!

D. JULIAN. And Severo was in a rage.

TEODORA. Why, I wonder.

D. JULIAN. How do I know? On the other hand, Pepito chattered enough for both.

TEODORA. He always does, and nobody escapes his tongue.

D. JULIAN. He's a character for Ernest's play. (*Exeunt* TEODORA, *and* DON JULIAN *by right.*)

SCENE IV

ERNEST. Let Don Julian say what he will, I won't abandon the undertaking. That would be signal cowardice. Never retreat—always forward. (*Rises and begins to walk about in an agitated way. Then approaches the balcony.*) Protect me, night. In thy blackness, rather than in the azure clearness of day, are outlined the luminous shapes of inspiration. Lift your roofs, you thousand houses of this great town, as well for a poet in dire necessity as for the devil on two sticks who so wantonly exposed you. Let me see the men and women enter your drawing-rooms and boudoirs in search of the night's rest after fevered pleasures abroad. Let my acute hearing catch the stray words of all those who inquired for me of Don Julian and Teodora. As the scattered rays of light, when gathered to a focus by diaphanous crystal, strike flame, and darkness is forged by the crossed bars of shadow; as mountains are made from grains of earth, and seas from drops of water: so will I use your wasted words, your vague smiles, your eager glances, and build my play of all those thousand trivialities dispersed in *cafés,* at reunions, theaters, and spectacles, and that float now in the air. Let the modest crystal of my intelligence be the lens which will concentrate light and shadow, from which will spring the dramatic conflagration and the tragic explosion of the catastrophe. Already my play takes shape. It has even a title now, for there, under the lamp-shade, I see the immortal work of the immortal Florentine. It offers me in Italian what in good Spanish it would be risky and futile audacity either to write on paper or pronounce on the stage. Francesca and Paolo, assist me with the story of your loves! (*Sits down and prepares to write.*) The play . . . the play begins. . . . First page—there, 'tis no longer white. It has a name. (*Writing.*) *The Great Galeoto.* (*Writes feverishly.*)

END OF PROLOGUE

ACT I

SCENE—*A drawing-room in* DON JULIAN's *house. At the back of stage a large door, and beyond a passage separating it from the dining-room door, which remains closed throughout the act. On the left a balcony, and beyond it a door. On the right two doors. On the stage a table, an arm-chair, handsome and luxurious mounting. Hour, towards sunset.*

SCENE I

TEODORA *and* DON JULIAN. TEODORA *near the balcony;* DON JULIAN *seated on the sofa, lost in thought.*

TEODORA. What a lovely sunset! what clouds and light, and what a sky! Suppose it were true, as the poets say, and our fathers believed, that our fate is stamped upon the azure heaven! Were the mysterious secret of human destiny traced by the stars upon the sapphire sphere, and this splendid evening should hold the cipher of ours, what happiness it must disclose! what a smiling future! What a life in our life, and what radiance in our heaven! Is it not so, Julian? (*She approaches* DON JULIAN.) Ah, plunged in thought, I see! Come and look out. What, no word for me?

D. JULIAN (*Absently*). What is it?

TEODORA (*Coming near*). You have not been listening to me!

D. JULIAN. You have my heart ever—who are its magnet and its center. But my mind is apt to be besieged by preoccupations, cares, business——

TEODORA. They are the plague of my life, since they rob me, if not of my husband's affections, at least of some of his attention. But what is the matter, Julian? (*Affectionately.*) Something worries you. Is it serious, that you are so solemn and so silent? If it should be trouble, Julian, remember that I have a right to share it. My joys are yours, and your sorrows are no less mine.

D. JULIAN. Sorrows! Troubles! Are you not happy? Do I not possess in you the living embodiment of joy? With those cheeks so ruddy in the glow of health, and those dear eyes, clear like your soul and resplendent as the sky, and I the owner of all you, could pain, or shadow, or grief teach me I am other than the happiest man alive?

TEODORA. It is a business annoyance, perhaps?

D. JULIAN. Money never yet forced sleep or appetite to forsake me. I have never felt aversion, much less contempt for it, so it follows that the article has flowed easily into my coffers. I was rich, I am rich; and until Don Julian of Garagarga dies of old age, please God and his own good fortune, he will remain, if not the wealthiest, certainly the surest, banker of Madrid, Cadiz, and Opporto.

TEODORA. Then what is your preoccupation?

D. JULIAN. I was thinking—'tis a good thought, too.

TEODORA. Naturally, since 'tis yours.

D. JULIAN. Flatterer! you would spoil me.

TEODORA. But I am still unenlightened.

D. JULIAN. There is an important matter I want to achieve.

TEODORA. Connected with the new works?

D. JULIAN. No; it has nothing to do with stone or iron.

TEODORA. What, then?

D. JULIAN. It is a question of kindness—a sacred debt of old date.

TEODORA (*Gleefully*). Oh, I can guess now.

D. JULIAN. So!

TEODORA. You mean Ernest.

D. JULIAN. You are right.

TEODORA. Yes, yes, you must. Poor lad! he's so good and noble and generous.

D. JULIAN. Quite his father's son—the model of a loyal hidalgo.

TEODORA. And then so clever! Only twenty-six, and a prodigy! what doesn't he know?

D. JULIAN. Know! I should think he *did* know. That's nothing—rather, that's the worst of it. While he is wandering in the sphere of sublime thought, I fear he's not likely to learn much of a world so deceptive and prosaic as ours, which takes no interest in the subtleties of the mind until three centuries after genius has been buried.

TEODORA. But with you for a guide, Julian—you don't intend to abandon him yet a while, surely?

D. JULIAN. God forbid. I should be black-hearted indeed if I would so readily forget all I owe his father. Don Juan of Acedo risked for my family name and wealth, ay, almost his life. Should this lad need mine, he might ask it, and welcome. 'Twould be but just payment of the debt my name represents.

TEODORA. Well said, Julian. It is like you.

D. JULIAN. You remember, about a year ago, I heard my good friend was dead, and his son was left badly off. I lost no time, caught the train to Gerona, nearly used force, and carried the boy back here. When he stood in the middle of this room I said to him: "You are master here; you may command me and mine. Since I owe your father everything, you must regard me in the light of his representative. If I fall short, my desire is to come as near as possible to him. As for the amount of affection I have to dispose of—we'll see if I don't outrace him there."

TEODORA. I remember it well. The soft-hearted fellow burst out crying, and clung to you like a child.

D. JULIAN. He's but a child, as you say. That's why we must think and plan for him. And 'twas of that I was so seriously thinking a moment ago. I was meditating a half-formed project, while you, dear, wanted me to contemplate a panorama of radiant cloud and scarlet sun that cannot compare with the sun that shines in my own heaven.

TEODORA. I cannot divine your idea. What is it you project doing for Ernest?

D. JULIAN. Those are my words.

TEODORA. But is there something yet undone that you expect to discover? He has lived with us for the past year like one of ourselves. Were he your son, or a brother of mine, could you show him more tenderness, I more affection?

D. JULIAN. It is much, but not enough.

TEODORA. Not enough! I fancy,——

D. JULIAN. You are thinking of the present, and I of the future.

TEODORA. Oh! the future! That is easily settled. See, he lives here with us as long as he likes, for years. It is his home. Then when the just and natural law prompts him to fall in love and desire another, we will marry him. You will nobly share your wealth with him, and we will lead them from the altar to their own house,—*he* and *she!* The proverb, you know, says wisely, "for each wedded pair a house." He will live just a little away from us, but that will be no reason for our forgetting him, or loving him less. I see it all distinctly. They are happy, and we even happier. They have children, of course, and we perhaps more—well, at least, one little girl, who will fall in love with Ernest's son, and to whom we will marry her by and by. (*Spoken playfully, with volubility, grace, blushes, and lively gesture, according to the actress's talents.*)

D. JULIAN. But where in heaven's name are you going to stop? (*Laughing.*)

TEODORA. You spoke of his future, Julian, and I've sketched it. If not this one, I will neither approve nor accept it.

D. JULIAN. How like you, Teodora! but——

TEODORA. Ah, there is a but already.

D. JULIAN. Listen, Teodora. It is but a debt we owe to look after the poor fellow as if he were a relative, and obligation runs with the exactions of our affection. So much for himself, so much for his father's son. But every human action is complex, has two points of view, and every medal has its reverse. Which means, Teodora, that you must understand it is a very different matter to give and receive favors; and that in the end Ernest might feel my protection a humiliation. He's a high-spirited, fine lad, a trifle haughty perhaps, and it is imperative there should be an end to his present position. We may, if we can, do more for him, but we must seem to do less.

TEODORA. How so?

D. JULIAN. We'll see—but here he comes—— (*Looks down the stage.*)

TEODORA. Hush!

SCENE II

DON JULIAN, TEODORA, *and* ERNEST *behind.*

D. JULIAN. Welcome!

ERNEST. Don Julian!—and Teodora! (*Salutes absently. Sits down near the table in pensive silence.*)

D. JULIAN (*Approaching him*). What's the matter?

ERNEST. Nothing.

D. JULIAN. You look as if something ailed you—your preoccupation reveals it. No trouble, I hope?

ERNEST. Nonsense.

D. JULIAN. Nor disappointment?

ERNEST. None whatever.

D. JULIAN. I don't annoy you?

ERNEST. You! good heavens! (*Rises and comes toward him effusively.*) You speak out of the right of friendship and affection, and you read me through and through. Yes, sir; there is indeed something the matter. I will tell you, if you, and you also, Teodora, out of your pity, will hold me excused. I am an ungrateful fool, a mere boy, in truth, deserving neither of your kindness nor of your affection. Possessing such a father and such a sister, I ought to be happy, with no care for the morrow. But it is not so. I blush to explain it,—can't you understand?—Yes, yes, you must see how false my position is. I live here on alms. (*With energy.*)

TEODORA. Such a word——

ERNEST. Teodora!

TEODORA. Affronts us.

ERNEST. I expressed myself ill—but it is so.

D. JULIAN. I say it is not so. If any one in this house lives upon alms, and those no slight ones, it is I and not you.

ERNEST. I am acquainted, sir, with the story of two loyal friends, and of some money matters long forgotten. It does honor to my father and to his hidalgic race. But I am shamed in profiting by it. I am young, Don Julian, and although I may not be worth much, there ought still to be some way for me to earn my bread. It may be pride or folly, I cannot say. But I remember what my father used to say: "What you can do yourself, never ask another to do. What you can earn, never owe to anyone else."

D. JULIAN. So that my services humiliate and degrade you. You count your friends importunate creditors.

TEODORA. Reason may be on your side, Ernest, and in knowledge you are not deficient, but, believe me, in this case the heart alone speaks with wisdom.

D. JULIAN. Your father did not find me so ungenerous or so proud.

TEODORA. Ah, friendship was then a very different thing.

ERNEST. Teodora!

TEODORA (*To* DON JULIAN). What a noble anxiety he displays!

ERNEST. I know I seem ungrateful—I feel it—and an idiot to boot. Forgive me, Don Julian.

D. JULIAN. His head is a forge.

TEODORA (*Also apart to Don Julian*). He doesn't live in this world.

D. JULIAN. Just so. He's full of depth and learning, and lets himself be drowned in a pool of water.

ERNEST (*Meditatively*). True, I know little of life, and am not well fitted to make my way through it. But I divine it, and shudder, I know not why. Shall I founder on the world's pool as upon the high sea? I may not deny that it terrifies me far more than the deep ocean. The sea only reaches the limit set by the loose sand: over all space travel the emanations of the pool. A strong man's arms can struggle with the waves of the sea, but no one can struggle against subtle miasma. But if I fall, I must not feel the humiliation of defeat. I wish and pray that at the last moment I may see the approach of the sea that will bear me away at its will; see the sword that is to pierce me, the rock against which I am to be crushed. I must measure my adversary's strength, and despise it falling, despise it dying, instead of tamely breathing the venom scattered through the ambient air.

D. JULIAN (*To* TEODORA). Didn't I tell you he was going out of his mind?

TEODORA. But, Ernest, where are you wandering?

D. JULIAN. Yes. What has all this to do with the matter?

ERNEST. Sir, I have come to the conclusion that others, seeing me housed and fed here, are saying of me what I long have thought. They see me constantly driving out with you, in the morning walking with Teodora or Mercedes, in your opera-box, hunting on your lands, and daily occupying the same place at your table. Though you would like to think otherwise, in one way or another the gossip runs: Who is he? Is he a relation? Not so. The secretary? Still less. A partner? If a partner, it may be accepted he brings little or nothing to the general fund. So they chatter.

D. JULIAN. By no means. You are raving.

ERNEST. I beg to contradict you.

D. JULIAN. Then give me a name.

ERNEST. Sir——

D. JULIAN. One will do.

ERNEST. There is one at hand—upstairs.

D. JULIAN. Name him.

ERNEST. Don Severo.

D. JULIAN. My brother?

ERNEST. Exactly, your brother? Will that suffice? or shall we add his respected wife, Doña Mercedes? and Pepito, their son? What have you to say then?

D. JULIAN. That Severo is a fool, Mercedes an idle chatterer, and the lad a puppy.

ERNEST. They only repeat what they hear.

D. JULIAN. It is not true. This is false reasoning. Between gentlemen, when the intention is honorable, what can the opinion of the world really matter? The meaner it is, the loftier our disdain of it.

ERNEST. 'Tis nobly said, and is what all well-bred men feel. But I have been taught that gossip, whether inspired by malice or not, which is according to each one's natural tendency, begins in a lie and generally ends in truth. Does gossip, as it grows, disclose the hidden sin? Is it a reflex of the past, or does it invent evil and give it existence? Does it set its accursed seal upon an existent fault, or merely breed that which was yet not, and furnish the occasion for wrong? Should we call the slanderer infamous or severe? the accomplice or the divulger? the public avenger or the tempter? Does he arrest or precipitate our fall? wound through taste or duty? and when he condemns, is it from justice or from spite? Perhaps both, Don Julian. Who can say? though time, occasion, and facts may show.

D. JULIAN. See here, Ernest, I don't understand an iota of all this philosophizing. I presume 'tis on such nonsense you waste your intelligence. But I don't want you to be vexed or worried. It's true—you really wish for austere independence, to stand alone at a post of honor?

ERNEST. Don Julian!

D. JULIAN. Answer me.

ERNEST (*Joyously*). Yes.

D. JULIAN. Then count it gained. At this very moment I have no secretary. I am expecting one from London. But nobody would suit me better than a certain young fool, who is enamored of poverty. (*Speaks in pleasant reproach.*) His work and salary will, of course, be settled as anyone else's, though he be a son to one who cherishes him as such.

ERNEST. Don Julian!

D. JULIAN (*Affecting comical severity*). Remember, I am an exacting businessman, and I have not the habit of giving my money away for nothing. I intend to get as much as possible out of you, and work you hard. In my house the bread of just labor alone is consumed. By the clock, ten hours, starting at daybreak, and when I choose to be severe, you will see that Severo himself is no match for me. So, before the world you pose as the victim of my selfishness . . . but in private, dear boy, ever the same, the center of my dearest affections. (*Unable to maintain former tone,* DON JULIAN *breaks off, and holds his hand out to* ERNEST.)

ERNEST (*Deeply moved*). Don Julian!

D. JULIAN. You accept, then?

ERNEST. I am yours to command.

TEODORA (*To* DON JULIAN). At last you have tamed the savage.

ERNEST (*To* DON JULIAN). Anything for your sake.

D. JULIAN. So would I have you always, Ernest. And now I have to write to my London correspondent, and thank him, and while recognizing the extraordinary merit of his Englishman, whom he extols to the skies, regret that I have already engaged a young man. (*Walks toward the first door on the right hand.*) This is how we stand for the present; but in the future—it will be as partners. (*Returns with an air of mystery.*)

TEODORA. Stop, Julian, I beg of you. Can't you see that he will take alarm?

(DON JULIAN *goes out on the right, and laughs to himself, looking back at* ERNEST.)

SCENE III

TEODORA *and* ERNEST. *Towards the end of the last scene twilight has fallen, so that at this moment the room is in deep shadow.*

ERNEST. I am dazed by so much kindness. How can I ever repay it? (*He sits down on the sofa, displaying great emotion.* TEODORA *walks over and stands beside him.*)

TEODORA. By ejecting the spirit of pride and distrust; by being sensible and believing that we truly love you, that we will never change; and by putting full faith in all Julian's promises. His word is sacred, Ernest, and in him you will always have a father, in me a sister.

SCENE IV

TEODORA, ERNEST, DOÑA MERCEDES, *and* DON SEVERO. *The latter remain standing behind as they enter. The room is quite dark, save for a glimmer of light shed from the balcony, whither* ERNEST *and* TEODORA *have moved.*

ERNEST. How good you are!

TEODORA. And you, what a boy! After today I hope you have done with sadness—eh?

ERNEST. Quite.

MERCEDES (*Outside, speaking low*). How dark it is!

SEVERO (*In same tone*). Come away, Mercedes.

MERCEDES (*Crossing the threshold*). There is nobody here.

SEVERO (*Detaining her*). Yes, there is. (*Both stand a while peering.*)

ERNEST. Teodora, my whole life, a thousand lives would still not be enough to offer you in return for your kindness. Don't judge me by my morose temper. I cannot lend a showy front to my affections, but, believe me, I do know how to love—and hate as well. My heart can beat to bursting under the lash of either sentiment.

MERCEDES (*To* SEVERO). What are they saying?

SEVERO. Something odd, but I hear imperfectly. (TEODORA *and* ERNEST *go out on the balcony, speaking low.*)

MERCEDES. 'Tis Ernest.

SEVERO. And she—I suppose—is——

MERCEDES. Teodora.

SEVERO. Their eternal tricks—always together. I can stand no more of this. And their words? I mustn't put it off any longer——

MERCEDES. True, Severo. Come away. It is certainly your duty, since everybody is talking.

SEVERO. Yes, I must open Julian's eyes—today, at once.

MERCEDES. The fellow has impudence enough, and to spare.

SEVERO. By all that's holy—so has she.

MERCEDES. Poor girl! She's but a child. Leave her to me.

TEODORA. Another house? Surely no. You wouldn't leave us? What an idea! Julian would never consent.

SEVERO (*To* DOÑA MERCEDES). I should think not indeed, neither would I. (*Aloud.*) Ah, Teodora, you didn't see me? This is how you receive your guests.

TEODORA (*Coming from the balcony*). Don Severo! I am delighted.

MERCEDES. Is there no dinner this evening? It's near the hour.

TEODORA. Mercedes too!

MERCEDES. Yes, Teodora.

SEVERO (*Aside*). She is a capital actress. What a creature!

TEODORA. I must ring for lights. (*Touches the bell on the table.*)

SEVERO. Quite so. Everyone likes plenty of light.

SERVANT. Madam?

TEODORA. Bring the lamps, Genaro. (*Exit servant.*)

SEVERO. He who follows the narrow path of loyalty and duty, and is always that which he appears to be, need never fear the light, nor blush in its glare.

(*The servant enters with lamps, the stage is brilliantly illuminated. After a pause.*)

TEODORA (*Laughing naturally*). So I should think, and such, I imagine, is the general opinion. (*Looks at Mercedes.*)

MERCEDES. I suppose so.

SEVERO. Hulloa, Don Ernest! what were you doing out there? Were you with Teodora when we came in! (*Speaks with marked intention.*)

ERNEST (*Coldly*). I was here as you see.

SEVERO. The deuce you were! It is rather dark to see. (*Approaches him with outstretched hand, looking fixedly at him.* TEODORA *and* MERCEDES *converse apart. Aside.*) His face is flushed, and he appears to have been crying. In this world only children and lovers weep. (*Aloud.*) And Julian?

TEODORA. He went away to write a letter.

ERNEST (*Aside*). Though I have patience to spare, this man tries me hard.

SEVERO (*To* TEODORA). I am going to see him. There is still time before dinner?

TEODORA. Plenty.

SEVERO. Good. Then to work. (*Aside, rubbing his hands, and looking back at* ERNEST *and* TEODORA. *Aloud.*) Goodbye.

TEODORA. Goodbye.

SEVERO (*Rancorously, from the door*). My faith!

SCENE V

TEODORA, DOÑA MERCEDES, *and* ERNEST. *The ladies occupy the sofa, and* ERNEST *stands near them.*

MERCEDES (*To* ERNEST). We did not see you today.

ERNEST. No, madam.

MERCEDES. Nor Pepito?

ERNEST. No.

MERCEDES. He is upstairs alone.

ERNEST (*Aside*). Let him stop there.

MERCEDES (*Gravely and mysteriously to* TEODORA). I wish he would go. I want to speak to you.

TEODORA. Indeed?

MERCEDES (*In same tone*). Yes, it is something very serious.

TEODORA. Well, begin!

MERCEDES. Why doesn't he go?

TEODORA (*In a low voice*). I don't understand you.

MERCEDES. Courage! (*Takes her hand and clasps it affectionately.* TEODORA *looks at her in somber question.*) Send him about his business.

TEODORA. If you insist. Ernest, will you do me a favor?

ERNEST. Gladly—with a thousand wills.

MERCEDES (*Aside*). One were still too many.

TEODORA. Then go upstairs—to Pepito—— But it might bore you to carry a message.

ERNEST. By no means.

MERCEDES (*Aside*). In what a sweet, soft voice he speaks to her!

TEODORA. Tell him—ask him if he has renewed our subscription at the Opera as I told him. He knows about it.

ERNEST. With pleasure—this very moment.

TEODORA. Thanks, Ernest, I am sorry——

ERNEST. Nonsense. (*Exit.*)

TEODORA. Adieu!

SCENE VI

TEODORA *and* DOÑA MERCEDES.

TEODORA. Something serious? You alarm me, Mercedes. Such mystery! What can it mean?

MERCEDES. It is indeed very serious.

TEODORA. Concerning whom?

MERCEDES. All of you.

TEODORA. All of us?

MERCEDES. Julian, Ernest, and you.

TEODORA. All three?

MERCEDES. Yes, all three. (*Short pause. Both women stare at each other.*)

TEODORA. Then make haste.

MERCEDES (*Aside*). I should like to——but, no; I must go gently in this unsavory affair. (*Aloud.*) Listen, Teodora. My husband is, after all, your husband's brother, and in life and death our fortunes are one. So that we owe one another in all things protection, help, and advice,—is it not so? Today it may be I who offer assistance, and tomorrow, should I need it, I unblushingly claim it of you.

TEODORA. You may count upon it, Mercedes. But come to the end of the matter now.

MERCEDES. Up to today, Teodora, I shrank from this step, but Severo urges me. "It can't go on," he insists. "My brother's honor and my own self-esteem forbid me to witness that which fills me with shame and sorrow. On all sides am I assailed with innuendoes, with the smiles, the covert glances and the reproaches of my friends. There must be an end to this low gossip about us."

TEODORA. Continue, pray.

MERCEDES. Then heed me. (*They exchange a prolonged gaze.*)

TEODORA. Tell me, what is the gossip?

MERCEDES. The murmuring of the river tells us that its waters are swollen.

TEODORA. I understand nothing of your river and its swollen waters, but do not drive me wild.

MERCEDES (*Aside*). Poor child! My heart grieves for her. (*Aloud.*) So you do not understand me?

TEODORA. I? not in the least.

MERCEDES (*Aside*). How stupid she is! (*Aloud, energetically.*) You make a laughing-stock of him.

TEODORA. Of whom?

MERCEDES. Why, of your husband, of course.

TEODORA (*Impetuously, rising*). Julian!

what a falsehood! What wretch could say so? Julian would strike him!

MERCEDES (*Endeavoring to soothe her and make her sit down*). He would need a good many hands, then; for, if report speak truly, he would have to strike the entire town.

TEODORA. But what does it all mean? What is the mystery, and what is this talk of the town?

MERCEDES. So you're sorry?

TEODORA. I am sorry. But what is it?

MERCEDES. You see, Teodora, you are quite a child. At your age one is so often thoughtless and light, and then such bitter tears are afterwards shed. You still don't understand me?

TEODORA. No, what has such a case to do with me?

MERCEDES. It is the story of a scoundrel and the story of a lady——

TEODORA (*Speaking eagerly*). Whose name——?

MERCEDES. Her name——

TEODORA. Oh, what does it matter?

(TEODORA *moves away from* MERCEDES, *who shifts her seat on the sofa to follow her. The double movement of repugnance and aloofness on* TEODORA's *part, and of insistence and protection on* MERCEDES', *is very marked.*)

MERCEDES. The man is a shabby-hearted betrayer, who, for one hour of pleasure, would thrust upon the woman a life of sorrow: the husband's dishonor, the ruin of a family, and she left shamed and condemned to social penitence in the world's disdain, and to keener punishment still at the whip of her own conscience.

(*Here* TEODORA, *avoiding* MERCEDES, *reaches the edge of the sofa, bows her head and covers her face with both hands. At last she understands.*)

MERCEDES (*Aside*). Poor little thing! She touches me. (*Aloud.*) This man is not worthy of you, Teodora.

TEODORA. But, madam, what is the drift of all this blind emotion? Do not imagine that my eyes are dimmed with fear or horror or tears. They burn with the flame of anger. To whom can such words be addressed? What man do you mean? Is it, perchance——?

MERCEDES. Ernest.

TEODORA. Ah! (*Pause.*) And the woman I? Not so? (MERCEDES *nods and* TEODORA *rises again.*) Then listen to me, though I may offend you. I know not who is the viler, the inventor of this tale or you who repeat it. Shame upon the meanness that formed the idea, and shame upon the villainy that spreads it! It is so abominable, so fatal, that I almost feel myself criminal because I cannot instantly reject the thought and forget it. Heavens! could I suppose or credit such baseness? Because of his misfortunes I loved him. He was like a brother to me, and Julian was his providence. And he so noble and thorough a gentleman! (*Stands staring at* MERCEDES, *then turns away her face. Aside.*) How she inspects me! I scarcely like to say a good word for him to her. My God! I am compelled already to act a part.

MERCEDES. Be calm, child.

TEODORA (*Raising her voice*). Oh, what anguish! I feel cold and inconsolable. Stained in this way by public opinion! Oh, my dearest mother, and you, Julian, my heart's beloved. (*She falls sobbing into a chair on the left, and* MERCEDES *strives to console her.*)

MERCEDES. I did not imagine—forgive me—don't cry. There, I didn't really believe it was serious. I knew your past exonerated you. But as the case stands, you must admit that out of every hundred a hundred would accuse you and Julian of excessive rashness, or say you had led the world to conclude the worst. You a girl of twenty, Julian a man of forty, and Ernest between you, with his head full of romantic thoughts. On the one hand, a husband given up to business, on the other a youth to dreams, every day bringing its opportunity, and you there, unoccupied, in the flush of romance. It was wrong for people to conclude the worst because they saw you walking with him, and saw him so often at the theater with you. But, Teodora, in reason and justice I think that, if the world was bent on seeing evil, you furnished the occasion. Permit me to point out to you that the fault which society most fiercely chastises, pursues most relentlessly and cruelly, and in every varied imaginable way, both in man and woman is—don't frown so, Teodora—is *temerity.*

TEODORA (*Turning to* MERCEDES *without having heard her*). And you say that Julian——

MERCEDES. Is the laughing-stock of the town, and you——

TEODORA. Oh, I! That's no matter. But Julian!—oh, oh, so good, so chivalrous! If he only knew——

MERCEDES. He will know, for at this very moment Severo is telling him.

TEODORA. What!

JULIAN (*Inside*). That will do.

TEODORA. Oh, goodness!

JULIAN. Let me alone.

TEODORA. Come away, quickly.

MERCEDES (*Rushing with* TEODORA *towards first door on the right*). Yes, yes, quickly. What folly! (TEODORA *and* MERCEDES *go to the right.*)

TEODORA (*Stopping suddenly*). But wherefore, since I am not guilty? Not only does miserable calumny stain us, but it degrades us. It is so steeped in evil, that, against all evidence, its very breath takes the bloom off our consciences. Why should an idle terror cast its mean influence over me? (*At this moment* DON JULIAN *appears on the threshold of the first door on the right hand side, and behind him stands* DON SEVERO.)

TEODORA. Julian!

D. JULIAN. Teodora! (*She runs over to*

him, *and he folds her in a passionate embrace.*) Here in my arms, dearest. It is the home of your honor.

SCENE VII

TEODORA, DOÑA MERCEDES, DON JULIAN, *and* DON SEVERO. DON JULIAN *and* DOÑA MERCEDES *form the center group.*

D. JULIAN. Let it pass for this once, but, please God! there's an end of it. Whoever in future shall stain this face with tears (*pointing to Teodora*), I swear, and mean it, will never again cross the threshold of my house—though he should be my own brother. (*Pause.* DON JULIAN *soothes and comforts* TEODORA.)

D. SEVERO. I only mentioned common report.

D. JULIAN. Infamous!

D. SEVERO. It may be so.

D. JULIAN. It is.

D. SEVERO. Well, let me tell you what everyone says.

D. JULIAN. Filth! abominable lies.

D. SEVERO. Then repeating them——

D. JULIAN. 'Tis not the way to put an end to them. (*Pause.*)

D. SEVERO. You are wrong.

D. JULIAN. Right—more than right. A fine thing it would be if I let you carry the mire of the street into my drawing-room!

D. SEVERO. But I will do so.

D. JULIAN. You shall not.

D. SEVERO. You bear my name.

D. JULIAN. Enough.

D. SEVERO. And your honor——

D. JULIAN. Remember that you are in my wife's presence. (*Pause.*)

D. SEVERO (*In a low voice to* DON JULIAN). If our father saw you——

D. JULIAN. What do you mean, Severo?

MERCEDES. Hush! Here is Ernest.

TEODORA (*Aside*). How dreadful! If he should know—— (TEODORA *turns away her face, and holds her head bent.* DON JULIAN *looks at her questioningly.*)

SCENE VIII

TEODORA, DOÑA MERCEDES, DON JULIAN, DON SEVERO, ERNEST *and* PEPITO *grouped from left to right. On entering,* PEPITO *stands on* DON JULIAN'*s side and* ERNEST *walks over to* TEODORA.

ERNEST (*Looking at* DON JULIAN *and* TEODORA. *Aside*). He and she! It is no illusion. Can it be what I feared? what that fool told me. (*Referring to* PEPITO, *who at that moment enters behind.*) It was not his invention.

PEPITO (*Staring strangely about*). My salutations to all, and good appetite—as it is dinner-time. Here are the tickets, Teodora. Don Julian——

TEODORA. Thanks, Pepito. (*Accepts them mechanically.*)

ERNEST (*To* DON JULIAN *in a low voice*). What's the matter with Teodora?

D. JULIAN. Nothing.

ERNEST (*In same tone*). She is pale, and has been crying.

D. JULIAN (*Angrily*). Don't busy yourself about my wife. (*Pause.* DON JULIAN *and* ERNEST *exchange glances.*)

ERNEST (*Aside*). The wretches! They've completed their work.

PEPITO (*In a low voice to his mother, pointing to* ERNEST). He ought to have a strait-jacket. I quizzed him about Teodora. Poof! 'Pon my word, I thought he'd kill me.

ERNEST (*Aloud, with resolution and sadness*). Don Julian, I have thought over your generous offer, and much as I've already abused your kindness, it goes sorely against me to refuse it now. But, sir, I feel that I ought to reject this post you offer me.

D. JULIAN. Why?

ERNEST. Because I am so fashioned,— a poet and a dreamer. My father, sir, trained me for no career. I want to travel; I am restless and liable to revolt. I am not capable of settling down like another. Like a new Columbus, I am bitten by the spirit of adventure. But we will appeal to Don Severo. He will decide if I am right.

D. SEVERO. You speak like the book of wisdom and like a man of sense. I have been thinking as you do for a long while.

D. JULIAN. Since when have you felt this itch for new worlds and travel? When did you make up your mind to leave us? And the means?—where are they?

D. SEVERO. He wants to go away—to some place more to his taste than here. To be just, Julian, the rest is your affair. Give him as much as he wants, too, for this is no time for economy.

ERNEST (*To* DON SEVERO). I don't traffic with dishonor, nor receive alms. (*Pause.*) Well, it must be so; and as our parting would be a sad one—for in this life, who knows? I may never come back, and may not see them again—it is better that we should shake hands now, here, Don Julian, and have it over. Thus we snap the tie, and you forgive my selfishness. (*Deeply moved.*)

D. SEVERO (*Aside*). How they stare at one another!

TEODORA (*Aside*). What a noble fellow!

ERNEST (*To* DON JULIAN). Why do you withhold your hand? It is our last adieu, Don Julian. (*Goes toward him with outstretched hands.* DON JULIAN *embraces him.*)

D. JULIAN. No, lad. The question well considered, this is neither the first nor the last. It is the cordial embrace of two honorable men. You must not mention your mad project again.

D. SEVERO. Then he is not going away?

D. JULIAN. Never. I have not the habit of changing my mind or the plans I have matured because of a boy's caprice or a madman's folly. And I have still less intention of weakly subjecting my actions to the town's idle gossip.

D. SEVERO. Julian!

D. JULIAN. Enough. Dinner is served.

ERNEST. Father, I cannot——

D. JULIAN. But what if I believe you can? Or does my authority begin to bore you?

ERNEST. I beg you——

D. JULIAN. Come, dinner is ready. Give your arm to Teodora, and take her in.

ERNEST (*Looking at her, but holding back*). To Teodora!

TEODORA (*With a similar emotion*). Ernest!

D. JULIAN. Yes, as usual.

(*There is a movement of uncertainty on both sides; finally* ERNEST *approaches and* TEODORA *takes his arm, but neither dares to look at the other, and both are abrupt and violently agitated.*)

D. JULIAN (*To* PEPITO). And you! The deuce, why don't you offer your arm to your mother? My good brother Severo will take mine. So, quite a family party, and now let pleasure flow with the wine in our glasses. So there are gossips about? Well, let them chatter and scream. A farthing for all they can say. I shouldn't object to a glass house, that they might have the pleasure of staring in at Teodora and Ernest together, and learn how little I care for their spite and their calumnies. Each man to his fancy.

(*Enter* SERVANT *in black suit and white tie.*)

SERVANT. Dinner is served.

(*The dining-room door opens and displays a well-appointed table.*)

D. JULIAN. Let us look after our life, since it will be the affair of others to look after our death. Come. (*Invites the others to pass.*)

TEODORA. Mercedes.

MERCEDES. Teodora.

TEODORA. I pray you, Mercedes.

(DOÑA MERCEDES *passes in with* PEPITO *and takes her place at the table.* ERNEST *and* TEODORA *stand plunged in thought*, ERNEST *looking anxiously at her.*)

D. JULIAN (*Aside*). He is looking at her, and there are tears in her eyes. (TEODORA, *walking unsteadily and struggling with emotion, slowly follows the others inside.*)

D. JULIAN (*To* SEVERO). Are they talking together?

D. SEVERO. I don't know, but I think it very probable.

D. JULIAN. Why are they looking back at us? Both! Did you notice? I wonder why.

D. SEVERO. You see, you are growing reasonable at last!

D. JULIAN. No, I've caught your madness. Ah, how sure a thing is calumny! It pierces straight to the heart.

ACT II

Scene represents a small room almost poorly furnished. Door at the end, on the right another door, and on the left a balcony. A book-case, a table, an arm-chair. On the table DON JULIAN'S *portrait in a frame, beside it an empty frame; both small and alike. On the table an unlighted lamp, the "Divina Commedia," open at the Francesca episode, and close to it a morsel of burned paper. Papers scattered about, and the MS. of a play. A few chairs. Time, day.*

SCENE I

Enter DON JULIAN. DON SEVERO *and* SERVANT *below.*

D. SEVERO. Don Ernest is out?

SERVANT. Yes, sir. He went out early.

D. SEVERO. No matter. We'll wait. I suppose he will be in sooner or later.

SERVANT. I should think so. Nobody could be more punctual than he.

D. SEVERO. That will do.

SERVANT. Certainly, sir. If you want anything, you'll find me downstairs. (*Exit* SERVANT.)

SCENE II

DON JULIAN *and* DON SEVERO.

D. SEVERO (*Looking round*). How modest!

D. JULIAN. Poor is a better word.

D. SEVERO. What a lodging! (*Opens the door and peeps in.*) An alcove, this study, and an outer room—and that's all.

D. JULIAN. And thereby hangs the devil's own tale of human ingratitude, of bastard sentiment, of miserable passions, and of blackguard calumny. And whether you tell it quickly or at length, there's never an end to it.

D. SEVERO. It is the work of chance.

D. JULIAN. Not so, my dear fellow. It was the work of—well, I know whom.

D. SEVERO. Meaning me?

D. JULIAN. Yes, you as well. And before you the empty-pated idlers whom it behooved to busy themselves shamelessly about my honor and my wife's. And I, coward, mean, and jealous, I let the poor fellow go, despite my evidence of his upright nature. I responded to his nobler conduct by black ingratitude. Yes, ingratitude. You see my ostentatious wealth, the luxury of my surroundings and equipages, and the credit of my firm. Well, do you know where all that comes from?

D. SEVERO. I have quite forgotten.

D. JULIAN. Justly said,—forgotten! Such is the natural reward of every generous action, of every unusual impulse that prompts one man to help another quietly, without a flourish of trumpet or self-advertisement—just for friendship's or for honesty's sake.

D. SEVERO. You are unjust to yourself.

To such an excess have you pushed gratitude, that you have almost sacrificed honor and fortune to it. What more could be expected—even of a saint? There's a limit to all things, good and evil. He is proud and obstinate, and, however much you may oppose him, 'tis none the less a fact that he's his own master. If he chooses to leave your palace in a fit of despair, for this shanty—'tis his right. I admit, my dear boy, that it's very sad— but then, who could have prevented it?

D. JULIAN. The world in general, if it would mind its own business instead of tearing and rending reputations by the movement of its tongue and the sign of its hand. What did it matter to the public if we, fulfilling a sacred duty, treated Ernest, I as a son, and Teodora as a brother? Is it reason enough to assume the worst, and trumpet scandal because a fine lad sits at my table, walks out with my wife, and has his seat in my opera-box? Is by chance impure love the sole supreme bond between man and woman in this world of clay? Is there no friendship, gratitude, sympathy, esteem, that youth and beauty should only meet in the mire? And even supposing that the conclusion of the fools was the right one, is it their business to avenge me? I have my own eyes to look after my own affairs, and to avenge my wrongs have I not courage, steel, and my own right hand?

D. SEVERO. Well, accepting that outsiders were wrong to talk, did you expect me, who am of your blood and bear your name, to hold my tongue?

D. JULIAN. By heavens, no! But you should have been more careful. You might have told me alone of this sorry business, and not have set flame to a conflagration under my very roof.

D. SEVERO. I erred through excess of affection, I admit. But while I confess that the world and I have done the mischief—it by inventing the situation, and I by weakly crediting, and by giving voice to the shabby innuendoes—you, Julian (*approaches him and speaks with tender interest*), have nothing to reproach yourself with. You have the consolation of having acted throughout as a gentleman.

D. JULIAN. I cannot so easily console myself, while my heart gives shelter to that same story which my lips and my intelligence reject. I indignantly turn away from the world's calumny, and to myself I say: "What if it should be no lie: if perchance the world should be right?" So I stand in strife between two impulses, sometimes judge, sometimes accomplice. This inward battle wears me out, Severo. Doubt increases and expands, and my heart groans, while before my bloodshot vision stretches a reddened field.

D. SEVERO. Delirium!

D. JULIAN. No, 'tis not raving. You see, I bare myself to you as a brother. Think you Ernest would have left my house if I had firmly stood in his way and opposed his crossing the threshold? If so, why does a traitorous voice keep muttering in my disturbed consciousness: " 'twere wise to leave the door open to his exit, and lock it well afterwards, for the confiding man is but a poor guardian of honor's fortress." In my heart I wish what my lips deny. "Come back, Ernest," aloud, and to myself "do not come back," and while I show him a frank front, I am a hypocrite and a coward, watchful and worn with mistrust. No, Severo, this is not to act like an honest man. (*He drops into the arm-chair beside the table in deep dejection.*)

D. SEVERO. It is how any husband would act who had a beautiful young wife to look after, especially one with a romantic temperament.

D. JULIAN. Don't speak so of Teodora. She is a mirror that our breath tarnishes by any imprudent effort to bring it to our level. It gave back the sun's pure light before the million vipers of the earth gathered to stare at it. Today they crawl

within the glass in its divine frame, but they are insubstantial shadows. My hand can wave them away, and once more you will see the clear blue of heaven.

D. SEVERO. All the better.

D. JULIAN. No, not so.

D. SEVERO. Then what the deuce do you want?

D. JULIAN. Oh, so much. I told you that this inward struggle of which I spoke is changing me to another man. Now my wife finds me always sad, always distant. I am not the man I was, and no effort will ever make me so again. Seeing me so changed, she must ask, "Where is Julian? this is not my dear husband; what have I done to forfeit his confidence, and what shabby feeling causes this aloofness?" a shadow lies between us, ever deepening, and slowly, step by step, we move more apart. None of the old dear confidence, none of the old delightful talks; smiles frozen, tones embittered, in me through unjust resentment, in her through tearful grief,—I wounded in my love, and she, by my hand, wounded in her woman's dignity. There's how we stand.

D. SEVERO. Then you stand upon the verge of perdition. If you see your position so plainly, why don't you remedy it?

D. JULIAN. 'Tis of no use. I know I am unjust to doubt her, nay, worse still. I don't doubt her now. But who will say that, I losing little by little, and he gaining as steadily, the lie of today will not tomorrow be truth? (*He seizes* DON SEVERO *by the arm, and speaks with voluble earnestness and increasing bitterness.*) I, jealous, somber, unjust and hard, he noble and generous, resigned and inalterably sweet-natured, with that halo of martyrdom which, in the eyes of women, sits so becomingly on the brow of a brave and handsome youth. Is it not clear that his is the better part, and that my loss is his gain? while I can do nothing to alter the injustice of it. You see it, too? And if the ignoble talk of the town should compel those two to treason, though they may now truthfully assert: "we are not lovers," the force of repetition of the word may eventually drive them to the fact.

D. SEVERO. If that's how you feel about it, Julian, I think the safest thing would be to let Ernest carry out his project.

D. JULIAN. That I've come to prevent.

D. SEVERO. Then you are insane. He purposes to go to Buenos Aires. Nothing could be better. Let him go—in a sailing vessel, fresh wind to his sail, and good speed.

D. JULIAN. Do you wish me to show myself so miserably ungrateful and jealous before Teodora? Don't you know, Severo, that a woman may despise a lover and love him still, but not so a husband? Contempt is his dishonor. You would not have my wife follow the unhappy exile across the ocean with sad regrets? And I, should I see the trace of a tear upon her cheek, the mere thought that it might be for Ernest would drive me to strangle her in my arms. (*Speaks with rancor and rage.*)

D. SEVERO. What is it then you do want?

D. JULIAN. I must suffer. The care of unraveling the knot belongs to the world that conceived the drama solely by looking at us,—so fertile is its glance for good and ill.

D. SEVERO (*Moving back*). I think somebody is coming.

SERVANT (*From without, not seen on the stage*). Don Ernest cannot be much later. (*Enter* PEPITO.)

SCENE III

DON JULIAN, DON SEVERO, *and* PEPITO.

D. SEVERO. You here?

PEPITO (*Aside*). By Jove, I see they know all about it. (*Aloud.*) We are all here. How do you do, uncle? How do, father? (*Aside.*) Easy. They know what's

in the wind. (*Aloud.*) What brings you? —but I suppose you are looking for Ernest.

D. SEVERO. What else could bring us here?

D. JULIAN. I daresay you know what this madman is up to?

PEPITO. What he's up to! Well, yes— rather. I know as much as another.

D. SEVERO. And it's tomorrow?

PEPITO. No, tomorrow he is going away, so it must be today.

D. JULIAN (*Surprised*). What do you say?

PEPITO. That's what Pepe Uceda told me last night at the club. He is Nebreda's second, so he ought to know. But why do you stare so oddly? Didn't you know——

D. JULIAN (*Hastily covering his brother's movement*). Everything.

D. SEVERO. We——

D. JULIAN (*Aside*). Hold your tongue, Severo.— He starts tomorrow, and today he stakes his life—and we are here, of course, to prevent both, the duel and the departure. (DON JULIAN *makes it evident that he is only sounding* PEPITO's *knowledge of facts, and that he is only aware of the pending departure.*)

D. SEVERO. What duel?

D. JULIAN (*Aside to* SEVERO). I know nothing about it, but I shall presently.

PEPITO (*Aside*). Come, I haven't been such a duffer after all.

D. JULIAN (*Speaking with an air of certainty*). We know there is a viscount——

PEPITO. Yes.

D. JULIAN. With whom Ernest proposes to fight—a certain trustworthy person has informed us, who was at once apprised of it. They say 'tis a serious matter (PEPITO *nods*), a disgraceful quarrel in the presence of several witnesses (PEPITO *nods again*)—the lie direct, and a deluge of bad language——

PEPITO (*Interrupts excitedly, glad of his more accurate information*). Language indeed!—a blow bigger than a monument.

D. SEVERO. On which side?

PEPITO. Ernest struck the viscount.

D. JULIAN. Of course Ernest struck the viscount. I thought you knew that, Severo. The viscount insulted him. Patience is not the lad's strong point—hence the blow.

PEPITO. Exactly.

D. JULIAN (*Confidently*). I told you we knew the whole story. (*Then anxiously.*) The affair is serious?

PEPITO. Most serious. I don't like discussing it, but since you know so much, there is no need for further mystery.

D. JULIAN. None whatever. (*He approaches* PEPITO *eagerly.*)

PEPITO (*After a pause, adopts an ominous air to announce bad news*). It is a matter of life and death. (*Looks round triumphantly.* DON JULIAN *and* DON SEVERO *start.*) The viscount is neither a chicken nor a skulk. He can handle a sword.

D. JULIAN. And the quarrel? What was it? Nebreda is supposed to be——

PEPITO. It was hardly a quarrel. I'll tell you the facts. (*Both men draw near eagerly.*) Ernest, you know, means to leave Madrid tomorrow, and take passage in the *Cid* lying in Cadiz. Luiz Alcaráz had promised him a letter of introduction, and the poor fellow went off to meet him at the *café* and get it, with the best of intentions. Luiz wasn't there, so he waited. Some of the frequenters of Alcaráz's table, who did not know him, were in the full swing of glorious slander, and did not notice his clenched teeth. A name mentioned meant a reputation blasted. Broad-handed, ready-tongued, every living soul passed in their review. In this asylum of charity, in the middle of more smoke than an express train emits, between lifted glass and dropped cigarette ashes, with here and there a lump of sugar, the marble was

converted for the nonce into a dissecting-table: each woman dishonored, another glass of the old tap: a shout of laughter for each tippler's cut. In four clippings these lads left reputations ragged and the ladies rent to tatters. Yet what did it all come to? They but echoed society at a *café*-table. I don't say all this for myself, nor think it, but 'twas how Ernest spoke when he recounted the quarrel to me.

D. JULIAN. Well, make an end of it.

PEPITO. The end of it is, that between name and name, there was mention of one that Ernest could not endure. "Who dares to ridicule an honorable man?" he shouts. Somebody retorts: "a lady," and names a woman. His head was instantly on fire, and he flings himself upon Nebreda. The poor viscount fell like a ninepin, and there you have an Agramante's camp. The day's business is now a duel—in a room somewhere—I don't know where.

D. JULIAN (*Seizing his arms*). The man was I!

PEPITO. Sir?

D. JULIAN. And Teodora the woman? How have we fallen—she, myself, our love? (*Sits down and covers his face with both hands.*)

SEVERO. What have you done, you blockhead!

PEPITO. Didn't he say he knew all about it? and I naturally believed him.

D. JULIAN. Dishonored, dishonored!

SEVERO (*Approaching him*). Julian, my dear fellow.

D. JULIAN. It is true. I ought to be calm, I know. But what heart can I have when faith is gone? (*Seizes his brother's hand.*) Just heaven! Why are we so disgraced? What reason have they to turn and throw mud at us? No matter. I know my duty as a gentleman. I can count on you, Severo?

SEVERO. On me? Till death, Julian. (*They shake hands cordially.*)

JULIAN (*To* PEPITO). The duel?

PEPITO. For three o'clock.

JULIAN (*Aside*). I'll kill him—yes, kill him. Come. (*To* SEVERO.)

SEVERO. Whither?

D. JULIAN. To look for this viscount.

SEVERO. Do you mean———?

D. JULIAN. I mean to do what I ought and can to avenge myself and save Don Juan of Acedo's son. Who are the seconds? (*To* PEPITO.)

PEPITO. Alcaráz and Rueda.

D. JULIAN. I know them both. Let him stay here (*pointing to* PEPITO), so that in the event of Ernest's return———

SEVERO. Of course.

D. JULIAN (*To* PEPITO). Without arousing his suspicion, find out where the duel takes place.

SEVERO. You hear.

D. JULIAN (*To his brother*). Come.

SEVERO. What's the matter with you. Julian?

D. JULIAN. 'Tis a long while since I've felt so overjoyed. (*Catches* SEVERO's *arm feverishly*.)

SEVERO. The deuce! overjoyed! You're beside yourself.

D. JULIAN. I shall meet that fellow.

SEVERO. Nebreda?

D. JULIAN. Yes. Observe, until today calumny was impalpable. There was no seizing its shape. I have now discovered it, and it has taken a human form. There it is at hand, in the person of a viscount. Swallowing blood and gall for the past three months—the devil!—and now—fancy, face to face—he and I! (*Exeunt* DON JULIAN *and* DON SEVERO.)

SCENE IV

PEPITO. Well, here we are in a nice fix, and all for nothing! However, in spite of my uncle's belief, it was little short of madness to leave a resplendent creature under the same roof and in continual contact with a handsome fellow like Ernest, with a soul on fire, or given to romanticism. He swears there's nothing in it, and that his feeling for her is pure affection, that he loves her like a sister, and that my uncle is a father to him. But I am a sly fox, and, young as I am, I know a thing or two of this world. I've no faith in this sort of relations, when the brother is young and the sister is beautiful, and brotherhood between them a fiction. But suppose it were as he says, all square. What do outsiders know about that? Nobody is under any obligation to think the best of his fellows. The pair are seen everywhere together, and, seeing them, haven't their neighbors a right to talk? No, swears Ernest. *We hardly ever went out alone.* Once, perhaps? That's enough. If a hundred persons saw them on that occasion, it is quite the same as if they had been seen in public a hundred times. Good Lord! How are you going to confront all the witnesses to prove whether it was once or often they chose to give an airing to this pure sympathy and brotherly love? 'Tis absurd—neither just nor reasonable. What we see we may mention—'tis no lie to say it. "I saw them once," says one, "and I," another. One and one make two. "And I also"—that makes three. And then a fourth, and a fifth, and so, summing which, you soon enough reach infinity. We see because we look, and our senses are there to help us to pass the time, without any thought of our neighbor. He must look out for himself, and remember that, if he shuns the occasion, calumny and peril will shun him. (*Pause.*) And take notice that I admit the purity of the affection, and this makes it so serious a matter. Now, in my opinion, the man who could be near Teodora, and not fall in love with her, must be a stone. He may be learned and philosophical, and know physics and mathematics, but he has a body like another, and she's there with a divine one, and, body of Bacchus! that's sufficient to found an accusation on. Ah! if these walls could speak. If Ernest's private thoughts, scattered here, could take tangible form! By Jove! what's this? An empty frame, and beside it Don Julian's likeness in its fellow. Teodora was there, the pendant of my respected uncle. Why has she disappeared? To avoid temptation? (*Sits down at the table.*) If that's the reason—it's bad. And still worse if the portrait has left its frame for a more honorable place near his heart. Come forth, suspected imps that float about, and weave invisible meshes. Ruthlessly denounce this mystic philosopher. (*Looks about the table and sees the open Dante.*) Here's another. I never come here but I find this divine book open on Ernest's table. The Divine Comedy! His favorite poem, and I note that he seems never to get beyond the Francesca page. I conceive two explanations of the fact. Either the fellow never reads it, or he never reads any other. But there's a stain, like a tear-drop. My faith! what mysteries and abysses! And what a difficult thing it is to be married and live tranquilly. A paper half burned—(*picks it up*)—there's still a morsel left. (*Goes over to the balcony trying to read it. At this moment* ERNEST *enters, and stands watching him.*)

SCENE V

PEPITO *and* ERNEST.

ERNEST. What are you looking at?

PEPITO. Hulloa! Ernest. Only a paper I caught on the wing. The wind blew it away.

ERNEST (*Takes it and returns it after a short inspection*). I don't remember what it is.

PEPITO. Verses. You may remember (*reads with difficulty*) "The flame that consumes me." (*Aside.*) Devora rhymes with Teodora.

ERNEST. It is nothing important.

PEPITO. No, nothing. (*Throws away the paper.*)

ERNEST. That worthless bit of paper is

a symbol of our life—a few sobs of sorrow, and a little flake of ashes.

PEPITO. Then they were verses?

ERNEST. Yes. When I've nothing better to do, sometimes—my pen runs away with me—I write them at night.

PEPITO. And to prick enthusiasm, and get into harness, you seek inspiration in the master's book.

ERNEST. It would seem——

PEPITO. Say no more. 'Tis truly a gigantic work. The episode of Francesca. (*Pointing to the page.*)

ERNEST (*Ironically and impatiently*). You can't guess wrong today.

PEPITO. Not entirely, by Jove. Here, where the book is open, I find something I can't guess, and you must explain it to me. Reading a love-tale together to pass the time, we are told that Francesca and Paolo reached that part where the gallant author, proving himself no amateur in the business, sings the loves of Launcelot and Queen Guinevere. The match fell pat. The kiss in the book was repeated by the passionate youth on the girl's mouth. And at this point of the story, with rare skill and sublime truth, the Florentine poet tells us what happens. (*Points to the line.*) But this is what I do not understand. *Galeoto was the book they were reading, and they read no more.* They stopped reading? That's easy enough to understand. But this Galeoto, tell me where he comes in, and who was he? You ought to know, since he has given his name to the play that is to make you famous. Let me see. (*Takes up the MS. and examines it.*)

ERNEST. Galeoto was the go-between for the Queen and Launcelot and in all loves the *third* may be truthfully nick-named Galeoto, above all when we wish to suggest an ugly word without shocking an audience.

PEPITO. I see, but have we no Spanish word to express it?

ERNEST. We have one, quite suitable

and expressive enough. 'Tis an office that converts desires into ducats, overcomes scruples, and is fed upon the affections. It has a name, but to use it would be putting a fetter upon myself, forcing myself to express what, after all, I would leave unsaid. (*Takes the MS. from* PEPITO *and flings it upon the table.*) Each especial case, I have remarked, has its own especial go-between. Sometimes it is the entire social mass that is Galeoto. It then unconsciously exercises the office under the influence of a vice of quite another aspect, but so dexterously does it work against honor and modesty that no greater Galeoto can ever be found. Let a man and woman live happily, in tranquil and earnest fulfillment of their separate duties. Nobody minds them, and they float along at ease. But God be praised, this is a state of things that does not last long in Madrid. One morning somebody takes the trouble to notice them, and from that moment, behold society engaged in the business, without aim or object, on the hunt for hidden frailty and impurity. Then it pronounces and judges, and there is no logic that can convince it, nor living man who can hope to persuade it, and the honestest has not a rag of honor left. And the terrible thing is, that while it begins in error it generally ends in truth. The atmosphere is so dense, misery so envelops the pair, such is the press and torrent of slander, that they unconsciously seek one another, unite lovelessly, drift toward their fall, and adore each other until death. The world was the stumbling-stone of virtue, and made clear the way for shame—was Galeoto and—(*aside*) stay! what mad thought inflames me!

PEPITO (*Aside*). If that's the way he discourses to Teodora, heaven help poor Don Julian. (*Aloud.*) I suppose last night's verses dealt with the subject.

ERNEST. Yes, they did.

PEPITO. How can you waste your time so coolly, and sit there so calm, doing nothing, when in another hour you will be measuring swords with Nebreda, who, for all his dandy's cane, is a man when put upon his mettle? Wouldn't it be saner and wiser to practice fencing instead of expounding questions of verse and rhyme? You look so mighty cool that I almost doubt if you regard your meeting with the viscount as serious.

ERNEST. No,—for a good reason. If I kill him, the world gains; if he kills me, I gain.

PEPITO. Well, that's good.

ERNEST. Don't say any more about it.

PEPITO (*Aside*). Now I must warily find out. (*Approaches him and speaks in a low voice.*) Is it for today?

ERNEST. Yes, today.

PEPITO. Outside the town?

ERNEST. No, there's no time for that. Besides, we wish to keep it quiet.

PEPITO. In a house, then?

ERNEST. So I proposed.

PEPITO. Where?

ERNEST. Upstairs. (*Speaks with cold indifference.*) There's a room unlet upstairs, with a side window, through which nobody can look. Under the circumstances it's better than a field, and will be had for a handful of silver.

PEPITO. And now all you need——

ERNEST. The swords!

PEPITO. I hear voices outside. Somebody is coming—the seconds?

ERNEST. May be.

PEPITO. It sounds like a woman's voice. (*Approaches the door.*)

ERNEST (*Approaching also*). But who's keeping them?

SCENE VI

ERNEST, PEPITO, *and* SERVANT.

SERVANT (*Mysteriously*). Somebody wants to see you, sir.

ERNEST. Who?

SERVANT. A lady.

ERNEST. How extraordinary!

PEPITO (*Aside to servant*). What does she want?

SERVANT (*To* PEPITO). She is crying.

PEPITO (*Aloud*). Is she young?

SERVANT. Really, sir, I can't say. It's very dark outside, and the lady's face is so thickly veiled that the devil himself couldn't tell what she's like, and she speaks so low you can't even hear her.

ERNEST. Who can she be?

PEPITO. Who could want to see you?

ERNEST. I cannot think.

PEPITO (*Aside*). This is startling. (*Takes up his hat and holds out his hand.*) Well, I'll leave you in peace. Goodbye and good luck. (*To the servant.*) What are you waiting for, you booby?

SERVANT. For orders to show the lady in.

PEPITO. In such a case 'tis your business to anticipate them. And afterwards, until the veiled one has departed, you mustn't let any one in unless the sky were falling.

SERVANT. Then I am to show her in?

ERNEST. Yes. (*To* PEPITO *at the door.*) Goodbye.

PEPITO. Goodbye, Ernest. (*Exeunt* SERVANT *and* PEPITO.)

ERNEST. A lady? on what pretext? What does this mean? (*Enter* TEODORA, *thickly veiled; she stands without approaching.*) Ah, there she is!

SCENE VII

TEODORA *and* ERNEST, *she behind not daring to advance, he turned toward her.*

ERNEST. You desire to speak to me, madam? Kindly be seated. (*Offers her a chair.*)

TEODORA (*Unveiling*). Forgive me, Ernest.

ERNEST. Teodora!

TEODORA. I am wrong to come—am I not?

ERNEST (*Abruptly and stammering*). I can't say—since I don't know to what I

owe this honor. But what am I saying? Alas! Here, in my rooms, madam, reverence attends you, than which you cannot find a greater (*with devotion*). But what wrong can you possibly fear here, lady?

TEODORA. None—and there was a time —but that *once* is forever past. No thought of doubt or fear was then. I might have crossed any room on your arm without blush or fluttering pulse. But now! They tell me that you are starting for America tomorrow—and I—yes— like those who go away—perhaps not to return—it is so sad to lose a friend!—be- fore Julian—before the whole world— thinking only of our affection—I myself, Ernest, would have held out my arms to you—in farewell.

ERNEST (*Starts and quickly restrains himself*). Oh, Teodora!

TEODORA. But now I suppose it is not the same thing. There is a gulf between us.

ERNEST. You are right, madam. We may no longer care for one another, be no longer brother and sister. The mutual touch of palm would leave our hands un- clean. 'Tis all forever past. What we have now to learn is to hate one another.

TEODORA (*In a naïve consternation*). Hate! surely not!

ERNEST. Have I used that word—and to you! poor child!

TEODORA. Yes.

ERNEST. Don't heed me. If you needed my life, and the occasion offered itself, claim it, Teodora, for, to give my life for you would be—— (*with passion*) it would be my duty. (*With a sudden change of voice. Pause.*) Hate! if my lips pronounced the word, I was thinking of the misery,—I was thinking of the injury I have unwittingly wrought one to whom I owe so much. Yes, you, Teodora, must hate me—but I—ah, no!

TEODORA (*Sadly*). They have made me shed tears enough; yes, you are right in that, Ernest (*with tenderness*), but you I

[233]

do not accuse. Who could condemn or blame you for all this talk? You have nothing to do with the venomous solicitude with which evil minds honor us, nor with poor Julian's clouded temper. It is sorrow that makes him restive, and his suffering wounds me, for I know that it springs from doubt of my devotion.

ERNEST. That is what I cannot understand (*angrily*), and in him less than in another. It is what drives me wild: by the living God, I protest it is not worthy of pity, and there is no excuse for it. That the man should exist who could doubt a woman like you!

TEODORA. Poor fellow, he pays a heavy price for his savage distrust.

ERNEST (*Horrified to find he has been blaming* DON JULIAN *to* TEODORA). What have I said? I don't accuse him—no—I meant——(*He hastens to exculpate* DON JULIAN *and modify his former words.*) Anybody might feel the same, that is, if he were very much in love. In our earthly egoism, don't we doubt the very God in heaven? And the owner of a treasure jealously watches it as gold, and cannot but fear for it. I, too, in his place, would be full of doubt,—yes—even of my own brother. (*Speaks with increasing fervor, and again restrains himself, perceiving that he is on the brink of a peril he would avoid.* TEODORA *hears voices outside and rushes to the door.*)

ERNEST. Whither are you leading me, rebel heart? What depth have I stirred? I accuse the world of calumny, and would now prove it right.

TEODORA. Do you hear? Somebody is coming.

ERNEST (*Following her*). It is hardly two o'clock. Can it be——?

TEODORA (*With terror*). It is Julian's voice.— He is coming in!

ERNEST. No, they have prevented him.

TEODORA (*Turns to* ERNEST, *still frightened*). If it were Julian? (*Moves towards the bedroom door.* ERNEST *detains her respectfully.*)

ERNEST. Should it be he, stay here. Loyalty is our shield. Were it one of those who distrust us—then there, Teodora. (*Points to the door.*) Ah, nobody. (*Listening.*)

TEODORA. How my heart throbs!

ERNEST. You need not be afraid. The person who wanted to come in has gone away—or it was an illusion. For God's sake, Teodora——! (*Advances up the stage.*)

TEODORA. I had so much to say to you, Ernest, and the time has passed so quickly.

ERNEST. The time has flown.

TEODORA. I wanted——

ERNEST. Teodora, pray forgive me—but is it prudent? If anyone came in—and, indeed, I fear someone will.

TEODORA. That is why I came—to prevent it.

ERNEST. So that——?

TEODORA. I know everything, and I am stricken with horror at the thought that blood should be shed on my account. My head is on fire, my heart is bursting. (*Strikes her breast.*)

ERNEST. It is the affront that burns and shames you until my hand has struck at Nebreda's life. He wanted mud! Well, let him have it stained with blood.

TEODORA. You would kill him?

ERNEST. Certainly. (*Represses* TEODORA'S *movement of supplication.*) You can dispose of me in all else but in this one thing. Do not ask me to feel compassion for a man whose insult I remember.

TEODORA (*Prayerfully, with a sob*). For my sake!

ERNEST. For your sake?

TEODORA. It would be such a horrible scandal.

ERNEST. That is possible.

TEODORA. You can say it so coolly, and not endeavor to avoid it, not even when it is I who implore you!

ERNEST. I cannot avoid it, but I can chastise it: so I think and say, and this is my business. Others will look for the insult, I for the punishment.

TEODORA (*Coming nearer and speaking softly, as if afraid of her own voice*). And Julian?

ERNEST. Well?

TEODORA. If he were to know about it?

ERNEST. He will know about it.

TEODORA. What will he say?

ERNEST. What?

TEODORA. That only my husband, the man who loves me, has a right to defend me.

ERNEST. Every honorable man has the right to defend a lady. He may not even know her, be neither a friend, nor a relative, nor a lover. It is enough for him to hear a woman insulted. Why do I fight this duel? Why do I defend her? Because I heard the calumny. Because I am myself. Who is so base as to give his protection by scale and measure? Was I not there? Then whoever it was—I or another—who was first on the scene——

TEODORA (*Listens eagerly, dominated by him, and holds out her hand to him*). This is noble and honorable, and worthy of you, Ernest (*then restrains herself and moves backward*). But it leaves Julian humiliated (*with conviction*).

ERNEST. He? humiliated!

TEODORA. Most surely.

ERNEST. Why?

TEODORA. For no reason whatever.

ERNEST. Who will say so?

TEODORA. Everybody.

ERNEST. But wherefore?

TEODORA. When the world hears of the affront, and learns that it was not my husband who avenged me, and above all (*drops her eyes ashamed*) that it was you

who took his place—have we not then a new scandal topping the old?

ERNEST (*Convinced but protests*). If one had always to think of what people will say, by Heaven there would be no manner or means of living then!

TEODORA. It is so, nevertheless.

ERNEST. Just so. 'Tis horrible.

TEODORA. Then yield.

ERNEST. Impossible.

TEODORA. I beseech you.

ERNEST. No. Looking into the matter, as nobody can know what will happen, it is better that I should face Nebreda. For, after all, if the fellow lack a sense of honor, he can use a sword.

TEODORA (*Wounded and humiliated in the protection* ERNEST *seems to offer* DON JULIAN). My husband is not lacking in courage.

ERNEST. Fatality again! Either I have expressed myself ill, or you do not understand me. I know his worth. But when a desperate injury lies between men of courage, who knows what may happen? which of them may fall, and which may kill? And if this man's sword must strike Don Julian or Ernest, can you doubt which it ought to be? (*Questions her with sad sincerity.*)

TEODORA (*In anguish*). You!—oh, no —not that either.

ERNEST. Why? If it is my fate? Nobody loses by my death, and I lose still less.

TEODORA. For Heaven's sake, do not say that! (*Barely able to repress her sobs.*)

ERNEST. What do I leave behind me? Neither friendship nor strong love. What woman is there to follow my corpse shedding a lover's tears?

TEODORA. Last night I prayed for you —and you say that nobody—— I could not bear you to die. (*Vehemently.*)

ERNEST. Ah, we pray for any one; we only weep for one. (*With passion.*)

TEODORA (*Startled*). Ernest!

ERNEST (*Terrified by his own words*). What!

TEODORA (*Moving further away*). Nothing.

ERNEST (*Also moving away and looking nervously down*). I told you a little while ago I was half mad. Do not heed me. (*Pause. Both remain silent and pensive, at some distance, not looking at each other.*)

TEODORA (*Starting and glancing anxiously down the stage*). Again!

ERNEST (*Following her movement*). Somebody has come.

TEODORA. They are trying to get in.

ERNEST (*Listening*). There can be no doubt of it. There, Teodora. (*Points to the bedroom door.*)

TEODORA. My honor is my shield.

ERNEST. But it is not your husband.

TEODORA. Not Julian?

ERNEST (*Leading her to the door*). No.

TEODORA. I hoped—— (*Detains him with an air of supplication.*) Will you give up this duel?

ERNEST. Give it up? When I've struck him!

TEODORA. I didn't know that. (*Despairingly, but understands that nothing can be done.*) Then fly.

ERNEST. I fly!

TEODORA. For my sake, for his sake—for God's sake!

ERNEST (*Despairingly*). You must loathe me to propose such a thing to me. Never!

TEODORA. One word only. Are they coming for you now?

ERNEST. It is not yet time.

TEODORA. Swear it to me.

ERNEST. Yes, Teodora. And you—say you don't hate me.

TEODORA. Never.

PEPITO (*Outside*). Nothing. I must see him.

ERNEST. Quickly.

TEODORA. Yes. (*Hides in the bedroom.*)

PEPITO. Why do you prevent me?

ERNEST. Ah, calumny is working to make the lie truth.

SCENE VIII

ERNEST *and* PEPITO, *without his hat, exhibiting strong excitement.*

PEPITO. Go to the devil—I will go in—Ernest.

ERNEST. What has happened?

PEPITO. I hardly know how to tell you—yet I must——

ERNEST. Speak.

PEPITO. My head is in a whirl. Christ above, who would think——

ERNEST. Quickly. A clear account of what has happened.

PEPITO. What has happened? A great misfortune. Don Julian heard of the duel. He came here to look for you, and you were out. He went away to find the seconds, and marched them off to Nebreda's house.

ERNEST. Nebreda's! How?

PEPITO. The Lord send you sense. Don Julian's way, of course, who makes short work of convention and the will of others.

ERNEST. Go on——

PEPITO (*Going to the door*). They're coming, I believe.

ERNEST. Who?

PEPITO. They—they're carrying Don Julian.

ERNEST. You terrify me. Explain at once. (*Catches his arm violently, and drags him forward.*)

PEPITO. He compelled him to fight. There was no way out of it. The viscount cried: "Very well, between us two." It was settled it should take place here. Don Julian came upstairs. Your servant sent him away, protesting you were engaged with a lady, and swearing nobody could enter.

ERNEST. And then?

PEPITO. Don Julian went downstairs muttering "better so. I have the day's work for myself." And he, my father, Nebreda and the seconds came back together, and went upstairs.

ERNEST. They fought?

PEPITO. Furiously, as men fight when their intent is deadly, and their enemy's heart is within reach of the sword's point.

ERNEST. And Don Julian! No—it must be a lie.

PEPITO. Here they are.

ERNEST. Silence. Tell me who it is, but speak softly.

PEPITO. There. (*Enter* DON JULIAN, DON SEVERO, *and* RUEDA. *The two men support* DON JULIAN, *who is badly wounded.*)

ERNEST. Heaven preserve us!

SCENE IX

ERNEST, PEPITO, DON JULIAN, DON SEVERO, *and* RUEDA.

ERNEST. Don Julian! my friend, my father, my benefactor! (*Hurries excitedly toward him, and speaks brokenly.*)

D. JULIAN (*Weakly*). Ernest!

ERNEST. Oh, wretched I!

SEVERO. Quick, come away.

ERNEST. Father!

SEVERO. He is fainting with pain.

ERNEST. For my sake!

JULIAN. It is not so.

ERNEST. Through me—pardon! (*Takes* DON JULIAN'*s hand and bends on one knee before him.*)

JULIAN. No need to ask it, lad. You did your duty, and I did mine.

SEVERO. A couch. (*Loosens his hold of* DON JULIAN, *and* PEPITO *takes his place.*)

PEPITO (*Pointing to the bedroom*). Let us carry him in there.

ERNEST (*Shouting terribly*). Nebreda!

SEVERO. Let there be an end to folly. Is it your intention to kill him outright?

ERNEST (*With frenzy*). Folly, oh, we'll

see. I have two to avenge now. It is my right. (*Rushes down the stage.*)

SEVERO (*Moving to the right*). We'll take him into your room and lay him on the bed. (*Ernest wheels round in terror.*)

ERNEST. Where?

SEVERO. In here.

PEPITO. Yes.

ERNEST. No. (*Strides back, and stands before the door. The group are on the point of lifting* DON JULIAN, *desist, and stare at* ERNEST *in indignant surprise.*)

SEVERO. You forbid it?

PEPITO. Are you mad?

SEVERO. Back: can't you see he is dying?

D. JULIAN. What is it? He doesn't wish it? (*Raises himself and looks at* ERNEST *in distrust and fear.*)

RUEDA. I don't understand it.

PEPITO. Nor I.

ERNEST. He is dying—and implores me—and doubts me—father!

SEVERO. Come, we must. (*Pushes open the door above* ERNEST'*s shoulder.* TEODORA *is discovered.*)

ERNEST. My God!

SEVERO and PEPITO. She!

RUEDA. A woman!

TEODORA (*Coming forward to her husband and embracing him*). Julian!

D. JULIAN. Who is it? (*Pushes her away to stare at her, drags himself to his feet with a violent effort, and shakes himself free of all aid.*) Teodora! (*Falls lifeless to the ground.*)

ACT III

The same decoration as first act: an arm-chair instead of a sofa. It is night; a lighted lamp stands on the table.

SCENE I

PEPITO *listening at the door on the right, then comes back into the middle of the stage.*

PEPITO. The crisis is past at last. I hear nothing. Poor Don Julian! He's in a sad way. His life hangs in the balance: on one side death awaits him, and on the other another death, that of the soul, of honor—either abyss deeper than hopeless love. The devil! All this tragedy is making me more sentimental than that fellow with his plays and verses. The tune of disaster, scandal, death, treason, and disgrace, hums in my brain. By Jove, what a day, and what a night! and the worst is yet to come. Well, it certainly was madness to move him in his condition; but when once my uncle gets an idea into his head, there's no reasoning with him. And, after all, he was right. No honorable man, in his place, could have stayed, and he is a man of spirit. Who is coming? my mother, I believe—yes. (*Enter* DOÑA MERCEDES.)

SCENE II

PEPITO *and* DOÑA MERCEDES.

MERCEDES. Where's Severo?

PEPITO. He has not left my uncle for a moment. I had no idea he was so attached to him. If what I fear should happen——

MERCEDES. How is your uncle?

PEPITO. He suffers greatly, but says nothing. Sometimes he calls out "Teodora" in a low harsh voice, and sometimes "Ernest"; and then he tugs violently at the sheets, and lies quiet again as a statue, staring vacantly into space. Now his brow is bathed in the cold sweat of death, and then fever seizes him. He sits up in bed, listens attentively, and shouts that *he* and *she* are waiting for him. He tries to jump out of bed to rush at them, and all my father's entreaties and commands barely suffice to restrain him or soothe him. There's no quieting him. Anger races hot through his veins, and thought is a flame. It is shocking, mother, to see the bitter way his lips contract, and how his fingers close in a vise, with head all wild, and pupils dilated as though they drank in with yearning and despair every shadow that floats around the chamber.

MERCEDES. How does your father bear it?

PEPITO. He groans and breathes of vengeance. He, too, mutters the names of Teodora and Ernest. I hope to God he will not meet either, for if he should, small chance there is of restraining his fury.

MERCEDES. Your father is a good man.

PEPITO. Yes, but with a temper——

MERCEDES. It is not easily aroused, however. But when he has cause——

PEPITO. With all due respect, he's then a very tiger.

MERCEDES. Only when provoked.

PEPITO. I don't know about other occasions, but this time he certainly has provocation enough. And Teodora?

MERCEDES. She is upstairs. She wanted to come down—and cried—like a Magdalen.

PEPITO. Already! Repentant or erring?

MERCEDES. Don't speak so. Unhappy girl, she is but a child.

PEPITO. Who, innocent and candid, sweet and pure and meek, kills Don Julian. So that, if I am to accept your word, and regard her as a child, and such is her work on the edge of infancy, we may pray God in his mercy to guard us from her when she shall have put on years.

MERCEDES. She is hardly to be blamed. The infamy lies with your fine friend—he of the dramas, the poet and dreamer. He it is who is the culprit.

PEPITO. I don't deny it.

MERCEDES. Where is he?

PEPITO. Where is he? At this moment racing about the streets and public places, flying from his conscience, and unable to get away from it.

MERCEDES. He has a conscience?

PEPITO. So it would seem.

MERCEDES. Oh, what a tragedy!

PEPITO. A misfortune!

MERCEDES. Such a deception!

PEPITO. A cruel one.

MERCEDES. What shocking treason!

PEPITO. Unparalleled.

MERCEDES. Poor Julian!

PEPITO. Melancholy fate! (*Enter* SERVANT.)

SCENE III

DOÑA MERCEDES, PEPITO, *and* SERVANT.

SERVANT. Don Ernest.

MERCEDES. He dares——

PEPITO. This is too much.

SERVANT. I thought——

PEPITO. You had no business to think anything.

SERVANT. He is only passing. There is a cab waiting, so——

PEPITO. What are we to do?

MERCEDES. Let him come in. (*Exit* SERVANT.)

PEPITO. I'll give him his dismissal.

MERCEDES. Do it cleverly.

SCENE IV

DOÑA MERCEDES, PEPITO, *and* ERNEST. DOÑA MERCEDES *seated in the arm-chair,* PEPITO *standing, and* ERNEST *behind, whom neither salute nor look at.*

ERNEST (*Aside*). Hostile silence, anger, and contempt. Through no fault of my own, I now appear to them a prodigy of evil and insolence, and they all despise me.

PEPITO. Listen to me, Ernest. (*Turns round to him and speaks in a hard voice.*)

ERNEST. Well.

PEPITO. I have to tell you——

ERNEST. To go away, perhaps.

PEPITO (*Changing his tone*). Good heavens! What a notion! I only—wanted to ask you—if it is true (*hunts for something to say*) that you afterwards—the iscount, you know?

ERNEST (*Gloomily looking away*). Yes.

PEPITO. How did it happen?

ERNEST. I ran downstairs—half mad—I found them—we went upstairs again—locked the door. Two men—two witnesses—two swords—and afterwards—I hardly know what happened. Swords clashed—there was a cry—a thrust—blood spouted—an assassin stood—and a man lay stretched on the ground.

PEPITO. The devil! Sharp work. Did you hear, mother?

MERCEDES. More blood shed.

PEPITO. Nebreda deserved it.

ERNEST (*Approaching her*). Mercedes, for pity's sake—one word—Don Julian? How is he? If you could know what my anguish is—my sorrow—what do they say?

MERCEDES. That the wound, since his removal, is mortal, and it would be worse for him if you went near the bed of suffering and death. Leave this house.

ERNEST. I must see him.

MERCEDES. Go, instantly.

ERNEST. I will not.

PEPITO. What insolence!

ERNEST. It is befitting. (*To* PEPITO.) Pardon me, madam (*turning respectfully to* MERCEDES); you see I am achieving the general opinion of me.

MERCEDES. For pity's sake, Ernest——

ERNEST. Listen, Mercedes. When a man such as I am is abused, and for no reason on earth treated as a blackguard, and finds himself snared, with crime thrust upon him, 'tis indeed a perilous case,—for others rather than for himself. I, in this fierce struggle with miserable fate, have lost honor, friendship and love, and have now nothing more to lose but the shabby shreds of an insipid and dreary existence. I have come here solely to know if there is any hope—only for that—and then—but you cannot deny me so slight a consolation? (*Pleading.*) One word!

MERCEDES. Very well. They say—that he is better.

ERNEST. True? You are not deceiving me? You are sure—quite sure? Oh! you are merciful, you are kind. It is true, quite true! May God spare him! Not his death. Let him live and be happy once more; let him forgive me and embrace me once again! Only let me see him. (*Falls into the arm-chair beside the table sobbing, and covers his face with his hands. Pause.*)

MERCEDES. If your father should hear —if he should come out. Courage, Ernest, be sensible. (DOÑA MERCEDES *and* PEPITO *endeavor to screen* ERNEST.)

PEPITO. These nervous creatures are terrible. They sob and kill in the same breath.

ERNEST. If you see me crying, while sobs shake my throat in an hysterical convulsion, and I seem as weak as a child, or a woman, believe me, it is not for myself, but for him—for her—for their lost happiness for this indelible blot upon their name,—for the affront I am the cause of, in return for all their love and kindness. It is not my fault, but my utter misfortune. That is why I weep. My God, if I could wipe out this wretched past with tears, I would gladly weep away by blood to the last drop.

MERCEDES. Silence, I implore!

PEPITO. There, we will discuss tears and sorrows another time.

ERNEST. If everybody else is discussing them today, why should we too not speak of them? The whole town is astir and on tiptoe with excitement. It has swallowed up, devoured and blighted three reputations, three names, three persons, and floated them on the froth of laughter and a wave of degrading chatter down the straits of human misery, into the social abysm of shame, where for ever lie engulfed the conscience, and fame, and future of the unfortunates.

MERCEDES. Not so loud, Ernest.

ERNEST. Why? since the others are not murmurs, but voices, that thunder through the air? The tragic event is known all over the town, and each one has his own way of telling it. Wonderful! everything is known except the truth. 'Tis fatality. (DOÑA MERCEDES *and* PEPITO *exhibit keen interest in hearing the reports.*) Some say that Don Julian discovered Teodora in my rooms, and that I attacked him in blind fury and killed him on the spot. Others—and these would seem to be my friends, since they raise me from the rank of vulgar assassin to the noble level of duelist—aver that we fought loyally like gentlemen. And there are others, again, who have the tale more accurately, and recount how Don Julian took my place in the arranged meeting with Nebreda—that I arrived late on the scene—either from design or fear, or because I was in the arms—but, no; it would burn my lips to give this version— the thought of it sets my brain on fire. Seek the basest, the vilest, that which most blackens—the filth of the mind, the mire of the soul, the dross of degraded consciences; cast it to the wind as it whistles along the streets upon bespattering tongues, and you will have the tale, and may see what reputation remains for an innocent woman and two honest men when the town takes to jabbering about them.

MERCEDES. It is sad, I admit; but perhaps public opinion is not altogether to blame.

PEPITO. Teodora did go to your rooms —she was there——

ERNEST. To prevent the duel with Nebreda.

PEPITO. Then why did she hide herself?

ERNEST. Because we feared her presence would be misconstrued.

PEPITO. The explanation is easy and

simple. The difficult thing, Ernest, is to get us to believe it, for there is another still more easy and simple.

ERNEST. Which dishonors more, and that's the beauty of it.

PEPITO. Well, at least, admit that Teodora was giddy, if not really culpable.

ERNEST. Guilt is prudent and cautious. On the other hand, how imprudent is innocence!

PEPITO. Look here, if your rule holds good for everybody, the worst of us is an angel or a saint.

ERNEST. You are right. What does it matter? What is the weight or value of such calumny? The worst of it is that thought is degraded by mean contact with a mean idea. From force of dwelling upon a crime, the conscience becomes familiar with it. It shows itself terrible and repellent—*but it shows itself*—at night, in dark solitude! Yes—(*aside*) but what! why are they listening to me so strangely, almost in suspense? (*Aloud*) I am myself; my name is an honorable one. If I killed Nebreda solely because of a lie, what would I not do to myself if guilt threatened to give the truth to calumny?

PEPITO (*Aside to* MERCEDES). He denied it! Why, it is as clear as daylight.

MERCEDES (*Aside to* PEPITO). He's wandering.

PEPITO. 'Tis only his confession he's making.

MERCEDES (*Aloud*). That will do, Ernest. Go, now.

ERNEST. Impossible, madam. I should go mad if I had to spend tonight away from this sick-room—out of my mind.

MERCEDES. But if Severo came and found you?

ERNEST. What do I care? He is a loyal gentleman. Better still, let him come. We fly from fear, and only the guilty are afraid. Nothing will make me run away, or acknowledge fear.

PEPITO (*Listening*). Somebody is coming.

MERCEDES. Is it he?

PEPITO (*Going down the stage*). No, 'tis Teodora.

ERNEST. Teodora! Teodora! I want to see her.

MERCEDES (*Sternly*). Ernest!

ERNEST. Yes, I must ask her to forgive me.

MERCEDES. You don't remember——

ERNEST. I remember everything and understand. We two together! Ah, no. Enough. You need not fear. For her would I shed my blood, lay down my life, sacrifice my future, honor—all! But see her? never. 'Tis no longer possible. The mist of blood has risen between us. (*Goes out on the left.*)

SCENE V

DOÑA MERCEDES *and* PEPITO.

MERCEDES. Leave me alone with her. Go inside to your father. I want to see into her heart, and shall be able to probe its depths with my tongue.

PEPITO. Then I will leave you together.

MERCEDES. Goodbye.

PEPITO. Goodbye. (*Goes out on the right.*)

MERCEDES. Now to put my plan into work.

SCENE VI

TEODORA *and* DOÑA MERCEDES. TEODORA *enters timidly, and stands near* DON JULIAN's *door on the right, listening anxiously, and muffling her sobs with her handkerchief.*

MERCEDES. Teodora.

TEODORA. It is you. (*Advances to her.*)

MERCEDES. Courage! what good does crying do?

TEODORA. How is he? how is he? the truth!

MERCEDES. Much better.

TEODORA. Will he recover?

MERCEDES. I think so.

TEODORA. My God! My life for his.

MERCEDES (*Draws her affectionately forward*). And then—I have faith in your good sense. I can measure your remorse by your tears and anxiety.

TEODORA. Yes (DOÑA MERCEDES *sits down with a satisfied air*), I did wrong, I know, in going to see him (DOÑA MERCEDES *looks disappointed the confession is no worse*), but last night you told me about the outrage and the duel. I was grateful to you for doing so, although I did not then suspect the harm you did me, nor could I now explain it to you. Oh, what a night! (*Crosses her hands and glances upward.*) I have cried and raved, thinking of Julian's plight, of the scandal, of the violent quarrel and the bloodshed. Everything passed before my eyes—and then—poor Ernest dying, perhaps, for my sake! But why do you look at me so strangely? there can be no harm in it, surely! Or are you unconvinced, and do you think as the rest do?

MERCEDES (*Drily*). I think your fear for that fellow's life altogether superfluous.

TEODORA. Why? with so skilled an antagonist! You have seen it—Julian——

MERCEDES. Julian has been avenged. The man who killed him no longer lives, so that you have been wasting your fears and your tears. (*With deliberate hardness.*)

TEODORA (*Eagerly*). It was Ernest——

MERCEDES. Yes, Ernest.

TEODORA. He met the viscount?

MERCEDES. Face to face.

TEODORA (*Unable to restrain herself*). How noble and brave!

MERCEDES. Teodora!

TEODORA. What do you mean? Tell me.

MERCEDES (*Sternly*). I can read your thought.

TEODORA. My thought!

MERCEDES. Yes.

TEODORA. Which?

MERCEDES. You know very well.

TEODORA. Have I no right to be glad because Julian is avenged? Is that an impulse I could be expected to repress?

MERCEDES. That was not your feeling.

TEODORA. You know so much more about it than I do!

MERCEDES (*Pointedly*). Believe me, admiration is not far from love.

TEODORA. What do I admire?

MERCEDES. This youth's courage.

TEODORA. His nobility.

MERCEDES. Quite so, but that's the beginning.

TEODORA. What folly!

MERCEDES. It *is* folly—but on your side.

TEODORA. You persist! Ever this accursed idea!—while it is with immense, with infinite pity that I am filled.

MERCEDES. For whom?

TEODORA. For whom else but Julian?

MERCEDES. Have you never learned, Teodora, that in a woman's heart pity and forgetfulness may mean one and the same thing?

TEODORA. I beseech you—Mercedes—silence!

MERCEDES. I wish to let light in upon the state of your mind,—to turn upon it the lamp of truth, lit by my experience.

TEODORA. I hear you, but while I listen, it seems no longer a sister, a friend, a mother that speaks to me, so hateful are your words. Your lips seem to speak at inspiration of the devil's prompting. Why should you strive to convince me that little by little I am ceasing to love my husband, and that more and more I am imbued with an impure tenderness, with a feeling that burns and stains? I who love Julian as dearly as ever, who would give the last drop of blood in my body for a single breath of life for him—for him, from whom I am now separated— (*points to his room*)—why, I should like to go in there this moment, if your husband did not bar my way, and press

Julian once more in my arms. I would so inundate him with my tears, and so close him round with the passion of my love, that its warmth would melt his doubts, and his soul would respond to the fervor of mine. But it is not because I adore my husband that I am bound to abhor the faithful and generous friend who so nobly risked his life for me. And if I don't hate him, is that a reason to conclude that I love him? The world can think such things. I hear such strange stories, and such sad events have happened, and calumny has so embittered me, that I find myself wondering if public opinion can be true,—in doubt of myself. Can it be that I really am the victim of a hideous passion, unconsciously influenced by it? and in some sad and weak moment shall I yield to the senses, and be subjugated by this tyrannous fire?

MERCEDES. You are speaking the truth?

TEODORA. Can you doubt it?

MERCEDES. You really do not love him?

TEODORA. Mercedes, what words have I that will convince you? At another time, such a question would drive the blood of anger to my brow, and today, you see, I am discussing with you whether I am honest or not. Yes, am I really so? To the depth of the soul? No, for endurance of this humiliation proves me worthy of it. (*Hides her face in her hands and flings herself down in the armchair.*)

MERCEDES. Do not cry so, Teodora. I believe in you. Enough. No more tears. Let me but add one more word, and there's an end to the matter. Ernest is not what you believe him to be. He is not worthy of your trust.

TEODORA. He is good, Mercedes.

MERCEDES. No.

TEODORA. He is fond of Julian.

MERCEDES. He would betray him.

TEODORA. Again! My God!

MERCEDES. I no longer accuse you of responding to his passion, but I only assert—I would warn you that *he loves you.*

TEODORA (*Rising in anger*). Loves me!

MERCEDES. It is known to everybody. In this very room, a moment ago, before Pepito and me—you understand?

TEODORA. No, explain at once—what?

MERCEDES. He openly confessed it. He made a violent declaration, swore that he was ready to sacrifice life, honor, soul and conscience for you. And when you came, he wanted to see you. He only yielded to the force of my entreaties and went away. I tremble lest he should meet Severo and their encounter lead to an explosion. And you—what have you to say now?

TEODORA (*Who has listened to* MERCEDES *intently, held in an indefinable gloomy terror*). Heavens above! Can it be true? and I who felt—who professed so sincere an affection for him!

MERCEDES. There, you are on the point of crying again.

TEODORA. The heart has no tears for the manifold deceptions of this miserable life. A lad so pure and finely natured,—and to see him now so debased and spotted! And you say that he actually uttered those words here—he!—Ernest. Oh, oh, Mercedes! send him away from this house.

MERCEDES. Ah, that is what I wanted. Your energy consoles me. (*With evidence of honest satisfaction.*) Pardon me —now I fully believe you. (*Embraces her.*)

TEODORA. And before? No? (*The actress must strongly accentuate this line.*)

MERCEDES. Hush! He is coming back.

TEODORA (*Impetuously*). I will not see him. Tell him so. Julian expects me. (*Goes to the right.*)

MERCEDES (*Detaining her*). Impossible! You must know it. He will not heed my orders, and now that I understand so fully how you feel for him, I should be glad to have him suffer at your hands the contempt he has already endured at mine.

TEODORA. Then leave me. (*Enter* ERNEST.)

ERNEST. Teodora!

MERCEDES (*Aside to Teodora*). It is late, do your duty quickly. (*Aloud to* ERNEST.) The command you heard a little while ago from me, you will receive again from Teodora's lips, and she is the mistress of this house.

TEODORA (*In a low voice to* MERCEDES). Don't go away.

MERCEDES (*To* TEODORA). Are you afraid?

TEODORA. I afraid! I am afraid of nothing. (*Makes a sign for her to go. Exit* DOÑA MERCEDES *on the right.*)

SCENE VII

TEODORA *and* ERNEST.

ERNEST. The command was—that I should go away. (*Pause. Both remain silent without looking at each other.*) And you? Are you going to repeat it? (TEODORA *nods, but still does not look at him.*) Have no fear, Teodora. I will respect and obey your order. (*Submissively.*) The others could not get me to obey them, little as they may like to hear it (*harshly*), but nothing you could say, even though you wound me— From you I will endure anything! (*Sadly.*)

TEODORA. I wound you! No, Ernest, you cannot believe that—— (*Still does not look at him, is half vexed and afraid.*)

ERNEST. I do not believe it. (*Pause.*)

TEODORA. Adieu. I wish you all happiness.

ERNEST. Adieu, Teodora. (*Remains waiting for a moment to see if she will turn and offer him her hand. Then walks down the stage, turns back again, and approaches her.* TEODORA *shows that she feels his movement, and is distressed, but continues to keep her face averted.*) If with my death at this very instant I could blot out all the misery that lies to my account, not through any fault of mine, but through an implacable fate, I should not now be standing here alive. You may believe it on the word of an honorable man. No shadow of the past would remain,—neither sighs nor pain to remember, nor that sorrowful pallor of your face (TEODORA *starts and glances at him in terror*), nor the grieved fear of those eyes, nor sobs that tear the throat, nor tears that line the cheek. (TEODORA *sobs.*)

TEODORA (*Aside, moving further away*). Mercedes was right, and I, blind and thoughtless that I was——

ERNEST. Bid me goodbye—once—for kindness's sake.

TEODORA. Goodbye! Yes; and I forgive you all the injury you have done us.

ERNEST. I, Teodora!

TEODORA. Yes, you.

ERNEST. What a look! What a tone!

TEODORA. No more, Ernest, I beseech you.

ERNEST. What have I done to deserve——?

TEODORA. It is all over between us. Regard me as one who no longer exists for you.

ERNEST. Is this contempt?

TEODORA. Go.

ERNEST. Go? in this way?

TEODORA. My husband is dying in there—and here I feel as if I too were dying. (*Staggers back and clutches the arm-chair to keep from falling.*)

ERNEST. Teodora. (*Rushes forward to support her.*)

TEODORA (*Angrily drawing herself away*). Don't touch me. (*Pause.*) Ah, breathe again more freely. (*Tries to walk, staggers again weakly, and a sec-*

ond time ERNEST *offers to assist her. She repulses him.*)

ERNEST. Why not, Teodora?

TEODORA. Your touch would soil me.

ERNEST. I soil you!

TEODORA. Exactly.

ERNEST. I! (*Pause.*) What does she mean, Almighty God! She also! Oh, it is not possible! Oh, death is preferable to this—It cannot be true—I am raving—Say it is not true, Teodora—only one word—for justice—one word of pardon, of pity, of consolation, madam. I am resigned to go away, never to see you again, although 'twere to break, and mutilate, and destroy my life. But it will, at least, be bearable if I may carry into solitude your forgiveness, your affection, your esteem—only your pity, then. So that I still may think you believe me loyal and upright—that I could not, that I have not degraded you, much less be capable of insulting you. I care nothing about the world, and despise its affronts. Its passions inspire me with the profoundest disdain. Whether its mood be harsh or cruel, however it may talk of me and of what has happened, it will never think so ill of me as I do of it. But you, the purest dream of man's imagining—you for whom I would gladly give,—not only my life, but my right to heaven, ay, a thousand times—eagerly, joyously,—You, to suspect me of treason, of hypocrisy! Oh, this, Teodora—I cannot bear! (*Deeply moved, speaks despairingly.*)

TEODORA (*With increasing nervousness*). You have not understood me, Ernest. We must part.

ERNEST. But not like this!

TEODORA. Quickly, for mercy's sake. Julian suffers. (*Points to the sick-room.*)

ERNEST. I know it.

TEODORA. Then we should not forget it.

ERNEST. No; but I also suffer.

TEODORA. You, Ernest! why?

ERNEST. Through your contempt.

TEODORA. I feel none.

ERNEST. You have expressed it.

TEODORA. It was a lie.

ERNEST. No; not entirely. So that our sufferings are not equal. In this implacable strife *he* suffers as those on earth suffer, *I* as those in hell.

TEODORA. Spare me, Ernest—my head is on fire.

ERNEST. And my heart aches.

TEODORA. That will do, Ernest. I entreat you to pity me.

ERNEST. That was all I asked of you.

TEODORA. Mercy.

ERNEST. Yes, mercy. But why should you claim it? What is it you fear? of what are you thinking? (*Approaches her.*)

TEODORA. Forgive me if I have offended you.

ERNEST. Offended me, no! The truth, that is what I crave,—and I implore it on my knees. See, Teodora, my eyes are wet. (*Bends his knee before her and takes her hand.* DON JULIAN's *door opens, and* DON SEVERO *stands staring at them.*)

D. SEVERO (*Aside*). Miserable pair!

TEODORA. Don Severo!

SCENE VIII

TEODORA, ERNEST, *and* DON SEVERO. ERNEST *stands apart on the right.* DON SEVERO *places himself between him and* TEODORA.

D. SEVERO (*In a low voice of concentrated anger, so that* DON JULIAN *may not hear*). I can find no word or epithet adequate to the passion of contempt I would express, so I must be content to call you a blackguard. Leave this house at once.

ERNEST (*Also in a low voice*). My respect for Teodora, for this house, and for the sick man lying in yonder room, sir, compels me to put my retort—in silence.

D. SEVERO (*Ironically, under the impression that* ERNEST *is going*). It's the best thing you can do—obey and hold your tongue.

ERNEST. You have not understood me. I do not intend to obey.

SEVERO. You remain?

ERNEST. Until Teodora commands me to go. I was on the point of going away forever a moment ago, but the Almighty or the devil deterred me. Now you come and order me out, and as if your insult were an infernal message, it roots my heels to the floor in revolt.

SEVERO. We'll see that. There are servants to kick you out, and sticks if necessary.

ERNEST. Try it. (*Approaches* DON SEVERO *with a threatening air.* TEODORA *rushes between them.*)

TEODORA. Ernest! (*Turns commandingly to* DON SEVERO.) You seem to forget that this is my house as long as my husband lives and is its owner. Only one of us two has the right to command here. (*Softens to* ERNEST.) Not for him—but for my sake, because I am unhappy——

ERNEST (*Unable to contain his joy at hearing himself defended by* TEODORA). You wish it, Teodora?

TEODORA. I beg it. (ERNEST *bows and turns away.*)

SEVERO. Your audacity confounds and shocks me as much—no, far more, than his. (*Strides menacingly towards her.* ERNEST *turns swiftly round, then makes a strong effort to control himself and moves away again.*) You dare to raise your head, wretched woman, and before me too! Shame on you! (ERNEST *repeats previous movements and gestures, but this time more accentuated.*) You, so fearful and cowardly, where have you found courage to display this energy in his defense? How eloquent is passion! (ERNEST *stands, looking back.*) But you forget that, before pitching him out, I had the authority to forbid the door of this house to you, who have stained its threshold with Julian's blood. Why have you returned? (*Seizes her brutally and drags her roughly toward himself.*)

ERNEST. No, I can't stand this—I cannot! (*He thrusts himself between* SEVERO *and* TEODORA.) Off, you scoundrel.

SEVERO. Again!

ERNEST. Again.

SEVERO. You have dared to return?

ERNEST. You insolently affront Teodora. I still live. What do you expect me to do, if not return and chastise you, and brand you as a coward?

SEVERO. Me?

ERNEST. Precisely.

TEODORA. No!

ERNEST. He has brought it on himself. I have seen him lift his hand in anger to you—you, you! So now—— (*Seizes* DON SEVERO *violently.*)

SEVERO. You impudent puppy!

ERNEST. True, but I'll not release you. You loved and respected your mother, I presume. For that reason you must respect Teodora, and humbly bow before a sorrow so immense as hers. This woman, sir, is purer, more honest than the mother of such a man as you.

SEVERO. This to me?

ERNEST. Yes, and I have not yet done.

SEVERO. Your life——

ERNEST. Oh, my life, as much as you like—but afterwards. (TEODORA *endeavors to part them, but he pushes her gently away, without releasing* DON SEVERO.) You believe in a God—in a Maker—in hope. Well, then, as you bend your knee before the altar of that God above, so will I compel you to kneel to Teodora,—and that instantly, sir. Down —in the dust.

TEODORA. For mercy's sake——

ERNEST. To the ground! (*Forces* DON SEVERO *to kneel.*)

TEODORA. Enough, Ernest.

SEVERO. A thousand thunders.

ERNEST. At her feet!

SEVERO. You!

ERNEST. Yes, I.

SEVERO. For her?

ERNEST. For her.

TEODORA. That will do. Hush! (*She points in terror to* DON JULIAN's *door.* ERNEST *releases* DON SEVERO, *who rises and moves backward.* TEODORA *retreats and forms with* ERNEST *a group in the background.*)

SCENE IX

TEODORA, ERNEST, DON SEVERO. *Afterwards* DON JULIAN *and* DOÑA MERCEDES.

D. JULIAN (*Inside*). Let me go.

MERCEDES (*Inside*). No. You must not.

D. JULIAN. It is they. Don't you hear them?

TEODORA (*To* ERNEST). Go.

SEVERO (*To* ERNEST). Avenged!

ERNEST. I don't deny it. (*Enter* DON JULIAN, *pale and dying, leaning on* DOÑA MERCEDES' *arm.* DON SEVERO *stations himself on the right,* ERNEST *and* TEODORA *remain in the background.*)

D. JULIAN. Together! Where are they going? Who detains them here? Away with you, traitors. (*Wants to rush at them, but strength fails him, and he staggers back.*)

SEVERO (*Hurrying to his assistance*). No, no.

D. JULIAN. Severo; they deceived me—they lied to me—the miserable pair! (*While he speaks* DON SEVERO *and* DOÑA MERCEDES *lead him to the arm-chair.*) There, look at them—both—she and Ernest! Why are they together?

TEODORA AND ERNEST (*Separating.*) No.

D. JULIAN. Why don't they come to me? Teodora!

TEODORA (*Stretches out her arms but does not advance.*) Julian!

D. JULIAN. Here in my arms. (TEODORA *runs forward and flings herself into* DON JULIAN's *arms, who clasps her feverishly. Pause.*) You see—you see— (*to* DON SEVERO) I know well enough they are deceiving me. I hold her thus in my arms. I crush and subdue her— I might

kill her—so! and 'tis only what she deserves. But I look at her—*I look at her*—and then I cannot!

TEODORA. Julian——

D. JULIAN (*Pointing to* ERNEST). And that fellow?

ERNEST. Sir!

D. JULIAN. I loved him! Silence, and come hither. (ERNEST *approaches.*) You see, I am still here owner. (*He holds* TEODORA *more tightly clasped.*)

TEODORA. Yes,—I am yours.

D. JULIAN. Drop pretense. Don't lie.

MERCEDES (*Striving to soothe him*). For pity's sake——

D. SEVERO. Julian!

D. JULIAN (*To both*). Peace. (*To* TEODORA.) I see through you. I know well that you love him. (TEODORA *and* ERNEST *try to protest, but he will not let them.*) All Madrid knows it too—all Madrid.

ERNEST. No, father.

TEODORA. No.

D. JULIAN. They deny it—they deny it! Why, it is as clear as noonday. Why, I feel it in every fiber,—by the beat of fevered pulse, by the consuming flame of inward illumination!

ERNEST. It is the fever of your blood and the delirium of bodily weakness that feed the delusion. Listen to me, sir——

D. JULIAN. To hear how well you can lie?

ERNEST (*Pointing to* TEODORA.) She is innocent.

D. JULIAN. But I do not believe you.

ERNEST. Sir, by my father's memory——

D. JULIAN. Don't insult his name and memory.

ERNEST. By my mother's last kiss——

D. JULIAN. That kiss has long since been wiped from your brow.

ERNEST. What then do you want, father? I will swear by anything you wish. Oh, my father!

D. JULIAN. No oaths, or protests, or deceitful words.

ERNEST. Then what? Only tell me.

TEODORA. Yes, what, Julian?

D. JULIAN. Deeds.

ERNEST. What does he wish, Teodora? What does he ask of us?

TEODORA. I don't know. Oh, what are we to do, Ernest?

D. JULIAN (*Watching them in feverish distrust*). Ah, you would even deceive me to my face! You are plotting together, wretched traitors! I see it.

ERNEST. It is fever that misleads you—not the testimony of your eyes.

D. JULIAN. Fever, yes. And since fever is fire, it has burned away the bandage with which before you two had blinded me, and at last I see you for what you are. And now!—but why these glances at one another? Why, traitors? Why do your eyes gleam so? Tell me, Ernest. There are no tears in them to make them shine. Come nearer—nearer to me. (*Draws* ERNEST *to him, bends his head, and then succeeds in thrusting him upon his knees. Thus* TEODORA *is on one side of* DON JULIAN *and* ERNEST *at his feet.* DON JULIAN *passes his hand across the young man's eyes.*) You see—no tears— they are quite dry.

ERNEST. Forgive me, forgive me!

D. JULIAN. You ask my forgiveness? Then you acknowledge your sin?

ERNEST. No.

D. JULIAN. Yes.

ERNEST. I say it is not so.

D. JULIAN. Then here before me, look at her.

D. SEVERO. Julian!

MERCEDES. Sir!

D. JULIAN (*To* TEODORA *and* ERNEST). Perhaps you are afraid? So it is not like a brother that you cherish her? If so, prove it. Let me see what sort of light shines in your eyes as they meet—whether, to my close inspection, the rays dart passion's flame, or mild affection. Come here, Teodora. Both—so—still nearer. (*Drags* TEODORA *until she stumbles, so that both faces are compelled towards each other.*)

TEODORA (*Frees herself with a violent effort*). Oh, no.

ERNEST (*Also strives to free himself, but is held in* DON JULIAN'S *grasp*). I cannot.

D. JULIAN. You love one another—you can't deny it, for I've seen it. (*To* ERNEST.) Your life!

ERNEST. Yes.

D. JULIAN. Your blood!

ERNEST. All.

D. JULIAN (*Forcing him to his knees*). Stay still.

TEODORA. Julian!

D. JULIAN. Ah, you defend him, you defend him.

TEODORA. Not for his sake.

D. SEVERO. In God's name——

D. JULIAN (*To* SEVERO). Silence. (*Still holds* ERNEST *down.*) Bad friend, bad son!

ERNEST. My father.

D. JULIAN. Disloyal! Traitor!

ERNEST. No, father.

D. JULIAN. Here is my shameful seal upon your cheek— Today with my hand —soon with steel—so! (*With a supreme effort strikes* ERNEST. ERNEST *jumps up with a terrible cry, and turns away, covering his face.*)

ERNEST. Oh!

D. SEVERO (*Stretches out his hand to* ERNEST). Justice.

TEODORA. My God! (*Hides her face in both hands, and drops on a chair.*)

MERCEDES (*Turning to* ERNEST *to exculpate* DON JULIAN). It was only delirium. (*These four exclamations very hurried. A moment of stupor.* DON JULIAN *stands still staring at* ERNEST, *and* DOÑA MERCEDES *and* DON SEVERO *endeavor to calm him.*)

D. JULIAN. It was not delirium, it was chastisement, Heaven be praised. What did you think, ungrateful boy?

MERCEDES. That will do.

D. SEVERO. Come, Julian.

D. JULIAN. Yes, I am going. (*Is led away with difficulty between* DON SEVERO *and* DOÑA MERCEDES, *and stops to look back to* TEODORA *and* ERNEST.)

MERCEDES. Quickly, Severo.

D. JULIAN. Look at them, the traitors! It was only justice—was it not? Say so— at least I believe it.

D. SEVERO. For God's sake, Julian— well, at any rate, for *mine*——

D. JULIAN. Yes, for yours, Severo, only for yours. You alone have loved me truly. (*Embraces him.*)

D. SEVERO. Yes, yes, it is so.

D. JULIAN (*Stops at the door and looks back again*). She is crying for him—and does not follow me. Not even a look. She does not see that I am dying—yes, dying.

D. SEVERO. Julian, Julian!

D. JULIAN (*On the threshold*). Wait, wait. Dishonor for dishonor. Goodbye, Ernest. (*Exeunt* DON JULIAN, DON SEVERO, *and* MERCEDES.)

SCENE X

TEODORA *and* ERNEST. ERNEST *drops into a chair near the table.* TEODORA *remains standing on the right. Pause.*

ERNEST (*Aside*). What is the use of loyalty?

TEODORA. And what is the use of innocence?

ERNEST. Conscience grows dark.

TEODORA. Pity, my God! Pity!

ERNEST. Pitiless destiny.

TEODORA. Oh, most miserable fate!

ERNEST. Poor child!

TEODORA. Poor Ernest! (*Both remain apart until now.*)

D. SEVERO (*In anguish from within*). My brother.

MERCEDES. Help!

PEPITO. Quickly. (ERNEST *and* TEODORO *move together.*)

TEODORA. They are crying.

ERNEST. He is dying.

TEODORA. Come at once.

ERNEST. Where?

TEODORA. To him.

ERNEST. We cannot. (*Detains her.*)

TEODORA. Why not? I want him to live.

ERNEST. And I!—but I cannot. (*Points to* DON JULIAN'S *room.*)

TEODORA. Then I will. (*Rushes to the door.*)

LAST SCENE

TEODORA, ERNEST, DON SEVERO *and* PEPITO. ERNEST *stands on the right in the middle of the stage,* TEODORA *near the door of* DON JULIAN'S *room.* PEPITO *and, behind him,* DON SEVERO, *bar the way.*

PEPITO. Where are you going?

TEODORA (*In desperation*). I must see him.

PEPITO. It is impossible.

D. SEVERO. She cannot pass. This woman must not remain in my house —turn her out at once. (*To* PEPITO.) No compassion—this very moment.

ERNEST. What!

TEODORA. My mind is wandering.

D. SEVERO. Though your mother should stand in front of that woman, Pepito, you have my orders. Obey them. Never mind her prayers or supplications. If she should cry—then let her cry. (*With concentrated fury.*) Away with her, away—else I might kill her.

TEODORA. Julian orders——

D. SEVERO. Yes, Julian.

ERNEST. Her husband! It cannot be.

TEODORA. I must see him.

D. SEVERO. Very well. Look at him, once more—and then—depart.

PEPITO (*Interfering*). Father——

D. SEVERO (*Pushing him away*). Stop, sir.

TEODORA. It can't be true.

PEPITO. This is too horrible.

TEODORA. It is a lie.

D. SEVERO. Come, Teodora—come and see. (*Seizes her arm and leads her to the door.*)

TEODORA. Oh! My husband! Julian—dead. (*Staggers shudderingly back, and falls half senseless.*)

ERNEST (*Covering his face*). My father! (*Pause.* DON SEVERO *watches them rancorously.*)

D. SEVERO (*To his son*). Turn her out.

ERNEST (*Placing himself before* TEODORA). What cruelty!

PEPITO (*Doubting*). Sir——

SEVERO (*To* PEPITO). Such are my orders. Do you doubt my word?

ERNEST. Pity.

D. SEVERO (*Pointing to the death-chamber*). Yes, such pity as she showed him.

ERNEST. Fire races through my veins. I will leave Spain, sir.

D. SEVERO. It makes no difference.

ERNEST. She will die.

D. SEVERO. Life is short.

ERNEST. For the last time——

D. SEVERO. No more. (*To his son.*) Ring.

ERNEST. But I tell you she is innocent. I swear it.

PEPITO (*Interceding*). Father——

D. SEVERO (*With a contemptuous gesture*). That fellow lies.

ERNEST. You impel me with the current. Then I will not struggle against it. I go with it. I cannot yet know what may be her opinion (*pointing to* TEODORA) of others, and of your outrages. Her lips are silent, mute her thoughts. But what I think of it all—yes, I will tell you.

D. SEVERO. It is useless. It won't prevent me from—— (*Approaches* TEODORA.)

PEPITO (*Restraining him*). Father——

ERNEST. Stay. (*Pause.*) Let nobody touch this woman. She is mine. The world has so desired it, and its decision I accept. It has driven her to my arms. Come, Teodora. (*He raises her, and sustains her.*) You cast her forth from here. We obey you.

D. SEVERO. At last, you blackguard!

ERNEST. Yes; now you are right. I will confess now. Do you want passion? Then passion and delirium. Do you want love? Then love—boundless love. Do you want more? Then more and more. Nothing daunts me. Yours the invention, I give it shelter. So you may tell the tale. It echoes through all this heroic town. But should anyone ask you who was the infamous intermediary in this infamy, you will reply "ourselves, without being aware of it, and with us the stupid chatter of busybodies." Come, Teodora; my mother's spirit kisses your pure brow. Adieu, all. She belongs to me, and let heaven choose its day to judge between you and me. (*Gathers* TEODORA *into his embrace, with a glance of defiance around.*)

CURTAIN

THE LIFE AND WORKS OF

JOSÉ ECHEGARAY

By JEAN CAMP

WHEN ONE reads the works of the dramatist José Echegaray today, it is difficult to imagine the enormous success he had in Spain at the end of the last century. Nothing like it had been seen since Spain's golden age, as the Spanish theater, through lack of subjects of universal appeal and through the absence of any eminent dramatic writers, seemed to have lost its supremacy since the end of the eighteenth century.

Echegaray's first nights were awaited with eager impatience. The merits of his plays were passionately disputed. People praised his theatrical effects and his talent for the outrageous; the more fastidious took pleasure in criticizing the writer's baroque style and his fantastic and melodramatic love of emotion. What bombastic tirades, what conflicts so near to madness, and what fruitless beating of wings to reach the heights—and all to do with bourgeois problems that would leave today's public either quite indifferent or completely skeptical.

Don José de Echegaray y Eizaguirre was born in Madrid in 1833. He studied at the *Instituto* in Murcia and afterward in Madrid, where he became an engineer in the public works department and a professor at the School of Roads and Bridges. He launched an attack on the political economy and became a determined supporter of free trade. After the revolution of 1868, and the installation of a revolutionary *junta* in Madrid, he was made director of public works (1869–1872) under King Amadeo of Savoy. The fall of Amadeo sent him into temporary exile in Paris, where he was able to indulge his already keen taste for the theater. After his return, he became minister of finance and founded the Bank of Spain in 1874; that same year he wrote his first play, *El Libro Talonario* (Book of Accounts), under the pseudonym of Jorge Hayaseca.

René Bazin described "this astonishing Echegaray" in his beautifully written book on Spain. Bazin had the good luck to meet him while passing through Madrid: "He must have been fair-haired and is still slightly so. He looks like Frédéric Mistral, except for the moustache, which is waxed: a powerful, military face, light, bright eyes of a pale green that quickly change color, an easy manner and a look of one of those free spirits with the gift of understanding all about life, to whom everything comes easily."

It is coincidental that he so much resembled Mistral, because he shared the Nobel Prize with him in 1904. But the two men had few other characteristics in common. Mistral was a poet who resuscitated a dead language and a forgotten literature; Echegaray placed a steady talent at the service of his national theater.

Echegaray was a man of his time, a real prototype of the beginning of the twentieth century. Science was the new religion, attracting neophytes everywhere, and Echegaray was a scientist. He was also a politician, and was dazzled by the theatrical elegance of the great democrat Castelar; but he was a liberal in his own way, and the sworn enemy of "neos" of every kind and of atheists.

Apart from his plays, his literary work includes numerous articles on popular science, parts of which have been published in two collections, *Ciencia Popular* (Popular Science, 1905), and *Vulgarización Científica* (Scientific Vulgarization, 1910), not to mention his numerous parliamentary and academic speeches and his *Recuerdos* (Memoirs, 1917), in which the age he lived in comes to life.

He was a romantic whose lyrical outbursts were a strange combination of the easy verve of José Zorrilla, the undoubted leader of Romanticism at its height, and the intimate anxieties of a Spanish Ibsen. He was eager for greatness and eternal fame, and was the herald of national honor in the manner of Calderón.

His art, the success he achieved, and the reactions he caused partly explain the advent of Jacinto Benavente, the playwright, who was the second Spaniard to win the Nobel Prize, in 1922. Benavente, at the beginning of this century, took over the Castillian scene to show, in a long series of satirical works, that "life is a comedy and it is foolish to try and turn it into a tragedy," in complete opposition to his illustrious predecessor, Echegaray.

Echegaray had a formidable rival in the great novelist Pérez Galdós. Besides his enormous output of short stories,

Galdós was the author of much important dramatic work of undeniable tragic power, notably *El Abuelo* (*The Ancestor*, 1897). This is a remarkable play and is full of life, characters, and passions; it has a very well-portrayed hero, a fair and attractive humanism, and emotion which owes nothing to melodramatic emphasis. But Galdós wrote in a direct, simple, and sometimes vulgar style, still immersed in the purrings of the Romantic movement, which was calculated to draw applause from the audience in the pit. Although he knew how to portray the problems of his age and the hardships of daily life with fairness and feeling, he lacked the panache demanded by the public of his time; this, however, did not worry him at all. But Galdós's generosity of mind, his basic goodness, and his idealism, in which he resembled Echegaray fairly closely, paled beside Echegaray's theatrical scenes.

The Romantic theater was a long time dying, and it still aroused the feelings of those Spaniards who had seen the pathetic end of the reign of Isabella II and the advent of the ephemeral Alfonso XII. People were looking for a remedy to present-day evils in the pageantry of a national theater full of swagger and flourish. The outbursts of revolt and individualism suited the spectators' temperament so well that applause poured forth in torrents, no matter whether the protagonists' language was clothed in good poetry or bad. The speeches against tyranny, the evocation of past glory, and the most sordid concessions to the unrestrained excitement of the crowd easily roused this frenzied audience. The people were greedy for strong emotions, and they reveled in the violent contrasts provided by Echegaray's work, with its parricides, its dishonors, and its suicides.

But these unnaturally heroic characters, squeezed into their period frock coats, who seem to have formed a gigantic coalition with implacable society, are luckily not the only heroes to be found in Echegaray's prolific work; elsewhere, it contains passages of incomparable beauty.

Echegaray followed *El libro talonario* with a whole series of neo-Romantic plays, such as *La esposa del vengador* (The Avenger's Wife, 1874), *En el puño de la espada* (The Sword's Handle, 1875), and *En el pilar y en la cruz* (The Stake and the Cross, 1878). In these plays, history and chivalrous adventures combine to produce a kind of hysterical fever oscillating between grandeur and caricature. The author's poetic style was rough and forced, and not the kind of poetry that flowed easily from an expert's pen; but nevertheless it managed to win the approval of the public. His plays, far from being spontaneous, were the result of prolonged reflection, and his poetry, which he wrote only later in life, was laboriously polished, showing evidence of determined effort and patient research.

The writers who influenced him were many and various. He had read most of the works of his older compatriots, Espronceda, Hartzenbusch, and Zorrilla, and also those of Balzac, Eugène Sue, and Dumas. Among his contemporaries he valued Lopez de Ayala, a learned and subtle dramatist, and Tamayo y Baus, the famous author of *Lances de honor* (*Affairs of Honor,* 1863), of which Echegaray wrote an eloquent eulogy. He also studied the dramatists of the Romantic age and the seventeenth century; and toward the end of his life he was influenced by the Nordic writers: Ibsen above all others, Björnson, Strindberg, Sudermann, and Hartmann.

But as soon as Echegaray touched on foreign themes, in *Harold the Norman* or *A Miracle in Egypt,* the standard of his works dropped to the level of the libretto of *Aïda* without the excuse of the music which makes it possible.

One of Echegaray's most successful works, *El gran Galeoto* (*The Great Galeoto*), is solidly constructed and filled with powerful theatrical inspiration. But unfortunately it is written in such prosaic verse that the strong, evocative effect is spoiled and with it the genuine psychological insight.

But deep down in Echegaray lay the splendid and terrible ambition to rejuvenate the deep metaphysical theater of Pedro Calderón. He admired Calderón's sense of honor, the decorative richness of his baroque style, and his poetry, high-flown and human at the same time, which expresses itself through the most moving symbols. He attempted to choose from among Calderón's ideas those national sentiments that still throbbed in the hearts of the men of his own time. This was his purpose when he transposed the best Catalan plays of Angel Guimerá into Castillian: *Maria-Rosa* and *Terra Baixa.* Guimerá had resuscitated a kind of realistic Lope de Vega in his own vernacular, and had evoked the eternal conflict between the peasants and their masters with fairness and sincerity. Although Guimerá's straining for effect was undeniable, it was supported by relevant social truth and a simplicity of expression that sprang spontaneously from the frustrated beings it depicted: there was no pasteboard scenery or mediaeval disguise to cheapen the play or dazzle the spectator. Echegaray provided the Catalan author with a wider public by conferring the universality of Castillian on him, enabling him to reach the distant Americas.

Echegaray continued to learn, and it was now that he refreshed his style by reading Ibsen. Without *Ghosts,* Echegaray would never have written *Son of Don Juan* (1892), nor would the Ibsen-like Brand figure have appeared in shadowy outline behind the protagonist of *El loco Dios* (The Mad God, 1900). Echegaray was already in the middle of his career as a dramatist when he discovered his Nordic colleague. From that moment it was as though he were obsessed by the problem of insanity.

In 1882, in emulation of Ibsen, he started to think out a play which at first he called "A Neo and an Atheist." He changed the title to *Dos fanatismos* (Two Fanaticisms), and it was produced in Madrid on January 15, 1887. Two famous actors, Antonio and Rafael Calvo, turned it into a triumphant success.

The theme of the play is the struggle between love and social and ideological prejudices, a struggle that is only tragically resolved by death. In spite of its undoubted period flavor, the play does not completely justify its title. One of the fanatics is nearer to the portrait of a Pharisee, and the other represents brute force: they are the fathers of two traditional lovers. The depth of maternal love is the only thing described with subtlety and sensibility. Nevertheless, in this play Echegaray makes a praiseworthy effort to escape from scenes that are outrageously overdramatized and he tries to maintain a family atmosphere where the muted monotones can show up the unfolding tragedy in higher relief.

This work is also interesting because it deals with the religious or clerical problem, which also preoccupied Tamayo and Galdós; when treating it they both used their talent with the very firm intention of fighting its harmful excesses. Echegaray's spiritual position was different, and he tried to be more impartial. His materialistic hero Pedregal, who has made a fortune in the Americas, represents modern man, the Darwinian positivist, even the Nietzschean, who bases his whole existence on will power. "Is life anything other than a struggle? Is the will anything other than the strength which enables man to conquer? Is our body anything other than a seething mass of appetites

that stimulate our energies, amplify our existence, and fill the atmosphere which surrounds us with powerful undercurrents?" He compared the muscular colonials of the wide-open spaces overseas with the tired sons of Europe, exclaiming in his strangely characteristic style: "We, the men of America's virgin lands, we have redder blood than the buffalo, calm and obedient nerves like the wires of a two-way or a four-way telegraphic system, the muscles of old Atlantis, and brains which are as precise and clear as adding machines. As well as all this, we have plenty of pluck, and you must realize, my dear Lorenzo, that your scruples are of no use now, and they do not in the least affect the vigorous organism of Martin Pedregal. The Californian miner and New York banker, an American to the core, is the sworn enemy of all that is vile, old, diseased, and hypocritical, everywhere."

In contrast to Pedregal, Lorenzo is not a real Christian; he is sure of his faith but is timorous, conservative, and devout, and all his arguments seem very weak. The three heroines of the play are the only ones who breathe the true Christian spirit and express it lucidly. Julian, the young lover, tries to explain the author's ideas unequivocally: religion is the concern not only of women but of all humanity. Technical progress is by no means incompatible with religious tradition, and all ideological conflict can be resolved by charity.

Echegaray was a liberal parliamentarian in the style of Lamartine and he extolled the freedom of religious belief on the platform: he could see no other solution to the problem except through the most facile and lamentable romanticism, which ended in the tragic deaths of all his heroes.

Another of his works has a similar Don Quixote quality, *O locura ó santidad* (*Madman or Saint*, 1877), which made the greatest possible stir not only in Spain but also in the rest of the world. To some people, the basis of the conflict enacted in this play is a struggle of conscience, an intimate tragedy played out among the mists of spiritual contradictions.

Much of Echegaray's work is centered on the tragedy of madness; to this he adds the problem of material interests in conflict with duty, in which idealism is the generator of further conflict. In *Madman or Saint* the hero is a kind of layman saint who discovers that he is the master of his fortune through a mistake; he wants to give it all up immediately. Gradually the poor hero is brought to the verge of madness and condemned by society. Fortunately the work is in prose and stirs the audience's emotions violently enough without lapsing into facile melodrama, thanks to the noble nature of the principal character and to the ideal that both exalts him and overwhelms him at the same time.

But Echegaray's greatest triumph was on March 19, 1891, when *The Great Galeoto* appeared. In this play he strongly condemns contemporary society, and rises up in indignation against the calumnies, the scandals, and the prejudices that engender so much social conflict.

The concentrated action, the weightiness of the theme, and the structural ingenuity of the subject all contributed to the fame of this work; in Spain and a number of other countries it achieved a real triumph.

In *Son of Don Juan,* he deals with the question of hereditary pathology. Although he gives the theme an original slant of his own, he sincerely acknowledges his debt to Ibsen. He also adds a highly moral lesson with the punishment of the sins of the fathers. In the painful childhood of the invalid son it is as though he sees the renewal of a purified world. This play is noticeably direct and analytical and is filled with intimate dramatic poetry, always enhanced by scenic skill that is consistent throughout. The play successfully revives the legendary Don Juan without the murders and the violence; it is filled with a pure sense of the morals of everyday life.

Ibsen's shadow fell once more on Echegaray in 1900, when his *El loco Dios* (The Mad God) appeared. In this play the principal character, Gabriel, is a superman in love with goodness and justice. Ultimately he believes himself to be God, but in fact he ends by merely becoming a hospital case. The play alternates between the facts of this case (which are really rather banal and only of scientific interest) and an immense twilight of the gods confronting a society withered by self-interest and envy.

Echegaray's plays were frequently written for some particular actor or actress and in an important first series he made use of the talents of Antonio Vico, Rafael and Ricardo Calvo, Elisa Boldun, and Elisa Mendoza Tenorio. Later, he wrote for the famous pair of comedians, the sovereigns of the Spanish stage, Maria Guerrero and Fernando Diaz de Mendoza. In particular these two made the following plays famous: *La Duda* (Doubt), *El estigma* (The Stigmata), *Mancha que limpia* (Spot that Cleans), *Mariana,* and *A fuerza de arrastrarse* (By Dint of Crawling, 1905).

Echegaray also wrote a play on the life and death of Michel Servet, set in the gloom of Calvinist Geneva, called *La muerte en los labios* (Death on the Lips). It is a human tragedy, an appeal to tolerance, which does not distort history unduly.

Among his later works, *Mariana* is one that returns to the theme of honor pursued by a kind of mortal obsession. The disposition of the scenes, the skillful dialogue, the poetry mixed with genuine realism, and the grandeur of the central character make it one of the author's most important works.

After 1905, Echegaray was not heard again, and Benavente took his place in the theaters of Madrid.

There is no doubt that Echegaray loved to overdramatize the problems of conscience and moral conflict. But this was how he perpetuated the essential inspiration of the theater of the golden age, in which he was completely immersed. His vision of man is more external than internal. There is no painstaking analysis of a passion or a character, and he allows himself to be carried away by arbitrariness, or by a taste for shaking the spectators' nerves.

Echegaray also seems obsessed by abnormality, and perhaps it is pertinent to search for the cause of this in his early memories. In his youth there had at times been signs of monomania; as a small child he had reduced his family to despair by refusing to eat. His mother, a vital and devout Basque woman, endowed him with some of the characteristics of her strong personality, whereas his Aragonese father bequeathed him only an undeniable obstinacy.

As an exile in Paris, he lived under conditions of fairly severe adversity. Critical opinion in Madrid at that time did not spare him at all; the public refused to consider him as anything other than an amateur, and dismissed him as a mere scientist. And yet no other writer at that time possessed his warm, pulsating lyricism, which unfortunately he could express only in hard, forced verse. No one else wrote with the conciseness of the classical tradition that characterizes all his work, and he was, more than any other writer, the legitimate descendant of Calderón, whose dramatic genius had pervaded the whole of the seventeenth century. Echoes of *Life Is a Dream* can be heard in many of his works, with that strange mixture of dream and reality in which all frontiers are undefined. There is the same intense need to bring to life the longing and the melancholy that spring from the impossibility of that dream, to which the dreamer clings with such despairing faith.

Perhaps this explains the somewhat artificial character of his dramatic work: most of the plots were written before the play itself, which is therefore subordinated. Furthermore, he always preferred to use exceptional, surprising, or extraordinary situations rather than natural human actions, to the detriment of simplicity and verisimilitude. There is also some obscurity of thought and a certain coldness in the expression of feeling.

Nevertheless, Echegaray, who claimed to love mathematics, literature, and politics equally, is one of the most important figures in the nineteenth-century theater. He wrote plays of unquestionable power which stir human emotions with a heartening warmth and eloquence that carry the audience away. His tragic figures are grand and his subjects are many and various. He is the obvious link between moribund Romanticism and the realistic and symbolist plays that were to occupy the Spanish theater after him. Certain of his plays even foreshadow the masterpieces produced during his brief career by Federico García Lorca, of whom the contemporary theater had such high hopes.

Jean Camp is professor of literature in Aix-en-Provence.
Translated by Camilla Sykes.

THE 1904 PRIZE

By GUNNAR AHLSTRÖM

IT SEEMED both well-advised and fair to divide the Literature Prize of 1904 between Frédéric Mistral and José Echegaray. But in actual fact this decision was of a kind to raise psychological problems and stir up divergent opinions. How would the chosen writers welcome this division, and what would people say in the two countries concerned? Were "half-masters" and "half-laureates" about to be honored? This fine gesture might stir up rivalries and provoke polemical comparisons.

Without any doubt, Mistral, the master of Maillane, was the more accessible of the two, enjoyed the greater popularity, and was haloed in the balmy light of the skies of Provence. Echegaray was more cerebral, more difficult. It was indeed possible to celebrate in him the incarnation of the Latin spirit—as Paul Déroulède hastened to do in *Le Gaulois* —and even to applaud this double choice by recognizing it as a triumph of the common heritage of the Mediterranean peoples. However, the *Journal des Débats* took a rather severe line, and was not the only one to do so: "The choice of Mistral should not and does not meet with anything except unanimous approval. That of José Echegaray, on the other hand, is more debatable. A mathematician turned poet late in life, a statesman and dramatist, José Echegaray's work presents a strange combination of contradictory talents. Although his long career has shown him to be endowed with great ability, and although his plays are sometimes original and interesting, Monsieur Echegaray has not written a single masterpiece, and in the world literature of our epoch posterity will not place him in the first rank."

As both of the winners were full of years they did not attempt the journey to Stockholm for the ceremony of December 10, and they could not exchange smiles of friendship on the same platform: but each of them, from his home, tried to outdo the other in an exchange of courtesies from a distance. Echegaray hastened to enter into relations with Mistral in a series of letters of immense courtesy and subtlety. This written dialogue is significant, not only of the high-mindedness of the two laureates, but also of the fact that this dividing of the Prize assumed the importance of a sacred union between French and Spanish literature. Certain commentators observed that the Pyrenees had once again bowed graciously and melted away. It was in this same spirit that Echegaray sent a few lines to *L'Illustration*, which were as flattering to the two men who had received the Prize as to the people who had awarded it: "The illustrious Swedish Academy, which so worthily represents the powerful intellectual element of these Northern regions, has this year united two sister literatures in the Nobel Prize. A nation which exerts itself so valiantly still further to tighten the bonds between two peoples thereby remains united to them by a similar feeling of universal brotherhood."

These gentlemen of Stockholm, who thus found themselves integrated into universal brotherhood in this rather off-hand way, had a very special reason to look toward Spain. Madrid and its Real Academia Española was entitled to a certain consideration. The venerable assembly beyond the Pyrenees, founded in 1719, was, with the Académie Française, the only sister literary society to which the Swedish Academy could turn for help in the proposal of candidates. This, moreover, is what had happened, and the answers were quickly forthcoming. Thus it was that in 1901 the elderly poet Gaspar Núñez de Arce was proposed by the permanent secretary of the Spanish Academy, and his name was again brought forward by the official spokesman in 1902 and in 1903. José Echegaray was proposed in 1902 in a petition signed by twelve Academicians, and again proposed the following year, this time backed by fourteen signatures. After the death of Núñez de Arce in 1903, there were no further doubts as to the choice.

In his autobiography Wedel Jarlsberg devotes a chapter to the Echegaray episode. In the spring of 1904 the Swedish Academy asked him to present the half–

Nobel Prize to its Spanish winner, with suitable ceremony. In this world of blue-blooded *hidalgos* he considered that the accomplishment of this mission should be the occasion for special display. It was not enough to gather together a certain number of unimportant notables for a ceremony in the Teatro Real: it was the easiest thing in the world to organize a trifle of this kind, and in fact it took place on the evening of March 18. A beautifully drilled procession marched off from the Plaza Oriental and filed past as far as the Palacio de los Bibliotecas, situated at the opposite end of the capital. The blare of trumpets mixed with the roll of drums. Detachments of the army and navy marched at the head, followed by delegations from the literary and scientific societies and the welfare associations. Other corporations helped to swell this enormous procession of thirty thousand participants carrying two hundred banners. The immense parade at last arrived at the Senate, and a grand ceremony was held in the assembly hall.

On the platform the young and charming monarch, Alfonso XIII, took his place, surrounded by dignitaries of the Court, ministers and members of the diplomatic corps. All the literary, artistic, and scientific world of Madrid was represented at this gathering. The Swedish Minister expressed his admiration for José Echegaray in eloquent terms and requested the privilege of conveying the diploma and the gold medal of the Nobel Prize to him, by the hand of His Majesty the King.

Translated by Camilla Sykes.

T. S. Eliot

1948

"For his outstanding, pioneer

contribution to present-day poetry"

Illustrated by CARZOU

PRESENTATION ADDRESS

By ANDERS ÖSTERLING

PERMANENT SECRETARY
OF THE SWEDISH ACADEMY

IN THE IMPRESSIVE succession of Nobel Prizewinners for Literature, T. S. Eliot marks a departure from the type of writer that has most frequently gained that distinction. The majority have been representatives of literature which seeks its natural contacts in the public consciousness, and which, to attain this goal, avails itself of the media lying more or less ready at hand. This year's Prizewinner has chosen to take another path. His career is remarkable in that, from an extremely exclusive and consciously isolated position, he has gradually come to exercise a very far-reaching influence. At the outset he appeared to address himself to but a small circle of initiates, but this circle slowly widened, without his appearing to will it himself. Thus in Eliot's verse and prose there was quite a special accent, which compelled attention just in our own time, a capacity to cut into the consciousness of our generation with the sharpness of a diamond.

In one of his essays Eliot himself has advanced, as a purely objective and quite uncategorical assumption, that poets in our present civilization have to be difficult to approach. "Our civilization," he says, "comprehends great variety and complexity, and this variety and complexity, playing upon a refined sensibility, must produce various and complex results. The poet must become more and more comprehensive, more allusive, more indirect, in order to force, to dislocate if necessary, language into his meaning."

Against the background of such a pronouncement, we may test his results and learn to understand the importance of his contribution. The effort is worthwhile. Eliot first gained his reputation as the result of his magnificent experiment in poetry, *The Waste Land,* which appeared in 1922 and then seemed bewildering in several ways, because of its complicated symbolic language, its mosaic-like technique, and its apparatus of erudite allusion. It may be recalled that this work appeared in the same year as another pioneer work, which had a still more sensational effect on modern literature, the much discussed *Ulysses,* from the hand of an Irishman, James Joyce. The parallel is by no means fortuitous, for these products of the nineteen-twenties are closely akin to one another, in both spirit and mode of composition.

The Waste Land—a title whose terrifying import no one can help feeling, when the difficult and masterly word-pattern has finally yielded up its secrets. The melancholy and somber rhapsody aims at describing the aridity and impotence of modern civilization, in a series of sometimes realistic and sometimes mythological episodes, whose perspectives impinge on each other with an indescribable total effect. The cycle of poems consists of 436 lines, but actually it contains more than a packed novel of as many pages. *The Waste Land* now lies a quarter of a century back in time, but unfortunately it has proved that its catastrophic visions still have undiminished actuality in the shadow of the atomic age.

Since then Eliot has passed on to a series of poetic creations of the same brilliant concentration, in pursuance of the agonized, salvation-seeking main theme. The *horror vacui* of modern man in a secularized world, without order, meaning, or beauty, here stands out with poignant sincerity. In his latest work *Four Quartets* (1943), Eliot has arrived at a meditative music of words, with almost liturgical refrains and fine, exact expressions of his spiritual experiences. The transcendental superstructure rises ever clearer in his world picture. At the same time a manifest striving after a positive, guiding message emerges in his dramatic art, especially in the mighty historical play about Thomas of Canterbury, *Murder in the Cathedral* (1935), but also in *The Family Reunion* (1939), which is a bold attempt to combine such different conceptions as the Christian dogma of original sin and the classical Greek myths of fate, in an entirely modern environment, with the scene laid in a country house in northern England.

The purely poetical part of Eliot's work is not quantitatively great, but as it now stands out against the horizon, it rises from the ocean like a rocky peak and indisputably forms a landmark, sometimes assuming the mystic contours of a cathedral. It is poetry impressed with the stamp of strict responsibility and extraordinary self-discipline, remote from all emotional clichés, concentrated entirely on essential things, stark, granitic, and unadorned, but from time to time illuminated by a sudden ray from the timeless space of miracles and revelations.

Insight into Eliot must always present certain problems to be overcome, obstacles which are at the same time stimulating. It may appear to be contradictory to say that this radical pioneer of form, the initiator of a whole revolution in style within present-day poetry, is at the same time a coldly reasoning, logically subtle theorist, who never wearies of defending historical perspectives and the necessity of fixed norms for our existence. As early as the 1940's, he had become a convinced supporter of the Anglican Church in religion and of classicism in literature. In view of this philosophy of life which implies a consistent return to ideals standardized by age, it might seem that his modernistic practice would clash with his traditional theory. But this is hardly the case. Rather, in his capacity as an author, he has uninterruptedly and with varying success worked to bridge this chasm, the existence of which he must be fully and perhaps painfully conscious of. His earliest poetry, so convulsively disintegrated, so studiously aggressive in its whole technical form, can finally also be apprehended as a negative expression of a mentality which aims at higher and purer realities and must first free itself of abhorrence and cynicism. In other words, his revolt is that of the Christian poet. It should also be observed in this connection that, on the whole, Eliot is careful not to magnify the power of poetry in relation to that of religion. In one place, where he wishes to point out what poetry can really accomplish for our inner life, he does so with great caution and reserve: "It may make us from to time a little more aware of the deeper, unnamed feelings which form the substratum of our being, to which we rarely penetrate; for our lives are mostly a constant evasion of ourselves."

Thus, if it can be said with some justification that Eliot's philosophical position is based on nothing but tradition, it ought nevertheless to be borne in mind that he constantly points out how generally that word has been misused in today's debates. The word "tradition" itself implies movement, something which cannot be static, something which is constantly handed on and assimilated. In the poetic tradition, too, this living principle prevails. The existing monuments of literature form an idealistic order, but this is slightly modified every time a new work is added to the series. Proportions and values are unceasingly changing. Just as the old directs the new, this in its turn directs the old, and the poet who realizes this must also realize the scope of his difficulties and his responsiblity.

Externally, too, the now sixty-year-old Eliot has also returned to Europe, the ancient and storm-tossed, but still venerable, home of cultural traditions. Born an American, he comes from one of the Puritan families who emigrated from England at the end of the seventeenth century. His years of study as a young man at the Sorbonne, at Marburg, and at Oxford, clearly revealed to him that at bottom he felt akin to the historical milieu of the Old World, and since 1927 Mr. Eliot has been a British subject.

It is not possible in this presentation to indicate more than the most immediate fascinating features in the complicated multiplicity of Eliot's characteristics as a writer. The predominating one is the high, philosophically schooled intelligence, which has succeeded in enlisting in its service both imagination and learning, both sensitivity and the analysis of ideas. His capacity for stimulating a reconsideration of pressing questions within intellectual and aesthetic opinion is also extraordinary, and however much the appraisal may vary, it can never be denied that in his period he has been an eminent poser of questions, with a masterly gift for finding the apt wording, both in the language of poetry and in the defense of ideas in essay form.

Nor is it due only to chance that he has written one of the finest studies of Dante's work and personality. In his bitter moral pathos, in his metaphysical line of thought, and in his burning longing for a world order inspired by religion, a *civitas dei,* Eliot has indeed certain points of contact with the great Florentine poet. It redounds to his honor that, amidst the varied conditions of his milieu, he can be justly characterized as one of Dante's most recent successors. In his message we hear solemn echoes from other times, but that message does not by any means therefore become less real when it is given to our own time and to us who are now living.

Mr. Eliot—According to the diploma, the award is made chiefly in appreciation of your remarkable achievements as a pioneer in modern poetry. I have here tried to give a brief survey of this very important work of yours, which is admired by many ardent readers in this country.

Exactly twenty-five years ago, there stood where you are now standing another famous poet who wrote in the English tongue, William Butler Yeats. The honor now passes to you as being a leader and a champion of a new period in the long history of the world's poetry.

With the felicitations of the Swedish Academy, I now ask you to receive your Prize from the hands of His Royal Highness the Crown Prince.

ACCEPTANCE SPEECH

By T. S. ELIOT

When I began to think of what I should say to you this evening, I wished only to express very simply my appreciation of the high honor which the Swedish Academy has thought fit to confer upon me. But to do this adequately proved no simple task: my business is with words, yet the words were beyond my command. Merely to indicate that I was aware of having received the highest international honor that can be bestowed upon a man of letters, would be only to say what everyone knows already. To profess my own unworthiness would be to cast doubt upon the wisdom of the Academy; to praise the Academy might suggest that I, as a literary critic, approved the recognition given to myself as a poet. May I therefore ask that it be taken for granted, that I experienced, on learning of this award to myself, all the normal emotions of exaltation and vanity that any human being might be expected to feel at such a moment, with enjoyment of the flattery, and exasperation at the inconvenience, of being turned overnight into a public figure? Were the Nobel award similar in kind to any other award, and merely higher in degree, I might still try to find words of appreciation: but since it is different in kind from any other, the expression of one's feelings calls for resources which language cannot supply.

I must therefore try to express myself in an indirect way, by putting before you my own interpretation of the significance of the Nobel Prize for Literature. If this were simply the recognition of merit, or of the fact that an author's reputation has passed the boundaries of his own country and his own language, we could say that hardly any one of us at any time is, more than others, worthy of being so distinguished. But I find in the Nobel award something more and something different from such recognition. It seems to me more the election of an individual, chosen from time to time from one nation or another, and selected by something like an act of grace, to fill a peculiar role and to become a peculiar symbol. A ceremony takes place, by which a man is suddenly endowed with some function which he did not fill before. So the question is not whether he was worthy to be so singled out, but whether he can perform the function which you have assigned to him: the function of serving as a representative, so far as any man can be, of something of far greater importance than the value of what he himself has written.

Poetry is usually considered the most local of all the arts. Painting, sculpture, architecture, music, can be enjoyed by all who see or hear. But language, especially the language of poetry, is a different matter. Poetry, it might seem, separates peoples instead of uniting them.

But on the other hand we must remember, that while language constitutes a barrier, poetry itself gives us a reason for trying to overcome the barrier. To enjoy poetry belonging to another language, is to enjoy an understanding of the people to whom that language belongs, an understanding we can get in no other way. We may think also of the history of poetry in Europe, and of the great influence that the poetry of one language can exert on another; we must remember the immense debt of every considerable poet to poets of other languages than his own; we may reflect that the poetry of every country and every language would decline and perish, were it not nourished by poetry in foreign tongues. When a poet speaks to his own people, the voices of all the poets of other languages who have influenced him are speaking also. And at the same time he himself is speaking to younger poets of other languages, and these poets will convey something of *his* vision of life and something of the spirit of *his* people, to their own. Partly through his influence on other poets, partly through translation, which must be also a kind of re-creation of his poems by other poets, partly through readers of his language who are not themselves poets, the poet can contribute toward understanding between peoples.

In the work of every poet there will certainly be much that can only appeal to those who inhabit the same region, or speak the same language, as the poet. But nevertheless there is a meaning to the phrase "the poetry of Europe," and even to the word "poetry" the world over. I think that in poetry people of different countries and different languages —though it be apparently only through a small minority in any one country—acquire an understanding of each other which, however partial, is still essential. And I take the award of the Nobel Prize in Literature, when it is given to a poet, to be primarily an assertion of the supra-national value of poetry. To make that affirmation, it is necessary from time to time to designate a poet: and I stand before you, not on my own merits, but as a symbol, for a time, of the significance of poetry.

POEMS

By T. S. ELIOT

THE LOVE SONG OF J. ALFRED PRUFROCK

S'io credesse che mia risposta fosse
A persona che mai tornasse al mondo,
Questa fiamma staria senza piu scosse.
Ma perciocche giammai di questo fondo
Non torno vivo alcun, s'i'odo il vero,
Senza tema d'infamia ti rispondo.

Let us go then, you and I,
When the evening is spread out against the sky
Like a patient etherized upon a table;
Let us go, through certain half-deserted streets,
The muttering retreats
Of restless nights in one-night cheap hotels
And sawdust restaurants with oyster-shells:
Streets that follow like a tedious argument
Of insidious intent
To lead you to an overwhelming question . . .
Oh, do not ask, "What is it?"
Let us go and make our visit.

In the room the women come and go
Talking of Michelangelo.

The yellow fog that rubs its back upon the window-panes,
The yellow smoke that rubs its muzzle on the window-panes
Licked its tongue into the corners of the evening,

Lingered upon the pools that stand in drains,
Let fall upon its back the soot that falls from chimneys,
Slipped by the terrace, made a sudden leap,
And seeing that it was a soft October night,
Curled once about the house, and fell asleep.

    And indeed there will be time
For the yellow smoke that slides along the street,
Rubbing its back upon the window-panes;
There will be time, there will be time
To prepare a face to meet the faces that you meet;
There will be time to murder and create,
And time for all the works and days of hands
That lift and drop a question on your plate;
Time for you and time for me,
And time yet for a hundred indecisions,
And for a hundred visions and revisions,
Before the taking of a toast and tea.

    In the room the women come and go
Talking of Michelangelo.

    And indeed there will be time
To wonder, "Do I dare?" and, "Do I dare?"
Time to turn back and descend the stair,
With a bald spot in the middle of my hair—
[They will say: "How his hair is growing thin!"]
My morning coat, my collar mounting firmly to the chin,
My necktie rich and modest, but asserted by a simple pin—
[They will say: "But how his arms and legs are thin!"]
Do I dare
Disturb the universe?
In a minute there is time
For decisions and revisions which a minute will reverse.

    For I have known them all already, known them all:—
Have known the evenings, mornings, afternoons,

have measured out my life with coffee spoons;
know the voices dying with a dying fall
Beneath the music from a farther room.
      So how should I presume?

      And I have known the eyes already, known them all—
The eyes that fix you in a formulated phrase,
And when I am formulated, sprawling on a pin,
When I am pinned and wriggling on the wall,
Then how should I begin
To spit out all the butt-ends of my days and ways?
      And how should I presume?

      And I have known the arms already, known them all—
Arms that are braceleted and white and bare
 But in the lamplight, downed with light brown hair!]
Is it perfume from a dress
That makes me so digress?
Arms that lie along a table, or wrap about a shawl.
      And should I then presume?
      And how should I begin?

                    .   .   .   .   .

Shall I say, I have gone at dusk through narrow streets
And watched the smoke that rises from the pipes
Of lonely men in shirt-sleeves, leaning out of windows? . . .

      I should have been a pair of ragged claws
Scuttling across the floors of silent seas.

                    .   .   .   .   .

And the afternoon, the evening, sleeps so peacefully!
Smoothed by long fingers,
Asleep . . . tired . . . or it malingers,
Stretched on the floor, here beside you and me.
Should I, after tea and cakes and ices,
Have the strength to force the moment to its crisis?
But though I have wept and fasted, wept and prayed,

Though I have seen my head [grown slightly bald] brought in upon a platter,
I am no prophet—and here's no great matter;
I have seen the moment of my greatness flicker,
And I have seen the eternal Footman hold my coat, and snicker,
And in short, I was afraid.

    And would it have been worth it, after all,
After the cups, the marmalade, the tea,
Among the porcelain, among some talk of you and me,
Would it have been worth while,
To have bitten off the matter with a smile,
To have squeezed the universe into a ball
To roll it toward some overwhelming question,
To say: "I am Lazarus, come from the dead,
Come back to tell you all, I shall tell you all"—
If one, settling a pillow by her head,
  Should say: "That is not what I meant at all.
  That is not it, at all."

    And would it have been worth it, after all,
Would it have been worth while,
After the sunsets and the dooryards and the sprinkled streets,
After the novels, after the teacups, after the skirts that trail along the floor—
And this, and so much more?—
It is impossible to say just what I mean!
But as if a magic lantern threw the nerves in patterns on a screen:
Would it have been worth while
If one, settling a pillow or throwing off a shawl,
And turning toward the window, should say:
  "That is not it at all,
  That is not what I meant, at all."

             . . . . .

No! I am not Prince Hamlet, nor was meant to be;
Am an attendant lord, one that will do
To swell a progress, start a scene or two,
Advise the prince; no doubt, an easy tool,
Deferential, glad to be of use,

Politic, cautious, and meticulous;
Full of high sentence, but a bit obtuse;
At times, indeed, almost ridiculous—
Almost, at times, the Fool.

I grow old . . . I grow old . . .
I shall wear the bottoms of my trousers rolled.

Shall I part my hair behind? Do I dare to eat a peach?
I shall wear white flannel trousers, and walk upon the beach.
I have heard the mermaids singing, each to each.

I do not think that they will sing to me.

I have seen them riding seaward on the waves
Combing the white hair of the waves blown back
When the wind blows the water white and black.

We have lingered in the chambers of the sea
By sea-girls wreathed with seaweed red and brown
Till human voices wake us, and we drown.

SWEENEY ERECT

> *And the trees about me,*
> *Let them be dry and leafless; let the rocks*
> *Groan with continual surges; and behind me*
> *Make all a desolation. Look, look, wenches!*

Paint me a cavernous waste shore
    Cast in the unstilled Cyclades,
Paint me the bold anfractuous rocks
    Faced by the snarled and yelping seas.

Display me Aeolus above
    Reviewing the insurgent gales

[275]

Which tangle Ariadne's hair
   And swell with haste the perjured sails.

Morning stirs the feet and hands
   (Nausicaa and Polypheme).
Gesture of orang-outang
   Rises from the sheets in steam.

This withered root of knots of hair
   Slitted below and gashed with eyes,
This oval O cropped out with teeth:
   The sickle motion from the thighs

Jackknifes upward at the knees
   Then straightens out from heel to hip
Pushing the framework of the bed
   And clawing at the pillow slip.

Sweeney addressed full length to shave
   Broadbottomed, pink from nape to base,
Knows the female temperament
   And wipes the suds around his face.

(The lengthened shadow of a man
   Is history, said Emerson
Who had not seen the silhouette
   Of Sweeney straddled in the sun.)

Tests the razor on his leg
   Waiting until the shriek subsides.
The epileptic on the bed
   Curves backward, clutching at her sides.

The ladies of the corridor
   Find themselves involved, disgraced,
Call witness to their principles
   And deprecate the lack of taste

Observing that hysteria
    Might easily be misunderstood;
Mrs. Turner intimates
    It does the house no sort of good.

But Doris, toweled from the bath,
    Enters padding on broad feet,
Bringing sal volatile
    And a glass of brandy neat.

MR. ELIOT'S SUNDAY MORNING SERVICE

Look, look, master, here comes two religious caterpillars.
THE JEW OF MALTA.

Polyphiloprogenitive
The sapient sutlers of the Lord
Drift across the window-panes.
In the beginning was the Word.

In the beginning was the Word.
Superfetation of τὸ ἕν,
And at the mensual turn of time
Produced enervate Origen.

A painter of the Umbrian school
Designed upon a gesso ground
The nimbus of the Baptized God.
The wilderness is cracked and browned

But through the water pale and thin
Still shine the unoffending feet
And there above the painter set
The Father and the Paraclete.

. . . . .

The sable presbyters approach
The avenue of penitence;
The young are red and pustular
Clutching piaculative pence.

Under the penitential gates
Sustained by staring Seraphim
Where the souls of the devout
Burn invisible and dim.

Along the garden-wall the bees
With hairy bellies pass between
The staminate and pistilate,
Blest office of the epicene.

Sweeney shifts from ham to ham
Stirring the water in his bath.
The master of the subtle schools
Are controversial, polymath.

SWEENEY AMONG THE NIGHTINGALES

ὤμοι, πέπληγμαι καιρίαν πληγὴν ἔσω.

Apeneck Sweeney spreads his knees
Letting his arms hang down to laugh,
The zebra stripes along his jaw
Swelling to maculate giraffe.

The circles of the stormy moon
Slide westward toward the River Plate,
Death and the Raven drift above
And Sweeney guards the hornèd gate.

Gloomy Orion and the Dog
Are veiled; and hushed the shrunken seas;

The person in the Spanish cape
Tries to sit on Sweeney's knees

Slips and pulls the table cloth
Overturns a coffee-cup,
Reorganized upon the floor
She yawns and draws a stocking up;

The silent man in mocha brown
Sprawls at the window-sill and gapes;
The waiter brings in oranges
Bananas figs and hothouse grapes;

The silent vertebrate in brown
Contracts and concentrates, withdraws;
Rachel *née* Rabinovitch
Tears at the grapes with murderous paws;

She and the lady in the cape
Are suspect, thought to be in league;
Therefore the man with heavy eyes
Declines the gambit, shows fatigue,

Leaves the room and reappears
Outside the window, leaning in,
Branches of wistaria
Circumscribe a golden grin;

The host with someone indistinct
Converses at the door apart,
The nightingales are singing near
The Convent of the Sacred Heart,

And sang within the bloody wood
When Agamemnon cried aloud,
And let their liquid siftings fall
To stain the stiff dishonored shroud.

LINES FOR CUSCUSCARAWAY AND
MIRZA MURAD ALI BEG

How unpleasant to meet Mr. Eliot!
With his features of clerical cut,
And his brow so grim
And his mouth so prim
And his conversation, so nicely
Restricted to What Precisely
And If and Perhaps and But.
How unpleasant to meet Mr. Eliot!
With a bobtail cur
In a coat of fur
And a porpentine cat
And a wopsical hat:
How unpleasant to meet Mr. Eliot!
                    (Whether his mouth be open or shut).

THE ELDER STATESMAN

By T. S. ELIOT

CHARACTERS

MONICA CLAVERTON-FERRY

CHARLES HEMINGTON

LAMBERT

LORD CLAVERTON

FEDERICO GOMEZ

MRS. PIGGOTT

MRS. CARGHILL

MICHAEL CLAVERTON-FERRY

ACT I

The drawing-room of LORD CLAVERTON's *London house.*
Four o'clock in the afternoon.

ACT II

The Terrace at Badgley Court. Morning.

ACT III

The Same. Late afternoon of the following day.

[281]

ACT ONE

The drawing-room of LORD CLAVERTON's *London house. Four o'clock in the afternoon.* (*Voices in the hall*)

CHARLES. Is your father at home today?

MONICA. You'll see him at tea.

CHARLES. But if I'm going to have you to myself
    There's really no point in my staying to tea.
    (*Enter* MONICA *and* CHARLES *carrying parcels*)

MONICA. But you *must* stay to tea. That was understood
    When you said you could give me the whole afternoon.

CHARLES. But I couldn't say what I wanted to say to you
    Over luncheon . . .

MONICA. That's your own fault.
    You should have taken me to some other restaurant
    Instead of to one where the *maître d'hôtel*
    And the waiters all seem to be your intimate friends.

CHARLES. It's the only place where I'm really well known
    And get well served. And when *you're* with me
    It must be a perfect lunch.

MONICA. It was a perfect lunch.
    But I know what men are—they like to show off.
    That's masculine vanity, to want to have the waiters
    All buzzing round you: and it reminds the girl
    That she's not the only one who's been there with him.

CHARLES. Well, tease me if you like. But a man does feel a fool
    If he takes you to a place where he's utterly unknown
    And the waiters all appear to be avoiding his eye.

MONICA. We're getting off the point . . .

CHARLES. You've got me off *my* point . . .
    I was trying to explain . . .

MONICA. It's simply the question
    Of your staying to tea. As you practically promised.

CHARLES. What you don't understand is that I have a grievance.
On Monday you're leaving London, with your father:
I arranged to be free for the whole afternoon
On the plain understanding . . .
MONICA. That you should stop to tea.
CHARLES. When I said that I was free for the whole afternoon,
That meant you were to give *me* the whole afternoon.
I couldn't say what I wanted to, in a restaurant;
And then you took me on a shopping expedition . . .
MONICA. If you don't like shopping with me . . .
CHARLES. Of course I like shopping with you.
But how can one *talk* on a shopping expedition—
Except to guess what you want to buy
And advise you to buy it.
MONICA. But why not stop to tea?
CHARLES. Very well then, I will stop to tea,
But you know I won't get a chance to talk to you.
You know that. Now that your father's retired
He's at home every day. And you're leaving London.
And because your father simply can't bear it
That any man but he should have you to himself,
Before I've said two words he'll come ambling in . . .
MONICA. You've said a good deal more than two words already.
And besides, my father doesn't amble.
You're not at all respectful.
CHARLES. I try to be respectful;
But you know that I shan't have a minute alone with you.
MONICA. You've already had several minutes alone with me
Which you've wasted in wrangling. But seriously, Charles,
Father's sure to be buried in the library
And he won't think of leaving it until he's called for tea.
So why not talk now? Though I know very well
What it is you want to say. I've heard it all before.
CHARLES. And you'll hear it again. You think I'm going to tell you
Once more, that I'm in love with you. Well, you're right.
But I've something else to say that I haven't said before,
That will give you a shock. I believe *you* love *me*.
MONICA. Oh, what a dominating man you are!

Really, you must imagine you're a hypnotist.

CHARLES. Is this a time to torment me? But I'm selfish
In saying that, because I think—
I think you're tormenting yourself as well.

MONICA. You're right. I am. Because I *am* in love with you.

CHARLES. So I was right! The moment I'd said it
I was badly frightened. For I didn't *know* you loved me—
I merely wanted to believe it. And I've made you say so!
But now that you've said so, you must say it again,
For I need so much assurance! Are you sure you're not mistaken?

MONICA. How did this come, Charles? It crept so softly
On silent feet, and stood behind my back
Quietly, a long time, a long long time
Before I felt its presence.

CHARLES. Your words seem to come
From very far away. Yet very near. You are changing me
And I am changing you.

MONICA. Already
How much of me is you?

CHARLES. And how much of me is you?
I'm not the same person as a moment ago.
What do the words mean now—*I* and *you?*

MONICA. In our private world—now we have our private world—
The meanings are different. Look! We're back in the room
That we entered only a few minutes ago.
Here's an armchair, there the table;
There's the door . . . and I hear someone coming:
It's Lambert with the tea . . .
(*Enter* LAMBERT *with trolley*)
                    and I shall say, "Lambert,
Please let his lordship know the tea is waiting."

LAMBERT. Yes, Miss Monica.

MONICA. I'm very glad, Charles,
That you *can* stay to tea.
                              (*Exit* LAMBERT)
—Now we're in the public world.

CHARLES. And your father will come. With his calm possessive air
And his kindly welcome, which is always a reminder

That I mustn't stay too long, for you belong to him.
He seems so placidly to take it for granted
That you don't really care for any company but his!

MONICA. You're not to assume that anything I've said to you
Has given you the right to criticize my father.
In the first place, you don't understand him;
In the second place, we're not engaged yet.

CHARLES. Aren't we? We're agreed that we're in love with each other,
And, there being no legal impediment
Isn't that enough to constitute an engagement?
Aren't you sure that you want to marry me?

MONICA. Yes, Charles. I'm sure that I want to marry you
When I'm free to do so. But by that time
You may have changed your mind. Such things have happened.

CHARLES. That won't happen to me.

(*Knock. Enter* LAMBERT)

LAMBERT. Excuse me, Miss Monica. His Lordship said to tell you
Not to wait tea for him.

MONICA. Thank you, Lambert.

LAMBERT. He's busy at the moment. But he won't be very long. (*Exit*)

CHARLES. Don't you understand that you're torturing me?
How long will you be imprisoned, alone with your father
In that very expensive hotel for convalescents
To which you're taking him? And what after that?

MONICA. There are several good reasons why I should go with him.

CHARLES. Better reasons than for marrying me?
What reasons?

MONICA. First, his terror of being alone.
In the life he's led, he's never had to be alone.
And when he's been at home in the evening,
Even when he's reading, or busy with his papers,
He needs to have someone else in the room with him,
Reading too—or just sitting—someone
Not occupied with anything that can't be interrupted.
Someone to make a remark to now and then.
And mostly it's been me.

CHARLES. I know it's been you.
It's a pity that you haven't had brothers and sisters

To share the burden. Sisters, I should say,
For your brother's never been of any use to you.

MONICA. And never will be of any use to anybody,
I'm afraid. Poor Michael! Mother spoiled him
And Father was too severe—so they're always at loggerheads.

CHARLES. But you spoke of several reasons for your going with your father.
Is there any better reason than his fear of solitude?

MONICA. The second reason is exactly the opposite:
It's his fear of being exposed to strangers.

CHARLES. But he's most alive when he's among people
Managing, maneuvering, cajoling or bullying—
At all of which he's a master. Strangers!

MONICA. You don't understand. It's one thing meeting people
When you're in authority, with authority's costume,
When the man that people see when they meet you
Is not the private man, but the public personage.
In politics Father wore a public label.
And later, as chairman of public companies,
Always his privacy has been preserved.

CHARLES. His privacy has been so well preserved
That I've sometimes wondered whether there was any . . .
Private self to preserve.

MONICA. There *is* a private self, Charles.
I'm sure of that.

CHARLES. You've given two reasons,
One the contradiction of the other.
Can there be a third?

MONICA. The third reason is this:
I've only just been given it by Dr. Selby—
Father is much iller than he is aware of:
It may be, he will never return from Badgley Court.
But Selby wants him to have every encouragement—
If he's hopeful, he's likely to live a little longer.
That's why Selby chose the place. A *convalescent* home
With the atmosphere of an hotel—
Nothing about it to suggest the clinic—
Everything about it to suggest recovery.

CHARLES. This is your best reason, and the most depressing;
    For this situation may persist for a long time,
    And you'll go on postponing and postponing our marriage.
MONICA. I'm afraid . . . not a very long time, Charles.
    It's almost certain that the winter in Jamaica
    Will never take place. "Make the reservations,"
    Selby said, "as if you were going."
    But Badgley Court's so near your constituency!
    You can come down at weekends, even when the House is sitting.
    And you can take me out, if Father can spare me.
    But he'll simply love having you to talk to!
CHARLES. I know he's used to seeing me about.
MONICA. I've seen him looking at you. He was thinking of himself
    When he was your age—when he started like you,
    With the same hopes, the same ambitions—
    And of his disappointments.
CHARLES. Is that wistfulness,
    Compassion, or . . . envy?
MONICA. Envy is everywhere.
    Who is without envy? And most people
    Are unaware or unashamed of being envious.
    It's all we can ask if compassion and wistfulness . . .
    And tenderness, Charles! Are mixed with envy:
    I do believe that he is fond of you.
    So you must come often. And oh, Charles dear—
    (*Enter* LORD CLAVERTON)
MONICA. You've been very long in coming, Father. What have you been
    doing?
LORD CLAVERTON. Good afternoon, Charles. You might have guessed,
    Monica,
    What I've been doing. Don't you recognize this book?
MONICA. It's your engagement book.
LORD CLAVERTON. Yes, I've been brooding over it.
MONICA. But what a time for your engagement book!
    You know what the doctors said: complete relaxation
    And to think about nothing. Though I know that won't be easy.
LORD CLAVERTON. That is just what I was doing.

[287]

MONICA. Thinking of nothing?

LORD CLAVERTON. Contemplating nothingness. Just remember:
Every day, year after year, over my breakfast,
I have looked at this book—or one just like it—
You know I keep the old ones on a shelf together;
I could look in the right book, and find what I was doing
Twenty years ago, today, at this hour of the afternoon.
If I've been looking at this engagement book, today,
Not over breakfast, but before tea,
It's the empty pages that I've been fingering—
The first empty pages since I entered Parliament.
I used to jot down notes of what I had to say to people:
Now I've no more to say, and no one to say it to.
I've been wondering . . . how many more empty pages?

MONICA. You would soon fill them up if we allowed you to!
That's my business to prevent. You know I'm to protect you
From your own restless energy—the inexhaustible
Sources of the power that wears out the machine.

LORD CLAVERTON. They've dried up, Monica, and you know it.
They talk of rest, these doctors, Charles; they tell me to be cautious,
To take life easily. Take life easily!
It's like telling a man he mustn't run for trains
When the last thing he wants is to take a train for anywhere!
No. I've not the slightest longing for the life I've left—
Only fear of the emptiness before me.
If I had the energy to work myself to death
How gladly would I face death! But waiting, simply waiting,
With no desire to act, yet a loathing of inaction.
A fear of the vacuum, and no desire to fill it.
It's just like sitting in an empty waiting room
In a railway station on a branch line,
After the last train, after all the other passengers
Have left, and the booking office is closed
And the porters have gone. What am I waiting for
In a cold and empty room before an empty grate?
For no one. For nothing.

MONICA. Yet you've been looking forward
    To this very time! You know how you grumbled
    At the farewell banquet, with the tributes from the staff,
    The presentation, and the speech you had to make
    And the speeches that you had to listen to!
LORD CLAVERTON (*pointing to a silver salver, still lying in its case*).
    I don't know which impresed me more, the insincerity
    Of what was said about me, or of my reply—
    All to thank them for that.
                        O the grudging contributions
    That bought this piece of silver! The inadequate levy
    That made the Chairman's Price! And my fellow directors
    Saying "we must put our hands in our pockets
    To double this collection—it must be something showy."
    This would do for visiting cards—if people still left cards
    And if I was going to have any visitors.
MONICA. Father, you simply want to revel in gloom!
    You know you've retired in a blaze of glory—
    You've read every word about you in the papers.
CHARLES. And the leading articles saying "we are confident
    That his sagacious counsel will long continue
    To be at the disposal of the Government in power."
    And the expectation that your voice will be heard
    In debate in the Upper House . . .
LORD CLAVERTON. The established liturgy
    Of the Press on any conspicuous retirement.
    My obituary, if I had died in harness,
    Would have occupied a column and a half
    With an inset, a portrait taken twenty years ago.
    In five years' time, it will be the half of that;
    In ten years' time, a paragraph.
CHARLES. That's the reward
    Of every public man.
LORD CLAVERTON. Say rather, the exequies
    Of the failed successes, the successful failures,
    Who occupy positions that other men covet.

When we go, a good many folk are mildly grieved,
And our closest associates, the small minority
Of those who really understand the place we filled
Are inwardly delighted. They won't want my ghost
Walking in the City or sitting in the Lords.
And I, who recognize myself as a ghost
Shan't want to be seen there. It makes me smile
To think that men should be frightened of ghosts.
If they only knew how frightened a ghost can be of men!
(*Knock. Enter* LAMBERT)
LAMBERT. Excuse me, My Lord. There's a gentleman downstairs
Is very insistent that he must see you.
I told him you never saw anyone, My Lord,
But by previous appointment. He said he knew that,
So he had brought this note. He said that when you read it
You would want to see him. Said you'd be very angry
If you heard that he'd gone away without your seeing him.
LORD CLAVERTON. What sort of a person?
LAMBERT. A foreign person
By the looks of him. But talks good English.
A pleasant-spoken gentleman.
LORD CLAVERTON (*after reading the note*). I'll see him in the library.
No, stop. I've left too many papers about there.
I'd better see him here.
LAMBERT. Very good, My Lord.
Shall I take the trolley, Miss Monica?
MONICA. Yes, thank you, Lambert.   (*Exit* LAMBERT)
CHARLES. I ought to be going.
MONICA. Let *us* go into the library. And then I'll see you off.
LORD CLAVERTON. I'm sorry to turn you out of the room like this,
But I'll have to see this man by myself, Monica.
I've never heard of this Señor Gomez
But he comes with a letter of introduction
From a man I used to know. I can't refuse to see him.
Though from what I remember of the man who introduces him
I expect he wants money. Or to sell me something worthless.

MONICA. You ought not to bother with such people now, Father.
  If you haven't got rid of him in twenty minutes
  I'll send Lambert to tell you that you have to take a trunk call.
  Come, Charles. Will you bring my coat?
CHARLES. I'll say goodbye, sir.
  And look forward to seeing you both at Badgley Court
  In a week or two.
  (*Enter* LAMBERT)
LAMBERT. Mr. Gomez, My Lord.
LORD CLAVERTON. Goodbye, Charles. And please remember
  That we both want to see you, whenever you can come
  If you're in the vicinity. Don't we, Monica?
MONICA. Yes, Father. (*To* CHARLES) We *both* want to see you.

  (*Exeunt* MONICA *and* CHARLES)

  (LAMBERT *shows in* GOMEZ)
LORD CLAVERTON. Good evening, Mr. . . . Gomez. You're a friend of Mr.
  Culverwell?
GOMEZ. We're as thick as thieves, you might almost say.
  Don't you know me, Dick?
LORD CLAVERTON. Fred Culverwell!
  Why do you come back with another name?
GOMEZ. You've changed your name too, since I knew you.
  When we were up at Oxford, you were plain Dick Ferry.
  Then, when you married, you took your wife's name
  And became Mr. Richard Claverton-Ferry;
  And finally, Lord Claverton. I've followed your example,
  And done the same, in a modest way.
  You know, where *I* live, people do change their names;
  And besides, my wife's name is a good deal more normal
  In my country, than Culverwell—and easier to pronounce.
LORD CLAVERTON. Have you lived out there ever since . . . you left Eng-
  land?
GOMEZ. Ever since I finished my sentence.
LORD CLAVERTON. What has brought you to England?
GOMEZ. Call it homesickness,
  Curiosity, restlessness, whatever you like.

[291]

But I've been a pretty hard worker all these years
And I thought, now's the time to take a long holiday,
Let's say a rest cure—that's what I've come for.
You see, I'm a widower, like you, Dick.
So I'm pretty footloose. Gomez, you see,
Is now a highly respected citizen
Of a Central American republic: San Marco.
It's as hard to become a respected citizen
Out there, as it is here. With this qualification:
Out there they respect you for rather different reasons.
LORD CLAVERTON. Do you mean that you've won respect out there
By the sort of activity that lost you respect
Here in England?
GOMEZ. Not at all, not at all.
I think that was rather an unkind suggestion.
I've always kept on the right side of the law—
And seen that the law turned its right side to *me*.
Sometimes I've had to pay pretty heavily;
But I learned by experience whom to pay;
And a little money laid out in the right manner
In the right places, pays many times over.
I assure you it does.
LORD CLAVERTON. In other words
You have been engaged in systematic corruption.
GOMEZ. No, Dick, there's a fault in your logic.
How can one corrupt those who are already corrupted?
I can swear that I've never corrupted anybody.
In fact, I've never come across an official
Innocent enough to be corruptible.
LORD CLAVERTON. It would seem then that most of your business
Has been of such a nature that, if carried on in England,
It might land you in jail again?
GOMEZ. That's true enough,
Except for a false inference. I wouldn't dream
Of carrying on such business if I lived in England.
I have the same standards of morality
As the society in which I find myself.

I do nothing in England that you would disapprove of.

LORD CLAVERTON. That's something, at least, to be thankful for.

I trust you've no need to engage in forgery.

GOMEZ. Forgery, Dick? An absurd suggestion!

Forgery, I can tell you, is a mug's game.

I say that—with conviction.

No, forgery, or washing checks, or anything of that nature,

Is certain to be found out sooner or later.

And then what happens? You have to move on.

That wouldn't do for me. I'm too domestic.

And by the way, I've several children,

All grown up, doing well for themselves.

I wouldn't allow either of my sons

To go into politics. In my country, Dick,

Politicians can't afford mistakes. The prudent ones

Always have airplane ready:

And keep an account in a bank in Switzerland.

The ones who don't get out in time

Find themselves in jail and not very comfortable,

Or before a firing squad.

You don't know what serious politics is like!

I said to my boys: "Never touch politics.

Stay out of politics, and play both parties:

What you don't get from one you may get from the other."

Dick, don't tell me that there isn't any whisky in the house?

LORD CLAVERTON. I can provide whisky. (*Presses the bell*) But why have
    you come?

GOMEZ. You've asked me that already!

To see you, Dick, a natural desire!

For you're the only old friend I can trust.

LORD CLAVERTON. You really trust me? I appreciate the compliment.

GOMEZ. Which you're sure you deserve. But when I say "trust" . . .

    (*Knock. Enter* LAMBERT)

LORD CLAVERTON. Lambert, will you bring in the whisky. And soda.

LAMBERT. Very good, My Lord.

GOMEZ. And some ice.

LAMBERT. Ice? Yes, My Lord.   (*Exit*)

[293]

GOMEZ. I began to say: when I say "trust"
    I use the term as experience has taught me.
    It's nonsense to talk of trusting people
    In general. What does that mean? One trusts a man
    Or a woman—in this respect or that.
    A won't let me down in this relationship,
    B won't let me down in some other connection.
    But, as I've always said to my boys:
    "When you come to the point where you need to trust someone
    You must make it worth his while to be trustworthy."
    (*During this* LAMBERT *enters silently, deposits tray and exit.*)
LORD CLAVERTON. Won't you help yourself?
    (GOMEZ *does so, liberally*)
GOMEZ. And what about you?
LORD CLAVERTON. I don't take it, thank you.
GOMEZ. A reformed character!
LORD CLAVERTON. I should like to know why you need to trust *me*.
GOMEZ. That's perfectly simple. I come back to England
    After thirty-five years. Can you imagine
    What it would be like to have been away from home
    For thirty-five years? I was twenty-five—
    The same age as you—when I went away,
    Thousands of miles away, to another climate,
    To another language, other standards of behavior,
    To fabricate for myself another personality
    And to take another name. Think what that means—
    To take another name.
    (*Gets up and helps himself to whisky*) But of course you know!
    Just enough to think you know more than you do.
    You've changed your name twice—by easy stages,
    And each step was merely a step up the ladder,
    So you weren't aware of becoming a different person:
    But where *I* changed my name, there was no social ladder.
    It was jumping a gap—and you can't jump back again.
    I parted from myself by a sudden effort,
    You, slowly and sweetly, that you've never waked up
    To the fact that Dick Ferry died long ago.

I married a girl who didn't know a word of English,
Didn't want to learn English, wasn't interested
In anything that happened four thousand miles away,
Only believed what the parish priest told her.
I made my children learn English—it's useful;
I always talk to them in English.
But do they think in English? No, they do not.
They think in Spanish, but their thoughts are Indian thoughts.
O God, Dick, *you* don't know what it's like
To be so cut off! Homesickness!
Homesickness is a sickly word.
You don't understand such isolation
As mine, you think you do . . .
LORD CLAVERTON. I'm sure I do,
   I've always been alone.
GOMEZ. Oh, loneliness—
   Everybody knows what that's like.
   Your loneliness—so cosy, warm and padded:
   You're not isolated—merely insulated.
   It's only when you come to see that you have lost *yourself*
   That you are quite alone.
LORD CLAVERTON. I'm waiting to hear
   Why you should need to trust me.
GOMEZ. Perfectly simple.
   My father's dead long since—that's a good thing.
   My mother—I dare say she's still alive.
   But she must be very old. And she must think I'm dead;
   And as for my married sisters—I don't suppose their hubands
   Were ever told the story. *They* wouldn't want to see me.
   No, I need one old friend, a friend whom I can trust—
   And one who will accept both Culverwell and Gomez—
   See Culverwell as Gomez—Gomez as Culverwell.
   I need you, Dick, to give me reality!
LORD CLAVERTON. But according to the description you have given
   Of trusting people, how do you propose
   To make it worth my while to be trustworthy?
GOMEZ. It's done already, Dick; done many years ago:

Adoption tried, and grappled to my soul
With hoops of steel, and all that sort of thing.
We'll come to that, very soon. Isn't it strange
That there should always have been this bond between us?
LORD CLAVERTON. It has never crossed my mind. Develop the point.
GOMEZ. Well, consider what we were when we went up to Oxford
And then what I became under your influence.
LORD CLAVERTON. You cannot attribute your . . . misfortune to *my* influence.
GOMEZ. I was just about as different as anyone could be
From the sort of men you'd been at school with—
I didn't fit in to your set, and I knew it.
When you started to take me up at Oxford
I've no doubt your friends wondered what you found in me—
A scholarship boy from an unknown grammar school.
I didn't know either, but I was flattered.
Later, I came to understand: you made friends with me
Because it flattered *you*—tickled your love of power
To see that I was flattered, and that I admired you.
Everyone expected that I should get a First.
I suppose your tutor thought you'd be sent down.
It went the other way. You stayed the course, at least.
I had plenty of time to think things over, later.
LORD CLAVERTON. And what is the conclusion that you came to?
GOMEZ. This is how it worked out, Dick. You liked to play the rake,
But you never went too far. There's a prudent devil
Inside you, Dick. He never came to *my* help.
LORD CLAVERTON. I certainly admit no responsibility,
None whatever, for what happened to you later.
GOMEZ. You led me on at Oxford, and left me to it.
And so it came about that I was sent down
With the consequences which you remember:
A miserable clerkship—which your father found for me,
And expensive tastes—which you had fostered in me,
And, equally unfortunate, a talent for penmanship.
Hence, as you have just reminded me

[296]

Defalcation and forgery. And then my stretch
Which gave me time to think it all out.

LORD CLAVERTON. That's the second time you have mentioned your re-
flections.
But there's just one thing you seem to have forgotten:
I came to your assistance when you were released.

GOMEZ. Yes, and paid my passage out. I know the reason:
You wanted to get rid of me. I shall tell you why presently.
Now let's look for a moment at *your* life history.
You had plenty of money, and you made a good marriage—
Or so it seemed—and with your father's money
And your wife's family influence, you got on in politics.
Shall we say that you did very well by yourself?
Though not, I suspect, as well as you had hoped.

LORD CLAVERTON. I was never accused of making a mistake.

GOMEZ. No, in England mistakes are anonymous
Because the man who accepts responsibility
Isn't the man who made the mistake.
That's your convention. Or if it's known you made it
You simply get moved to another post
Where at least you can't make quite the same mistake.
At the worst, you go into opposition
And let the other people make mistakes
Until your own have been more or less forgotten.
I dare say you did make some mistake, Dick . . .
That would account for your leaving politics
And taking a conspicuous job in the City
Where the Government could always consult you
But of course didn't have to take your advice . . .
I've made a point, you see, of following your career.

LORD CLAVERTON. I am touched by your interest.

GOMEZ. I have a gift for friendship.
I rejoiced in your success. But one thing has puzzled me.
You were given a ministry before you were fifty:
That should have led you to the very top!
And yet you withdrew from the world of politics

And went into the City. Director of a bank
And chairman of companies. You looked the part—
Cut out to be an impressive figurehead.
But again, you've retired at sixty. Why at sixty?
LORD CLAVERTON. Knowing as much about me as you do
   You must have read that I retired at the insistence of my doctors.
GOMEZ. Oh yes, the usual euphemism.
   And yet I wonder. It *is* surprising:
   You should have been good for another five years
   At least. Why did they let you retire?
LORD CLAVERTON. If you want to know, I had had a stroke.
   And I might have another.
GOMEZ. Yes. You might have another.
   But I wonder what brought about this . . . stroke;
   And I wonder whether you're the great economist
   And financial wizard that you're supposed to be.
   And I've learned something of other vicissitudes.
   Dick, I was very very sorry when I heard
   That your marriage had not been altogether happy.
   And as for your son—from what I've heard about *him,*
   He's followed your undergraduate career
   Without the protection of that prudent devil
   Of yours, to tell him not to go too far.
   Well, now, I'm beginning to be thirsty again.
   (*Pours himself whisky*)
LORD CLAVERTON. An interesting historical epitome.
   Though I cannot accept it as altogether accurate.
   The only thing I find surprising
   In the respected citizen of San Marco
   Is that in the middle of the engrossing business
   Of the nature of which dark hints have been given,
   He's informed himself so carefully about my career.
GOMEZ. I don't propose to give you a detailed account
   Of my own career. I've been very successful.
   What would have happened to me, I wonder,
   If I had never met you? I should have got my First,
   And I might have become the history master

In a school like that from which I went to Oxford.
As it is, I'm somebody—a more important man
In San Marco than I should ever have been in England.

LORD CLAVERTON. So, as you consider yourself a success . . .

GOMEZ. A worldly success, Dick. In another sense
We're both of us failures. But even so,
I'd rather be my kind of failure than yours.

LORD CLAVERTON. And what do you call failure?

GOMEZ. What do I call failure?
The worst kind of failure, in my opinion,
Is the man who has to keep on pretending to himself
That he's a success—the man who in the morning
Has to make up his face before he looks in the mirror.

LORD CLAVERTON. Isn't that the kind of pretense that you're maintaining
In trying to persuade me of your . . . worldly success?

GOMEZ. No, because I know the value of the coinage
I pay myself in.

LORD CLAVERTON. Indeed! How interesting!
I still don't know why you've come to see me
Or what you mean by saying you can trust me.

GOMEZ. Dick, do you remember the moonlight night
We drove back to Oxford? *You* were driving.

LORD CLAVERTON. That happened several times.

GOMEZ. One time in particular.
You know quite well to which occasion I'm referring—
A summer night of moonlight and shadows—
The night you ran over the old man in the road.

LORD CLAVERTON. You *said* I ran over an old man in the road.

GOMEZ. You knew it too. If you had been surprised
When I said "Dick, you've run over somebody"
Wouldn't you have shown it, if only for a second?
You never lifted your foot from the accelerator.

LORD CLAVERTON. We were in a hurry.

GOMEZ. More than in a hurry.
You didn't want it to be known where we'd been.
The girls who were with us (what were their names?
I've completely forgotten them) you didn't want *them*

To be called to give evidence. You couldn't face it.
Do you see now, Dick, why I say I can trust you?
LORD CLAVERTON. If you think that this story would interest the public
Why not sell your version to a Sunday newspaper?
GOMEZ. My dear Dick, what a preposterous suggestion!
Who's going to accept the unsupported statement
Of Federico Gomez of San Marco
About something that happened so many years ago?
What damages you'd get! The Press wouldn't look at it.
Besides, you can't think I've any desire
To appear in public as Frederick Culverwell?
No, Dick, your secret's safe with me.
Of course, I might give it to a few friends, in confidence.
It might even reach the ears of some of your acquaintance—
But you'd never know to whom I'd told it,
Or who knew the story and who didn't. I promise you.
Rely upon me as the soul of discretion.
LORD CLAVERTON. What do you want then? Do you need money?
GOMEZ. My dear chap, you are obtuse!
I said: "Your secret is safe with me,"
And then you . . . well, I'd never have believed
That you would accuse an old friend of . . . blackmail!
On the contrary, I dare say I could buy you out
Several times over. San Marco's a good place
To make money in—though not to *keep* it in.
My investments—not all in my own name either—
Are pretty well spread. For the matter of that,
My current account in Stockholm or Zurich
Would keep me in comfort for the rest of my life.
Really, Dick, you owe me an apology.
Blackmail! On the contrary
Any time you're in a tight corner
My entire resources are at your disposal.
You were a generous friend to me once
As you pointedly reminded me a moment ago.
Now it's my turn, perhaps, to do you a kindness.
(*Enter* LAMBERT)

LAMBERT. Excuse me, My Lord, but Miss Monica asked me
    To remind you there's a trunk call coming through for you
    In five minutes' time.
LORD CLAVERTON. I'll be ready to take it.   (*Exit* LAMBERT)
GOMEZ. Ah, the pre-arranged interruption
    To terminate the unwelcome intrusion
    Of the visitor in financial distress
    Well, I shan't keep you long, though I dare say your caller
    Could hang on for another quarter of an hour.
LORD CLAVERTON. Before you go—what is it that you want?
GOMEZ. I've been trying to make clear that I only want your friendship!
    Just as it used to be in the old days
    When you taught me expensive tastes. Now it's my turn.
    I can have cigars sent direct to you from Cuba
    If your doctors allow you a smoke now and then.
    I'm a lonely man, Dick, with a craving for affection.
    All I want is as much of your company,
    So long as I stay here, as I can get.
    And the more I get, the longer I may stay.
LORD CLAVERTON. This is preposterous!
    Do you call it friendship to impose your company
    On a man by threats? Why keep up the pretense?
GOMEZ. Threats, Dick! How can you speak of threats?
    It's most unkind of you. My only aim
    Is to renew our friendship. Don't you understand?
LORD CLAVERTON. I see that when I gave you my friendship
    So many years ago, I only gained in return
    Your envy, spite and hatred. That is why you attribute
    Your downfall to me. But how was I responsible?
    We were the same age. You were a free moral agent.
    You pretend that I taught you expensive tastes:
    If you had not had those tastes already
    You would hardly have welcomed my companionship.
GOMEZ. Neatly argued, and almost convincing:
    Don't you wish you could believe it?
LORD CLAVERTON. And what if I decline
    To give you the pleasure of my company?

GOMEZ. Oh, I can wait, Dick. You'll relent at last.

You'll come to feel easier when I'm with you

Than when I'm out of sight. You'll be afraid of whispers,

The reflection in the mirror of the face behind you,

The ambiguous smile, the distant salutation,

The sudden silence when you enter the smoking room.

Don't forget, Dick:

You *didn't stop!* Well, I'd better be going.

I hope I haven't outstayed my welcome?

Your telephone pal may be getting impatient.

I'll see you soon again.

LORD CLAVERTON. Not very soon, I think.

I am going away.

GOMEZ. So I've been informed.

I have friends in the press—if not in the peerage.

Goodbye for the present. It's been an elixir

To see you again, and assure myself

That we can begin just where we left off. (*Exit* GOMEZ)

(LORD CLAVERTON *sits for a few minutes brooding. A knock. Enter*
MONICA)

MONICA. Who was it, Father?

LORD CLAVERTON. A man I used to know.

MONICA. Oh, so you knew him?

LORD CLAVERTON. Yes. He'd changed his name.

MONICA. Then I suppose he wanted money?

LORD CLAVERTON. No, he didn't want money.

MONICA. Father, this interview has worn you out.

You must go and rest now, before dinner.

LORD CLAVERTON. Yes, I'll go and rest now. I wish Charles was dining
with us.

I wish we were having a dinner party.

MONICA. Father, can't you bear to be alone with me?

If you can't bear to dine alone with me tonight,

What will it be like at Badgley Court?

CURTAIN

ACT TWO

The terrace of Badgley Court. A bright sunny morning, several days later.
Enter LORD CLAVERTON *and* MONICA.

MONICA. Well, so far, it's better than you expected,
    Isn't it, Father? They've let us alone;
    The people in the dining room show no curiosity;
    The beds are comfortable, the hot water is hot,
    They give us a very tolerable breakfast;
    And the chambermaid really *is* a chambermaid:
    For when I asked about morning coffee
    She said "I'm not the one for eleven's,
    That's Nurse's business."
LORD CLAVERTON. So far, so good.
    I'll feel more confidence after a fortnight—
    After fourteen days of people not staring
    Or offering picture papers, or wanting a fourth at bridge;
    Still, I'll admit to a feeling of contentment
    Already. I only hope that it will last—
    The sense of wellbeing! It's often with us
    When we are young, but then it's not noticed;
    And by the time one has grown to consciousness
    It comes less often.
              I hope this benignant sunshine
    And warmth will last for a few days more.
    But this early summer, that's hardly seasonable,
    Is often a harbinger of frost on the fruit trees,
MONICA. Oh, let's make the most of this weather while it lasts.
    I never remember you as other than occupied
    With anxieties from which you were longing to escape;
    Now I want to see you learning to enjoy yourself!
LORD CLAVERTON. Perhaps I've never really enjoyed living
    As much as most people. At least, as they seem to do.
    Without knowing that they enjoy it. Whereas I've often known

[303]

That I didn't enjoy it. Some dissatisfaction
With myself, I suspect, very deep within myself
Has impelled me all my life to find justification
Not so much to the world—first of all to myself.
What is this self inside us, this silent observer,
Severe and speechless critic, who can terrorize us
And urge us on to futile activity,
And in the end, judge us still more severely
For the errors into which his own reproaches drove us?

MONICA. You admit that at the moment you find life pleasant,
That it really does seem quiet here and restful.
Even the matron, though she looks rather dominating,
Has left us alone.

LORD CLAVERTON. Yes, but remember
What she said. She said: "I'm going to leave you alone!
You want perfect peace: that's what Badgley Court is for."
I thought that very ominous. When people talk like that
It indicates a latent desire to interfere
With the privacy of others, which is certain to explode.

MONICA. Hush, Father. I see her coming from the house.
Take your newspaper and start reading to me.
(*Enter* MRS. PIGGOTT)

MRS. PIGGOTT. Good morning, Lord Claverton! Good morning, Miss
Claverton!
Isn't this a glorious morning!
I'm afraid you'll think I've been neglecting you;
So I've come to apologize and explain.
I've been in such a rush, these last few days,
And I thought, "Lord Claverton will understand
My not coming in directly after breakfast:
He's led a busy life, too." But I hope you're happy?
Is there anything you need that hasn't been provided?
All you have to do is to make your wants known.
Just ring through to my office. If I'm not there
My secretary will be—Miss Timmins.
She'd be overjoyed to have the privilege of helping you!

MONICA. You're very kind . . . Oh, I'm sorry,
We don't know how we ought to address you.
Do we call you "Matron"?

MRS. PIGGOTT. Oh no, not "Matron"!
Of course, I *am* a matron in a sense—
No, I don't simply mean that I'm a married woman—
A widow in fact. But I was a Trained Nurse,
And of course I've always lived in what you might call
A medical milieu. My father was a specialist
In pharmacology. And my husband
Was a distinguished surgeon. Do you know, I fell in love with him
During an appendicitis operation!
I was a theater nurse. But you mustn't call me "Matron"
At Badgley Court. You see, we've studied to avoid
Anything like a nursing-home atmosphere.
We don't want our guests to think of themselves as ill,
Though we never have guests who are perfectly well—
Except when they come like you, Miss Claverton.

MONICA. Claverton-Ferry. Or Ferry: it's shorter.

MRS. PIGGOTT. So sorry. Miss Claverton-Ferry. I'm Mrs. Piggott.
Just call me Mrs. Piggott. It's a short and simple name
And easy to remember. But, as I was saying,
Guests in perfect health are exceptional
Though we never accept any guest who's incurable.
You know, we've been deluged with applications
From people who wanted to come here to die!
We never accept them. Nor do we accept
Any guest who *looks* incurable—
We make that stipulation to all the doctors
Who send people here. When you go in to lunch
Just take a glance around the diningroom:
Nobody looks ill! They're all convalescents,
Or resting, like you. So you'll remember
Always to call me Mrs. Piggott, won't you?

MONICA. Yes, Mrs. Piggott, but please tell me one thing.
We haven't seen her yet, but the chambermaid

Referred to a nurse. When we see her
Do we address her as "Nurse"?

MRS. PIGGOTT. Oh yes, that's different.
She is a real nurse, you know, fully qualified.
Our system is very delicately balanced:
For me to be simply "Mrs. Piggott"
Reassures the guests in one respect;
And calling our nurses "Nurse" reassures them
In another respect.

LORD CLAVERTON. I follow you perfectly.

MRS. PIGGOTT. And now I must fly. I've so much on my hands!
But before I go, just let me tuck you up . . .
You must be very careful at this time of year;
This early warm weather can be very treacherous.
There, now you look more comfy. Don't let him stay out late
In the afternoon, Miss Claverton-Ferry.
And remember, when you want to be *very* quiet
There's the Silence Room. With a television set.
It's popular in the evenings. But not *too* crowded. (*Exit*)

LORD CLAVERTON. Much as I had feared. But I'm not going to say
Nothing could be worse. Where there's a Mrs. Piggott
There may be, among the guests, something worse than Mrs. Piggott.

MONICA. Let's hope this was merely the concoction
Which she decants for every newcomer.
Perhaps after what she considers proper courtesies,
She will leave us alone.
(*Re-enter* MRS. PIGGOTT)

MRS. PIGGOTT. I really *am* neglectful! Miss Claverton-Ferry, I ought to tell
you more
About the amenities which Badgley Court
Can offer to guests of the younger generation.
When there are enough young people among us
We dance in the evening. At the moment there's no dancing,
And it's still too early for the bathing pool.
But several of our guests are keen on tennis,
And of course there's always croquet. But I don't advise croquet
Until you know enough about the other guests

To know whom *not* to play with. I'll mention no names,
But there are one or two who don't like being beaten,
And that spoils any sport, in my opinion.

MONICA. Thank you, Mrs. Piggott. But I'm very fond of walking
And I'm told there are very good walks in this neighborhood.

MRS. PIGGOTT. There are indeed. I can lend you a map.
There are lovely walks, on the shore or in the hills,
Quite away from the motor roads. You must learn the best walks.
I won't apologize for the lack of excitement:
After all, peace and quiet is our *raison d'être*.
Now I'll leave you to enjoy it.   (*Exit*)

MONICA. I hope she won't remember anything else.

LORD CLAVERTON. She'll come back to tell us more about the peace and quiet.

MONICA. I don't believe she'll be bothering us again:
I could see from her expression when she left
That she thought she'd done her duty by us for today.
I'm going to prowl about the grounds. Don't look so alarmed!
If you spy any guest who seems to be stalking you
Put your newspaper over your face
And pretend you're pretending to be asleep.
If they think you *are* asleep they'll do something to wake you,
But if they see you're shamming they'll have to take the hint.   (*Exit*)
(*A moment later,* LORD CLAVERTON *spreads his newspaper over his face.
Enter* MRS. CARGHILL. *She sits in a deckchair nearby, composes herself
and takes out her knitting.*)

MRS. CARGHILL (*after a pause*). I hope I'm not disturbing you. I always
   sit here.
It's the sunniest and most sheltered corner,
And none of the other guests have discovered it.
It was clever of you to find it so quickly.
What made you choose it?

LORD CLAVERTON (*throwing down newspaper*). My daughter chose it.
She noticed that it seemed to offer the advantages
Which you have just mentioned. I am glad you can confirm them.

MRS. CARGHILL. Oh, so that *is* your daughter—that very charming girl?
And obviously devoted to her father.
I was watching you both in the diningroom last night.

You are the great Lord Claverton, aren't you?
Somebody said you were coming here—
It's been the topic of conversation.
But I couldn't believe that it would really happen!
And now I'm sitting here talking to you.
Dear me, it's astonishing, after all these years;
And you don't even recognize me! I'd know you anywhere.
But then, we've all seen your portrait in the papers
So often. And everybody knows *you*. But still,
    I wish you could have paid *me* that compliment, Richard.
LORD CLAVERTON. What!
MRS. CARGHILL. Don't you know me yet?
LORD CLAVERTON. I'm afraid not.
MRS. CARGHILL. There were the three of us—Effie, Maudie and me.
    That day we spent on the river—I've never forgotten it—
    The turning point of all my life!
    Now whatever were the names of those friends of yours
    And which one was it invited us to lunch?
    I declare, I've utterly forgotten their names.
    And you gave us lunch—I've forgotten what hotel—
    But such a good lunch—and we all went in a punt
    On the river—and we had a tea basket
    With some lovely little cakes—I've forgotten what you called them,
    And you made me try to punt, and I got soaking wet
    And nearly dropped the punt pole, and you all laughed at me.
    Don't you remember?
LORD CLAVERTON. Pray continue.
    The more you remind me of, the better I'll remember.
MRS. CARGHILL. And the three of us talked you over afterwards—
    Effie and Maud and I. What a time ago it seems!
    It's surprising I remember it all so clearly.
    You attracted me, you know, at the very first meeting—
    I can't think why, but it's the way things happen.
    I said "there's a man I could follow round the world!"
    But Effie it was—you know, Effie was very shrewd—
    Effie it was said "you'd be throwing yourself away.
    Mark my words," Effie said, "if you chose to follow *that* man

He'd give you the slip: he's not to be trusted.
That man is hollow." That's what she said.
Or did she say "yellow"? I'm not quite sure.
You do remember now, don't you, Richard?
LORD CLAVERTON. Not the conversation you have just repeated.
That is new to me. But I do remember you.
MRS. CARGILL. Time has wrought sad changes in me, Richard.
I was very lovely once. So *you* thought,
And others thought so too. But as you remember,
Please, Richard, just repeat my name—just once:
The name by which you knew me. It would give me such a thrill
To hear you speak my name once more.
LORD CLAVERTON. Your name was Maisie Batterson.
MRS. CARGHILL. Oh, Richard, you're only saying that to tease me.
You know I meant my stage name. The name by which you knew me.
LORD CLAVERTON. Well, then, Maisie Montjoy.
MRS. CARGHILL. Yes, Maisie Montjoy.
I was Maisie Montjoy once. And you didn't recognize me.
LORD CLAVERTON. You've changed your name, no doubt. And I've changed
mine.
Your name now and here . . .
MRS. CARGHILL. Is Mrs. John Carghill.
LORD CLAVERTON. You married, I suppose, many years ago?
MRS. CARGHILL. Many years ago, the first time. That didn't last long.
People sometimes say: "Make one mistake in love,
You're more than likely to make another."
How true that is! Algy was a weakling,
But simple he was—not sly and slippery.
Then I married Mr. Carghill. Twenty years older
Than me, he was. Just what I needed.
LORD CLAVERTON. Is he still living?
MRS. CARGHILL. He had a weak heart.
And he worked too hard. Have you never heard
Of Carghill Equipments? They make office furniture.
LORD CLAVERTON. I've never had to deal with questions of equipment.
I trust that the business was very successful . . .
I mean, that he left you comfortably provided for?

MRS. CARGHILL. Well, Richard, my doctor could hardly have sent me *here*
If I wasn't well off. Yes, I'm provided for.
But isn't it strange that you and I
Should meet here at last? Here, of all places!
LORD CLAVERTON. Why not, of all places? What I don't understand
Is why you should take the first opportunity,
Finding me here, to revive old memories
Which I should have thought we both preferred to leave buried.
MRS. CARGHILL. There you're wrong, Richard. Effie always said—
What a clever girl she was!—"he doesn't understand women.
Any woman who trusted *him* would soon find that out."
A man may prefer to forget all the women
He has loved. But a woman doesn't want to forget
A single one of her admirers. Why, even a faithless lover
Is still, in her memory, a kind of testimonial.
Men live by forgetting—women live on memories.
Besides a woman has nothing to be ashamed of:
A man is always trying to forget
His own shabby behavior.
LORD CLAVERTON. But we'd settled our account.
What harm was done? I learned my lesson
And you learned yours, if you needed the lesson.
MRS. CARGHILL. You refuse to believe that I was really in love with you!
Well, it's natural that you shouldn't want to believe it.
But you think, or try to think, that if I'd really suffered
I shouldn't want to let you know who I am,
I shouldn't want to come and talk about the past.
You're wrong, you know. It's both pain and pleasure
To talk about the past—about you and me.
These memories are painful—but I cherish them.
LORD CLAVERTON. If you had really been broken-hearted
I can't see how you could have acted as you did.
MRS. CARGHILL. Who can say whether a heart's been broken
Once it's been repaired? But I know what you mean.
You mean that I would never have started an action
For breach of promise, if I'd really cared for you.
What sentimental nonsense! One starts an action

Simply because one must do *something*.
Well, perhaps I shouldn't have settled out of court.
My lawyer said: "I advise you to accept,
Because Mr. Ferry will be standing for Parliament:
His father has political ambitions for him.
If he's lost a breach of promise suit
Some people won't want to appear as his supporters."
He said: "What his lawyers are offering in settlement
Is twice as much as I think you'd be awarded."
Effie was against it—she wanted you exposed.
But I gave way. I didn't want to ruin you.
If I'd carried on, it might have ended your career,
And then you wouldn't have become Lord Claverton.
So perhaps I laid the foundation of your fortunes!
LORD CLAVERTON. And perhaps at the same time of your own?
I seem to remember, it was only a year or so
Before your name appeared in very large letters
In Shaftesbury Avenue.
MRS. CARGHILL. Yes, I had my art.
Don't you remember what a hit I made
With a number called *It's Not Too Late for You to Love Me*?
I couldn't have put the feeling into it I did
But for what I'd gone through. Did you hear me sing it?
LORD CLAVERTON. Yes, I heard you sing it.
MRS. CARGHILL. And what did you feel?
LORD CLAVERTON. Nothing at all. I remember my surprise
At finding that I felt nothing at all.
I thought, perhaps, what a lucky escape
It had been, for both of us.
MRS. CARGHILL. That "both of us"
Was an afterthought, Richard. A lucky escape
You thought, for you. You felt no embarrassment?
LORD CLAVERTON. Why should I feel embarrassment? My conscience was
clear.
A brief infatuation, ended in the only way possible
To our mutual satisfaction.
MRS. CARGHILL. Your conscience was clear.

[311]

I've very seldom heard people mention their consciences
Except to observe that their consciences were clear.
You got out of a tangle for a large cash payment
And no publicity. So your conscience was clear.
At bottom, I believe you're still the same silly Richard
You always were. You wanted to pose
As a man of the world. And now you're posing
As what? I presume, as an elder statesman;
And the difference between being an elder statesman
And posing successfully as an elder statesman
Is practically negligible. And you look the part.
Whatever part you've played, I must say you've always looked it.
LORD CLAVERTON. I've no longer any part to play, Maisie.
MRS. CARGHILL. There'll always be some sort of part for you
    Right to the end. You'll still be playing a part
    In your obituary, whoever writes it.
LORD CLAVERTON. Considering how long ago it was when you knew me
    And considering the brevity of our acquaintance,
    You're surprisingly confident, I must say,
    About your understanding of my character.
MRS. CARGHILL. I've followed your progress year by year, Richard.
    And although it's true that our acquaintance was brief,
    Our relations were intense enough, I think,
    To have given me one or two insights into you.
    No, Richard, don't imagine that I'm still in love with you;
    And you needn't think I idolize your memory.
    It's simply that I feel that we belong together . . .
    Now, don't get alarmed. But you touched my soul—
    Pawed it, perhaps, and the touch still lingers.
    And I've touched yours.
    It's frightening to think that we're still together
    And more frightening to think that we may *always* be together.
    There's a phrase I seem to remember reading somewhere:
    Where their fires are not quenched. Do you know what I do?
    I read your letters every night.
LORD CLAVERTON. My letters!

MRS. CARGHILL. Have you forgotten that you wrote me letters?
Oh, not very many. Only a few worth keeping.
Only a few. But very beautiful!
It was Effie said, when the break came,
"They'll be worth a fortune to you, Maisie."
They would have figured at the trial, I suppose,
If there had been a trial. Don't you remember them?
LORD CLAVERTON. Vaguely. Were they very passionate?
MRS. CARGHILL. They were very loving. Would you like to read them?
I'm afraid I can't show you the originals;
They're in my lawyer's safe. But I have photostats
Which are quite as good, I'm told. And I like to read them
In your own handwriting.
LORD CLAVERTON. And have you shown these letters
To many people?
MRS. CARGHILL. Only a few friends.
Effie said: "If he becomes a famous man
And you should be in want, you could have these letters auctioned."
Yes, I'll bring the photostats tomorrow morning,
And read them to you.
                    —Oh, there's Mrs. Piggott!
She's bearing down on us. Isn't she frightful!
She never stops talking. Can you bear it?
If I go at once, perhaps she'll take the hint
And leave us alone tomorrow.
                         Good morning, Mrs. Piggott!
Isn't it a glorious morning!
(*Enter* MRS. PIGGOTT)
MRS. PIGGOTT. Good morning, Mrs. Carghill!
MRS. CARGHILL. Dear Mrs. Piggott!
It seems to me that you never sit still:
You simply sacrifice yourself for us.
MRS. PIGGOTT. It's the breath of life to me, Mrs. Carghill,
Attending to my guests. I like to feel they *need* me!
MRS. CARGHILL. You do look after us well, Mrs. Piggott:
You're so considerate—and so understanding.

[313]

MRS. PIGGOTT. But I ought to introduce you. You've been talking to Lord
   Claverton,
   The famous Lord Claverton. This is Mrs. Carghill.
   Two of our very nicest guests!
   I just came to see that Lord Claverton was comfortable:
   We can't allow him to tire himself with talking.
   What he needs is *rest!* You're not going, Mrs. Carghill?
MRS. CARGHILL. Oh, I knew that Lord Claverton had come for a rest cure,
   And it struck me that he might find it a strain
   To have to cope with both of us at once.
   Besides, I ought to do my breathing exercises.   (*Exit*)
MRS. PIGGOTT. As a matter of fact, I flew to your rescue
   (That's why I've brought your morning tipple myself
   Instead of leaving it, as usual, to Nurse)
   When I saw that Mrs. Carghill had caught you.
   You wouldn't know that name, but you might remember her
   As Maisie Montjoy in revue.
   She was well-known at one time. I'm afraid her name
   Means nothing at all to the younger generation,
   But you and I should remember her, Lord Claverton.
   That tune she was humming, *It's Not Too Late for You to Love Me,*
   Everybody was singing it once. A charming person,
   I dare say, but not quite your sort or mine.
   I suspected that she wanted to meet you, so I thought
   That I'd take the first opportunity of hinting—
   Tactfully, of course—that you should not be disturbed.
   Well, she's gone now. If she bothers you again
   Just let me know. I'm afraid it's the penalty
   Of being famous.
   (*Enter* MONICA)
                  Oh, Miss Claverton-Ferry!
   I didn't see you coming. Now I must fly.   (*Exit*)
MONICA. I saw Mrs. Piggott bothering you again
   So I hurried to your rescue. You look tired, Father.
   She ought to know better. But I'm all the more distressed
   Because I have some . . . not very good news for you.
LORD CLAVERTON. Oh, indeed. What's the matter?

MONICA. I didn't get far.

    I met Michael in the drive. He says he must see you.

    I'm afraid that something unpleasant has happened.

LORD CLAVERTON. Was he driving his car?

MONICA. No, he was walking.

LORD CLAVERTON. I hope he's not had another accident.

    You know, after that last escapade of his,

    I've lived in terror of his running over somebody.

MONICA. Why, Father, should you be afraid of that?

    This shows how bad your nerves have been.

    He only ran into a tree.

LORD CLAVERTON. Yes, a tree.

    It might have been a man. But it can't be that,

    Or he wouldn't be at large. Perhaps he's in trouble

    With some woman or other. I'm sure he has friends

    Whom he wouldn't care for you or me to know about.

MONICA. It's probably money.

LORD CLAVERTON. If it's only debts

    Once more, I expect I can put up with it.

    But where is he?

MONICA. I told him he must wait in the garden

    Until I have prepared you. I've made him understand

    That the doctors want you to be free from worry.

    He won't make a scene. But I can see he's frightened.

    And you know what Michael is like when he's frightened.

    He's apt to be sullen and quick to take offense.

    So I hope you'll be patient.

LORD CLAVERTON. Well, then, fetch him.

    Let's get this over.

MONICA (calls). Michael!

    (Enter MICHAEL)

LORD CLAVERTON. Good morning, Michael.

MICHAEL. Good morning, Father. (A pause) What a lovely day!

    I'm glad you're here, to enjoy such weather.

LORD CLAVERTON. You're glad I'm here? Did you drive down from London?

MICHAEL. I drove down last night. I'm staying at a pub

    About two miles from here. Not a bad little place.

LORD CLAVERTON. Why are you staying there? I shouldn't have thought
It would be the sort of place that you'd choose for a holiday.
MICHAEL. Well, this isn't a holiday exactly.
But this hotel was very well recommended.
Good cooking, for a country inn. And not at all expensive.
LORD CLAVERTON. You don't normally consider that a recommendation.
Are you staying there long? For the whole of this holiday?
MICHAEL. Well, this isn't a holiday, exactly.
Oh. I said that before, didn't I?
MONICA. I wish you'd stop being so polite to each other.
Michael, you know what you've come to ask of Father
And Father knows that you want something from him.
Perhaps you'll get to the point if I leave you together.   (*Exit*)
MICHAEL. You know, it's awfully hard to explain things to *you*.
You've always made up your mind that I was to blame
Before you knew the facts. The first thing I remember
Is being blamed for something I hadn't done.
I never got over that. If you always blame a person
It's natural he should end by getting into trouble.
LORD CLAVERTON. You started pretty early getting into trouble,
When you were expelled from your prep school for stealing.
But come to the point. You're in trouble again.
We'll ignore, if you please, the question of blame:
Which will spare you the necessity of blaming someone else.
Just tell me what's happened.
MICHAEL. Well, I've lost my job.
LORD CLAVERTON. The position that Sir Alfred Walter made for you.
MICHAEL. I'd stuck it for two years. And deadly dull it was.
LORD CLAVERTON. Every job is dull, nine-tenths of the time . . .
MICHAEL. I need something much more stimulating.
LORD CLAVERTON. Well?
MICHAEL. I want to find some more speculative business.
LORD CLAVERTON. I dare say you've tried a little private speculation.
MICHAEL. Several of my friends gave me excellent tips.
They always came off—tips I didn't take.
LORD CLAVERTON. And the ones you did take?
MICHAEL. Not so well, for some reason.

The fact is, I needed a good deal more capital
To make anything of it. If I could have borrowed more
I might have pulled it off.

LORD CLAVERTON. Borrowed? From whom?
Not . . . from the firm?

MICHAEL. I went to a lender,
A man whom a friend of mine recommended.
He gave me good terms, on the strength of my name:
The only good the name has ever done me.

LORD CLAVERTON. On the strength of your name. And what do you call
good terms?

MICHAEL. I'd nothing at all to pay for two years:
The interest was just added on to the capital.

LORD CLAVERTON. And how long ago was that?

MICHAEL. Nearly two years.
Time passes pretty quickly, when you're in debt.

LORD CLAVERTON. And have you other debts?

MICHAEL. Oh, ordinary debts:
My tailor's bill, for instance.

LORD CLAVERTON. I expected that.
It was just the same at Oxford.

MICHAEL. It's their own fault.
They won't send in their bills, and then I forget them.
It's being your son that gets me in debt.
Just because of your name they insist on giving credit.

LORD CLAVERTON. And your debts: are they the cause of your being discharged?

MICHAEL. Well, partly. Sir Alfred did come to hear about it,
And so he pretended to be very shocked.
Said he couldn't retain any man on his staff
Who'd taken to gambling. Called me a gambler!
Said he'd communicate with you about it.

LORD CLAVERTON. That accounts for your coming down here so precipi-
tately—
In order to let me have your version first.
I dare say Sir Alfred's will be rather different.
And what else did he say?

MICHAEL. He took the usual line,
    Just like the headmaster. And my tutor at Oxford.
    "Not what we expected from the son of your father"
    And that sort of thing. It's for your sake, he says,
    That he wants to keep things quiet. I can tell you, it's no joke
    Being the son of a famous public man.
    You don't know what I suffered, working in that office.
    In the first place, they all knew the job had been made for me
    Because I was your son. They considered me superfluous;
    They knew I couldn't be living on my pay;
    They had a lot of fun with me—sometimes they'd pretend
    That I was overworked, when I'd nothing to do.
    Even the office boys began to sneer at me.
    I wonder I stood it as long as I did.
LORD CLAVERTON. And does this bring us to the end of the list of your short-
    comings?
    Or did Sir Alfred make other unflattering criticisms?
MICHAEL. Well, there was one thing he brought up against me,
    That I'd been too familiar with one of the girls.
    He assumed it had gone a good deal further than it had.
LORD CLAVERTON. Perhaps it had gone further than you're willing to admit.
MICHAEL. Well, after all, she was the only one
    Who was at all nice to me. She wasn't exciting,
    But it served to pass the time. It would never have happened
    If only I'd been given some interesting work!
LORD CLAVERTON. And what do you now propose to do with yourself?
MICHAEL. I want to go abroad.
LORD CLAVERTON. You want to go abroad?
    Well, that's not a bad idea. A few years out of England
    In one of the Dominions, might set you on your feet.
    I have connections, or at least correspondents
    Almost everywhere. Australia—no.
    The men I know there are all in the cities:
    An outdoor life would suit you better.
    How would you like to go to Western Canada?
    Or what about sheep farming in New Zealand?
MICHAEL. Sheep farming? Good Lord, no.

That's not my idea. I want to make money.
I want to be somebody on my own account.
LORD CLAVERTON. But what do you want to do? Where do you want to go?
What kind of a life do you think you want?
MICHAEL. I simply want to lead a life of my own,
According to my own ideas of good and bad,
Of right and wrong. I want to go far away
To some country where no one has heard the name of Claverton;
Or where; if I took a different name—and I might choose to—
No one would know or care what my name had been.
LORD CLAVERTON. So you are ready to repudiate your family,
To throw away the whole of your inheritance?
MICHAEL. What is my inheritance? As for your title,
I know why you took it. And Mother knew.
First, because it gave you the opportunity
Of retiring from politics, not without dignity,
Being no longer wanted. And you wished to be Lord Claverton
Also, to hold your own with Mother's family—
To lord it over them, in fact. Oh, I've no doubt
That the thought of passing on your name and title
To a son, was gratifying. But it wasn't for *my* sake!
I was just *your* son—that is to say,
A kind of prolongation of your existence,
A representative carrying on business in your absence.
Why should I thank you for imposing this upon me?
And what satisfaction, I wonder, will it give you
In the grave? If you're still conscious after death,
I bet it will be a surprised state of consciousness.
Poor ghost! reckoning up its profit and loss
And wondering why it bothered about such trifles.
LORD CLAVERTON. So you want me to help you escape from your father!
MICHAEL. And to help my father to be rid of *me*.
You simply don't know how very much pleasanter
You will find life become, once I'm out of the country.
What I'd like is a chance to go abroad
As a partner in some interesting business.
But I might be expected to put up some capital.

LORD CLAVERTON. What sort of business have you in mind?

MICHAEL. Oh, I don't know. Import and export,
   With an opportunity of profits both ways.

LORD CLAVERTON. This is what I will do for you, Michael.
   I will help you to make a start in any business
   You may find for yourself—if, on investigation,
   I am satisfied about the nature of the business.

MICHAEL. Anyway, I'm determined to get out of England.

LORD CLAVERTON. Michael! Are there reasons for your wanting to go
   Beyond what you've told me? It isn't . . . manslaughter?

MICHAEL. Manslaughter? Why manslaughter? Oh, you mean on the road.
   Certainly not. I'm far too good a driver.

LORD CLAVERTON. What then? That young woman?

MICHAEL. I'm not such a fool
   As to get myself involved in a breach of promise suit
   Or somebody's divorce. No, you needn't worry
   About that girl—or any other.
   But I want to get out. I'm fed up with England.

LORD CLAVERTON. I'm sure you don't mean that. But it's natural enough
   To want a few years abroad. It might be very good for you
   To find your feet. But I shouldn't like to think
   That what inspired you was no positive ambition
   But only the desire to escape.

MICHAEL. I'm not a fugitive.

LORD CLAVERTON. No, not a fugitive from justice—
   Only a fugitive from reality.
   Oh Michael! If you had some aim of high achievement,
   Some dream of excellence, how gladly would I help you!
   Even though it carried you away from me forever
   To suffer the monotonous sun of the tropics
   Or shiver in the northern night. Believe me, Michael:
   Those who flee from their past will always lose the race.
   I know this from experience. When you reach your goal,
   Your imagined paradise of success and grandeur,
   You will find your past failures waiting there to greet you.
   You're all I have to live for, Michael—
   You and Monica. If I lived for twenty years

Knowing that my son had played the coward—
I should merely be another twenty years in dying.

MICHAEL. Very well: if you like, call me a coward.
I wonder whether you would play the hero
If you were in my place. I don't believe you would.
You didn't suffer from the handicap that I've had.
Your father was rich, but was no one in particular,
So you'd nothing to live up to. Those standards of conduct
You've always made so much of, for my benefit:
I wonder whether *you* have always lived up to them.
(MONICA *has entered unobserved*)

MONICA. Michael! How can you speak to Father like that?
Father! What has happened? Why do you look so angry?
I know that Michael must be in great trouble,
So can't you help him?

LORD CLAVERTON. I am trying to help him,
And to meet him half way. I have made him an offer
Which he must think over. But if he goes abroad
I want him to go in a very different spirit
From that which he has just been exhibiting.

MONICA. Michael! Say something.

MICHAEL. What is there to say?
I want to leave England, and make my own career:
And Father simply calls me a coward.

MONICA. Father! You know that I would give my life for you.
Oh, how silly that phrase sounds! But there's no vocabulary
For love within a family, love that's lived in
But not looked at, love within the light of which
All else is seen, the love within which
All other love finds speech.
This love is silent.
                    What can I say to you?
However Michael has behaved, Father,
Whatever Father has said, Michael,
You must forgive each other, you must love each other.

MICHAEL. I could have loved Father, if he'd wanted love,
But he never did, Monica, not from me.

[321]

You know I've always been very fond of you—
I've a very affectionate nature, really,
But . . .

(*Enters* MRS. CARGHILL *with dispatch-case*)

MRS. CARGHILL. Richard! I didn't think you'd still be here.
I came back to have a quiet read of your letters;
But how nice to find a little family party!
I know who you are! You're Monica, of course:
And this must be your brother, Michael.
I'm right, aren't I?

MICHAEL. Yes, you're right.
But . . .

MRS. CARGHILL. How did I know? Because you're so like your father
When he was your age. He's the picture of you, Richard,
As you were once. You're not to introduce us,
I'll introduce myself. I'm Maisie Montjoy!
That means nothing to you, my dears.
It's a very long time since the name of Maisie Montjoy
Topped the bill in revue. Now I'm Mrs. John Carghill.
Richard! It's astonishing about your children:
Monica hardly resembles you at all,
But Michael—your father has changed a good deal
Since I knew him ever so many years ago,
Yet you're the image of what he was then.
Your father was a very dear friend of mine once.

MICHAEL. Did he really look like me?

MRS. CARGHILL. You've his voice! and his way of moving! It's marvelous.
And the charm! He's inherited all of your charm, Richard.
There's no denying it. But who's this coming?
It's another new guest here. He's waving to us.
Do you know him, Richard?

LORD CLAVERTON. It's a man I used to know.

MRS. CARGHILL. How interesting! He's a very good figure.
And he's rather exotic-looking. Is he a foreigner?

LORD CLAVERTON. He comes from some place in Central America.

MRS. CARGHILL. How romantic! I'd love to meet him.

He's coming to speak to us. You must introduce him.

(*Enter* GOMEZ)

GOMEZ. Good morning, Dick.

LORD CLAVERTON. Good morning, Fred.

GOMEZ. You weren't expecting me to join you here, were you?
You're here for a rest cure. I persuaded my doctor
That I was in need of a rest cure too.
And when I heard you'd chosen to come to Badgley Court
I said to my doctor, "Well, what about it?
What better recommendation could I have?"
So he sent me here.

MRS. CARGHILL. Oh, you've seen each other lately?
Richard, I think that you might introduce us.

LORD CLAVERTON. Oh. This is . . .

GOMEZ. Your old friend Federico Gomez,
The prominent citizen of San Marco.
That's my name.

LORD CLAVERTON. So let me introduce you—by that name—
To Mrs. . . . Mrs. . . .

MRS. CARGHILL. Mrs. John Carghill.

GOMEZ. We seem a bit weak on the surnames, Dick!

MRS. CARGHILL. Well, you see, Señor Gomez, when we first become friends—
Lord Claverton and I—I was known by my stage name.
There was a time, once, when everyone in London
Knew the name of Maisie Montjoy in revue.

GOMEZ. If Maisie Montjoy was as beautiful to look at
As Mrs. Carghill, I can well understand
Her success on the stage.

MRS. CARGHILL. Oh, did you never see me?
That's a pity, Señor Gomez.

GOMEZ. I lost touch with things in England.
Had I been in London, and in Dick's position
I should have been your most devoted admirer.

MRS. CARGHILL. *It's Not Too Late for You to Love Me*! That's the song
That made my reputation, Señor Gomez.

GOMEZ. It will never be too late. Don't you agree, Dick?

[323]

—This young lady I take to be your daughter?
And this is your son?

LORD CLAVERTON. This is my son Michael,
And my daughter Monica.

MONICA. How do you do. Michael!

MICHAEL. How do you do.

MRS. CARGHILL. I don't believe you've known Lord Claverton
As long as I have, Señor Gomez.

GOMEZ. My dear lady, you're not old enough
To have known Dick Ferry as long as I have.
We were friends at Oxford.

MRS. CARGHILL. Oh, so you were at Oxford!
Is that how you come to speak such perfect English?
Of course, I could tell from your looks that you were Spanish.
I do like Spaniards. They're so aristocratic.
But it's very strange that we never met before.
You were a friend of Richard's at Oxford
And Richard and I became great friends
Not long afterwards, didn't we, Richard?

GOMEZ. I expect that was after I had left England.

MRS. CARGHILL. Of course, that explains it. After Oxford
I suppose you went back to . . . where is your home?

GOMEZ. The republic of San Marco.

MRS. CARGHILL. Went back to San Marco.
Señor Gomez, if it's true you're staying at Badgley Court,
I warn you—I'm going to cross-examine you
And make you tell me all about Richard
In his Oxford days.

GOMEZ. On one condition:
That you tell me all about Dick when you knew him.

MRS. CARGHILL (*pats her dispatch-case*).
Secret for secret, Señor Gomez!
You've got to be the first to put your cards on the table!

MONICA. Father, I think you should take your rest now.
—I must explain that the doctors were very insistent
That my father should rest and have absolute quiet
Before every meal.

LORD CLAVERTON. But Michael and I
  Must continue our discussion. This afternoon, Michael.
MONICA. No, I think you've had enough talk for today.
  Michael, as you're staying so close at hand
  Will you come back in the morning? After breakfast?
LORD CLAVERTON. Yes, come tomorrow morning.
MICHAEL. Well, I'll come tomorrow morning.
MRS. CARGHILL. Are you staying in the neighborhood, Michael?
  Your father is such an old friend of mine
  That it seems most natural to call you Michael.
  You don't mind, do you?
MICHAEL. No, I don't mind.
  I'm staying at the George—it's not far away.
MRS. CARGHILL. Then I'd like to walk a little way with you.
MICHAEL. Delighted, I'm sure.
GOMEZ. Taking a holiday?
  You're in business in London, aren't you?
MICHAEL. Not a holiday, no. I've been in business in London,
  But I think of cutting loose, and going abroad.
MRS. CARGHILL. You must tell me all about it. Perhaps I could advise you.
  We'll leave you now, Richard. Au revoir, Monica.
  And Señor Gomez, I shall hold you to your promise!
  (*Exeunt* MRS. CARGHILL *and* MICHAEL)
GOMEZ. Well, Dick, we've got to obey our doctors' orders.
  But while we're here, we must have some good talks
  About old times. Bye bye for the present.   (*Exit*)
MONICA. Father, those awful people. We mustn't stay here.
  I want you to escape from them.
LORD CLAVERTON. What I want to escape from
  Is myself, is the past. But what a coward I am,
  To talk of escaping! And what a hypocrite!
  A few minutes ago I was pleading with Michael
  Not to try to escape from his own past failures:
  I said I knew from experience. Do I understand the meaning
  Of the lesson I would teach? Come, I'll start to learn again.
  Michael and I shall go to school together.
  We'll sit side by side, at little desks

And suffer the same humiliations
At the hands of the same master. But have I still time?
There is time for Michael. Is it too late for me, Monica?

CURTAIN

ACT THREE

Same as Act Two. Late afternoon of the following day. MONICA *seated alone. Enter* CHARLES.

CHARLES. Well, Monica, here I am. I hope you got my message.

MONICA. Oh Charles, Charles, I'm so glad you've come!
  I've been so worried, and rather frightened.
  It was exasperating that they couldn't find me
  When you telephoned this morning. That Mrs. Piggott
  Should have heard my beloved's voice
  And I couldn't, just when I had been yearning
  For the sound of it, for the caress that is in it!
  Oh Charles, how I've wanted you! And now I *need* you.

CHARLES. My darling, what I want is to know that you need me.
  On that last day in London, you admitted that you loved me,
  But I wondered . . . I'm sorry, I couldn't help wondering
  How much your words meant. You didn't seem to need me then.
  And you said we weren't engaged yet . . .

MONICA. We're engaged now.
  At least *I'm* engaged. I'm engaged to you forever.

CHARLES. There's another shopping expedition we must make!
  But my darling, since I got your letter this morning
  About your father and Michael, and those people from his past,
  I've been trying to think what I could do to help him.
  If it's blackmail, and that's very much what it looks like,
  Do you think I could persuade him to confide in me?

MONICA. Oh Charles! How could anyone blackmail Father?
  Father, of all people the most scrupulous,
  The most austere. It's quite impossible.

[326]

Father with a guilty secret in his past!
I just can't imagine it.
   (CLAVERTON *has entered unobserved*)
MONICA. I never expected you from *that* direction, Father!
   I thought you were indoors. Where have you been?
LORD CLAVERTON. Not far away. Standing under the great beech tree.
MONICA. Why under the beech tree?
LORD CLAVERTON. I feel drawn to that spot.
   No matter. I heard what you said about guilty secrets.
   There are many things not crimes, Monica,
   Beyond anything of which the law takes cognizance:
   Temporary failures, irreflective aberrations,
   Reckless surrenders, unexplainable impulses,
   Moments we regret in the very next moment,
   Episodes we try to conceal from the world.
   Has there been nothing in your life, Charles Hemington,
   Which you wish to forget? Which you wish to keep unknown?
CHARLES. There are certainly things I would gladly forget, Sir,
   Or rather, which I wish had never happened.
   I can think of things you don't yet know about me, Monica,
   But there's nothing I would ever wish to conceal from you.
LORD CLAVERTON. If there's nothing, truly nothing, that you couldn't tell
   Monica
   Then all is well with you. You're in love with each other—
   I don't need to be told what I've seen for myself!
   And if there is nothing that you conceal from *her*
   However important you may consider it
   To conceal from the rest of the world—your soul is safe.
   If a man has one person, just one in his life,
   To whom he is willing to confess everything—
   And that includes, mind you, not only things criminal,
   Not only turpitude, meanness and cowardice,
   But also situations which are simply ridiculous,
   When he has played the fool (as who has not?)—
   Then he loves that person, and his love will save him.
   I'm afraid that I've never loved anyone, really.
   No, I do love my Monica—but there's the impediment:

It's impossible to be quite honest with your child
If you've never been honest with anyone older,
On terms of equality. To one's child one can't reveal oneself
While she is a child. And by the time she's grown
You've woven such a web of fiction about you!
I've spent my life in trying to forget myself,
In trying to identify myself with the part
I had chosen to play. And the longer we pretend
The harder it becomes to drop the pretense,
Walk off the stage, change into our own clothes
And speak as ourselves. So I'd become an idol
To Monica. She worshiped the part I played:
How could I be sure that she would love the actor
If she saw him, off the stage, without his costume and makeup
And without his stage words, Monica!
I've had your love under false pretenses.
Now, I'm tired of keeping up those pretenses,
But I hope that you'll find a little love in your heart
Still, for your father, when you know him
For what he is, the broken-down actor.
MONICA. I think I should only love you the better, Father,
The more I knew about you. I should understand you better.
There's nothing I'm afraid of learning about Charles,
There's nothing I'm afraid of learning about you.
CHARLES. I was thinking, Sir—forgive the suspicion—
From what Monica has told me about your fellow guests,
Two persons who, she says, claim a very long acquaintance—
I was thinking that if there's any question of blackmail,
I've seen something of it in my practice at the bar.
I'm sure I could help.
MONICA. Oh Father, do let him.
CHARLES. At least, I think I know the best man to advise you.
LORD CLAVERTON. Blackmail? Yes, I've heard that word before,
Not so very long ago. When I asked him what he wanted.
Oh no, he said, I want nothing from you
Except your friendship and your company.
He's a very rich man. And she's a rich woman.

If people merely blackmail you to get your company
I'm afraid the law can't touch them.
CHARLES. Then why should you submit?
Why not leave Badgley and escape from them?
LORD CLAVERTON. Because they are not real, Charles. They are merely
  ghosts:
Specters from my past. They've always been with me
Though it was not till lately that I found the living persons
Whose ghosts tormented me, to be only human beings,
Malicious, petty, and I see myself emerging
From my spectral existence into something like reality.
MONICA. But what did the ghosts mean? All these years
You've kept them to yourself. Did Mother know of them?
LORD CLAVERTON. Your mother knew nothing about them. And I know
That I never knew your mother, as she never knew me.
I thought that she would never understand
Or that she would be jealous of the ghosts who haunted me.
And I'm still of that opinion. How open one's heart
When one is sure of the wrong response?
How make a confession with no hope of absolution?
It was not her fault. We never understood each other.
And so we lived, with a deep silence between us,
And she died silently. She had nothing to say to me.
I think of your mother, when she lay dying:
Completely without interest in the life that lay behind her
And completely indifferent to whatever lay ahead of her.
MONICA. It is time to break the silence! Let us share your ghosts!
CHARLES. But these are only human beings, who can be dealt with.
MONICA. Or only ghosts, who can be exorcised!
Who are they, and what do they stand for in your life?
LORD CLAVERTON. . . . And yet they've done better for themselves
In consequence of it all. He admitted as much,
Fred Culverwell . . .
MONICA. Fred Culverwell?
Who is Fred Culverwell?
LORD CLAVERTON. He no longer exists,
He's Federico Gomez, the Central American,

A man who's made a fortune by his own peculiar methods,
A man of great importance and the highest standing
In his adopted country. He even has sons
Following in their father's footsteps
Who are also successful. What would *he* have been
If he hadn't known me? Only a schoolmaster
In an obscure grammar school somewhere in the Midlands.
As for Maisie Batterson . . .

MONICA. Maisie Batterson?
Who is Maisie Batterson?

LORD CLAVERTON. She no longer exists.
Nor the musical comedy star, Maisie Montjoy.
There is Mrs. John Carghill, the wealthy widow.
But Freddy Culverwell and Maisie Batterson,
And Dick Ferry too, and Richard Ferry—
These are my ghosts. They were people with good in them,
People who might all have been very different
From Gomez, Mrs. Carghill and Lord Claverton.
Freddy admired me, when we were at Oxford:
What did I make of his admiration?
I led him to acquire tastes beyond his means:
So he became a forger. And so he served his term.
Was I responsible for that weakness in him?
Yes, I was.
How easily we ignore the fact that those who admire us
Will imitate our vices as well as our virtues—
Or whatever the qualities for which they did admire us!
And that again may nourish the faults that they were born with.
And Maisie loved me, with whatever capacity
For loving she had—self-centered and foolish—
But we should respect love always when we meet it;
Even when it's vain and selfish, we must not abuse it.
That is where I failed. And the memory frets me.

CHARLES. But all the same, these two people mustn't persecute you.
We can't allow that. What hold have they upon you?

LORD CLAVERTON. Only the hold of those who know
Something discreditable, dishonorable . . .

MONICA. Then, Father, you should tell *us* what they already know.
   Why should you wish to conceal from those who love you
   What is known so well to those who hate you?
LORD CLAVERTON. I will tell you very briefly
   And simply. As for Frederick Culverwell,
   He re-enters my life to make himself a reminder
   Of one occasion the memory of which,
   He knows very well, has always haunted me.
   I was driving back to Oxford. We had two girls with us.
   It was late at night. A secondary road.
   I ran over an old man lying in the road
   And I did not stop. Then another man ran over him.
   A lorry driver. He stopped and was arrested,
   But was later discharged. It was definitely shown
   That the old man had died a natural death
   And had been run over after he was dead.
   It was only a corpse that we had run over
   So neither of us killed him. But *I* didn't stop.
   And all my life I have heard, from time to time,
   When I least expected, between waking and sleeping,
   A voice that whispered, "you didn't stop!"
   I knew the voice: it was Fred Culverwell's.
MONICA. Poor Father! All your life! And no one to share it with;
   I never knew how lonely you were
   Or why you were lonely.
CHARLES. And Mrs. Carghill:
   What has she against you?
LORD CLAVERTON. I was her first lover.
   I would have married her—but my father prevented that:
   Made it worth while for her not to marry me—
   That was his way of putting it—and of course
   Made it worth while for me not to marry her.
   In fact, we were wholly unsuited to each other,
   Yet she had a peculiar physical attraction
   Which no other woman has had. And she knows it.
   And she knows that the ghost of the man I was
   Still clings to the ghost of the woman who was Maisie.

[331]

We should have been poor, we should certainly have quarreled,
We should have been unhappy, might have come to divorce;
But she hasn't forgotten or forgiven me.

CHARLES. This man, and this woman, who are so vindictive:
Don't you see that they were as much at fault as you
And that they know it? That's why they are inspired
With revenge—it's their means of self-justification.
Let them tell their versions of their miserable stories,
Confide them in whispers. They cannot harm you.

LORD CLAVERTON. Your reasoning's sound enough. But it's irrelevant.
Each of them remembers an occasion
On which I ran away. Very well.
I shan't run away now—run away from *them*.
It is through this meeting that I shall at last escape them.
—I've made my confession to you, Monica:
That is the first step taken towards my freedom,
And perhaps the most important. I know what you think.
You think that I suffer from a morbid conscience,
From brooding over faults I might well have forgotten.
You think that I'm sickening, when I'm just recovering!
It's hard to make other people realize
The magnitude of things that appear to them petty;
It's harder to confess the sin that no one believes in
Than the crime that everyone can appreciate.
For the crime is in relation to the law
And the sin is in relation to the sinner.
What has made the difference in the last five minutes
Is not the heinousness of my misdeeds
But the fact of my confession. And to you, Monica,
To you, of all people.

CHARLES. I grant you all that.
But what do you propose? How long, Lord Claverton,
Will you stay here and endure this persecution?

LORD CLAVERTON. To the end. The place and time of liberation
Are, I think, determined. Let us say no more about it.
Meanwhile, I feel sure they are conspiring against me.
I see Mrs. Carghill coming.

MONICA. Let us go.

LORD CLAVERTON. We will stay here. Let her join us.

(*Enter* MRS. CARGHILL)

MRS. CARGHILL. I've been hunting high and low for you, Richard!

I've some very exciting news for you!

But I suspect . . . Dare I? Yes, I'm sure of it, Monica!

I can tell by the change in your expression today;

This must be your fiancé. Do introduce him.

MONICA. Mr. Charles Hemington. Mrs. Carghill.

CHARLES. How do you do.

MRS. CARGHILL. What a charming name!

CHARLES. I'm glad my name meets with your approval, Mrs. Carghill.

MRS. CARGHILL. And let me congratulate *you,* Mr. Hemington.

You're a very lucky man, to get a girl like Monica.

I take a great interest in her future.

Fancy, I've only known her two days!

But I feel like a mother to her already.

You may say that I just missed being her mother!

I've known her father for a very long time,

And there was a moment when I almost married him,

Oh so long ago. So you see, Mr. Hemington,

I've come to regard her as my adopted daughter.

So much so, that it seems odd to call you Mr. Hemington:

I'm going to call you Charles!

CHARLES. As you please, Mrs. Carghill.

LORD CLAVERTON. You said you had some exciting news for us.

Would you care to impart it?

MRS. CARGHILL. It's about dear Michael.

LORD CLAVERTON. Oh? What about Michael?

MRS. CARGHILL. He's told me all his story.

You've cruelly misunderstood him, Richard.

How he must have suffered! So I put on my thinking cap.

I know you've always thought me utterly brainless,

But I have an idea or two, now and then.

And in the end I discovered what Michael really wanted

For making a new start. He wants to go abroad!

And find his own way in the world. That's very natural.

So I thought, why not appeal to Señor Gomez?
He's a wealthy man, and very important
In his own country. And a friend of Michael's father!
And I found him only too ready to help.

LORD CLAVERTON. And what was Señor Gomez able to suggest?

MRS. CARGHILL. Ah! That's the surprise for which I've come to prepare you.
Dear Michael is so happy—all his problems are solved;
And he was so perplexed, poor lamb. Let's all rejoice together.

(*Enter* GOMEZ *and* MICHAEL)

LORD CLAVERTON. Well, Michael, you know I expected you this morning,
But you never came.

MICHAEL. No, Father. I'll explain why.

LORD CLAVERTON. And I learn that you have discussed your problems
With Mrs. Carghill and then with Señor Gomez.

MICHAEL. When I spoke, Father, of my wish to get abroad,
You couldn't see my point of view. What's the use of chasing
Half round the world, for the same sort of job
You got me here in London? With another Sir Alfred
Who'd constitute himself custodian of my morals
And send you back reports. Some sort of place
Where everyone would sneer at the fellow from London,
The limey remittance man for whom a job was made.
No! I want to go where I can make my own way,
Not merely be your son. That's what Señor Gomez sees.
He understands my point of view, if *you* don't.
And he's offered me a job which is just what I wanted.

LORD CLAVERTON. Yes, I see the advantage of a job created for you
By Señor Gomez . . .

MICHAEL. It's not created for me.
Señor Gomez came to London to find a man to fill it,
And he thinks I'm just the man.

GOMEZ. Yes, wasn't it extraordinary.

LORD CLAVERTON. Of course you're just the man that Señor Gomez wants,
But in a different sense, and for different reasons
From what you think. Let me tell you about Gomez.
He's unlikely to try to be custodian of your morals;
His real name is Culverwell . . .

GOMEZ. My dear Dick,
    You're wasting your time, rehearsing ancient history.
    Michael knows it already. I've told him myself.
    I thought he'd better learn the facts from me
    Before he heard your distorted version.
    But, Dick, I was nettled by that insinuation
    About my not being custodian of Michael's morals.
    That is just what I should be! And most appropriate,
    Isn't it, Dick, when we recall
    That you were once custodian of *my* morals:
    Though of course you went a little *faster* than I did.
LORD CLAVERTON. On that point, Fred, you're wasting *your* time:
    My daughter and my future son-in-law
    Understand that allusion. I have told them the story
    In explanation of our . . . intimacy
    Which they found puzzling.
MRS. CARGHILL. Oh, Richard!
    Have you explained to them our intimacy too?
LORD CLAVERTON. I have indeed.
MRS. CARGHILL. The romance of my life.
    Your father was simply *irresistible*
    In those days. I melted the first time he looked at me!
    Some day, Monica, I'll tell you all about it.
MONICA. I am satisfied with what I know already, Mrs. Carghill,
    About you.
MRS. CARGHILL. But I was very lovely then.
GOMEZ. We are sure of that! You're so lovely now
    That we can well imagine you at . . . what age were you?
MRS. CARGHILL. Just eighteen.
LORD CLAVERTON. Now, Michael,
    Señor Gomez says he has told you his story.
    Did he include the fact that he served a term in prison?
MICHAEL. He told me everything. It was his experience
    With you, that made him so understanding
    Of my predicament.
LORD CLAVERTON. And made him invent
    The position which he'd come to find the man for.

MICHAEL. I don't care about that. He's offered me the job
  With jolly good pay, and some pickings in commissions.
  He's made a fortune there. San Marco for me!
LORD CLAVERTON. And what are your duties to be? Do you know?
MICHAEL. We didn't go into details. There's time for that later.
GOMEZ. Much better to wait until we get there.
  The nature of business in San Marco
  Is easier explained in San Marco than in England.
LORD CLAVERTON. Perhaps you intend to change your name to Gomez?
GOMEZ. Oh no, Dick, there are plenty of other good names.
MONICA. Michael, Michael, you can't abandon your family
  And your very self—it's a kind of suicide.
CHARLES. Michael, you think Señor Gomez is inspired by benevolence—
MICHAEL. I told you he'd come to London looking for a man
  For an important post on his staff—
CHARLES. A post the nature of which is left very vague.
MICHAEL. It's confidential, I tell you.
CHARLES. So I can imagine:
  Highly confidential . . .
GOMEZ. Be careful, Mr. Barrister.
  You ought to know something about the law of slander.
  Here's Mrs. Carghill, a reliable witness.
CHARLES. I know enough about the law of libel and slander
  To know that you are hardly likely to invoke it.
  And, Michael, here's another point to think of:
  Señor Gomez has offered you a post in San Marco,
  Señor Gomez pays your passage . . .
MICHAEL. And an advance of salary.
CHARLES. Señor Gomez pays your passage . . .
GOMEZ. Just as many years ago
  His father paid mine.
CHARLES. This return of past kindness
  No doubt gives you pleasure?
GOMEZ. Yes, it's always pleasant
  To repay an old debt. And better late than never.
CHARLES. I see your point of view. Can you really feel confidence,
  Michael, in a man who aims to gratify, through you,

His lifelong grievance against your father?
Remember, you put yourself completely in the power
Of a man you don't know, of the nature of whose business
You know nothing. All you can be sure of
Is that he served a prison sentence for forgery.

GOMEZ. Well, Michael, what do you say to all this?

MICHAEL. I'll say that Hemington has plenty of cheek.
Señor Gomez and I have talked things over, Hemington . . .

GOMEZ. As two men of the world, we discussed things very frankly;
And I can tell you, Michael's head is well screwed on.
He's got brains, he's got flair. When he does come back
He'll be able to buy you out many times over.

MRS. CARGHILL. Richard, I think it's time *I* joined the conversation.
My late husband, Mr. Carghill, was a businessman—
I wish you could have known him, Señor Gomez!
You're very much alike in some ways—
So I understand business. Mr. Carghill told me so.
Now, Michael has great abilities for business.
I saw that, and so does Señor Gomez.
He's simply been suffering, poor boy, from frustration.
He's been waiting all this time for opportunity
To make use of his gifts; and now, opportunity—
Opportunity has come knocking at the door.
Richard, you must not bar his way. That would be shameful.

LORD CLAVERTON. I cannot bar his way, as you know very well.
Michael's a free agent. So if he chooses
To place himself in your power, Fred Culverwell,
Of his own volition to contract his enslavement,
I cannot prevent him. I have something to say to you,
Michael, before you go. I shall never repudiate you
Though you repudiate me. I see now clearly
The many many mistakes I have made
My whole life through, mistake upon mistake,
The mistaken attempts to correct mistakes
By methods which proved to be equally mistaken.
I see that your mother and I, in our failure
To understand each other, both misunderstood you

[337]

In our divergent ways. When I think of your childhood,
When I think of the happy little boy who was Michael,
When I think of your boyhood and adolescence,
And see how all the efforts aimed at your good
Only succeeded in defeating each other,
How can I feel anything but sorrow and compunction?

MONICA. Oh Michael, remember, you're my only brother
And I'm your only sister. You never took much notice of me.
When we were growing up we seldom had the same friends.
I took all that for granted. So I didn't know till now
How much it means to me to have a brother.

MICHAEL. Why of course, Monica. You know I'm very fond of you
Though we never really seemed to have much in common.
I remember, when I came home for the holidays
How it used to get on my nerves, when I saw you
Always sitting there with your nose in a book.
And once, Mother snatched a book away from you
And tossed it into the fire. How I laughed!
You never seemed even to want a flirtation,
And my friends used to chaff me about my highbrow sister.
But all the same, I was fond of you, and always shall be.
We don't meet often, but if we're fond of each other,
That needn't interfere with your life or mine.

MONICA. Oh Michael, you haven't understood a single word
Of what I said. You must make your own life
Of course, just as I must make mine.
It's not a question of your going abroad
But a question of the spirit which inspired your decision:
If you wish to renounce your father and your family
What is left between you and me?

MICHAEL. That makes no difference.
You'll be seeing me again.

MONICA. But who will you be
When I see you again? Whoever you are then
I shall always pretend that it is the same Michael.

CHARLES. And when do you leave England?

MICHAEL. When we can get a passage.
  And I must buy my kit. We're just going up to London.
  Señor Gomez will attend to my needs for that climate.
  And you see, he has friends in the shipping line
  Who he thinks can be helpful in getting reservations.
MRS. CARGHILL. It's wonderful, Señor Gomez, how you manage *everything!*
  —No sooner had I put my proposal before him
  Than he had it all planned out! It really was an inspiration—
  On my part, I mean. Are you listening to me, Richard?
  You look very *distrait*. You ought to be excited!
LORD CLAVERTON. Is this goodbye then, Michael?
MICHAEL. Well, that just depends.
  I could look in again. If there's any point in it.
  Personally, I think that when one's come to a decision,
  It's as well to say goodbye at once and be done with it.
LORD CLAVERTON. Yes, if you're going, and I see no way to stop you,
  Then I agree with you, the sooner the better.
  We may never meet again, Michael.
MICHAEL. I don't see why not.
GOMEZ. At the end of five years he will get his first leave.
MICHAEL. Well . . . there's nothing more to say, is there?
LORD CLAVERTON. Nothing at all.
MICHAEL. Then we might as well be going.
GOMEZ. Yes, we might as well be going.
  You'll be grateful to me in the end, Dick.
MRS. CARGHILL. A parent isn't always the right person, Richard,
  To solve a son's problems. Sometimes an outsider,
  A friend of the family, can see more clearly.
GOMEZ. Not that I deserve any credit for it.
  We can only regard it as a stroke of good fortune
  That I came to England at the very moment
  When I could be helpful.
MRS. CARGHILL. It's truly providential!
MONICA. Goodbye Michael. Will you let me write to you?
GOMEZ. Oh, I'm glad you reminded me. Here's my business card
  With the full address. You can always reach him there.

But it takes some days, you know, even by air mail.
MONICA. Take the card, Charles. If I write to you, Michael,
    Will you ever answer?
MICHAEL. Oh of course, Monica.
    You know I'm not much of a correspondent;
    But I'll send you a card, now and again,
    Just to let you know I'm flourishing.
LORD CLAVERTON. Yes, write to Monica.
GOMEZ. Well, goodbye Dick. And goodbye Monica.
    Goodbye, Mr. . . . Hemington.
MONICA. Goodbye Michael.   (*Exeunt* MICHAEL *and* GOMEZ)
MRS. CARGHILL. I'm afraid this seems awfully sudden to you, Richard;
    It isn't so sudden. We talked it all over.
    But I've got a little piece of news of my own:
    Next autumn, I'm going out to Australia,
    On my doctor's advice. And on my way back
    Señor Gomez has invited me to visit San Marco.
    I'm so excited! But what pleases me most
    Is that I shall be able to bring you news of Michael.
    And now that we've found each other again,
    We must always keep in touch. But you'd better rest now.
    You're looking rather tired. I'll run and see them off. (*Exit* MRS. CARGHILL)
MONICA. Oh Father, Father, I'm so sorry!
    But perhaps, perhaps, Michael may learn his lesson.
    I believe he'll come back. If it's all a failure
    Homesickness, I'm sure, will bring him back to us;
    If he prospers, that will give him confidence—
    It's only self-confidence that Michael is lacking.
    Oh Father, it's not you and me he rejects,
    But himself, the unhappy self that he's ashamed of.
    I'm sure he loves us.
LORD CLAVERTON. Monica my dear,
    What you say comes home to me. I fear for Michael;
    Nevertheless, you are right to hope for something better.
    And when he comes back, if he does come back,
    I know that you and Charles will do what you can
    To make him feel that he is not estranged from you.

CHARLES. We will indeed. We shall be ready to welcome him
    And give all the aid we can. But it's both of you together
    Make the force to attract him; you and Monica combined.
LORD CLAVERTON. I shall not be here. You heard me say to him
    That this might be a final goodbye.
    I am sure of it now. Perhaps it is as well.
MONICA. What do you mean, Father? You'll be here to greet him.
    But one thing I'm convinced of: you must leave Badgley Court.
CHARLES. Monica is right. You should leave.
LORD CLAVERTON. This may surprise you: I feel at peace now.
    It is the peace that ensues upon contrition
    When contrition ensues upon knowledge of the truth.
    Why did I always want to dominate my children?
    Why did I mark out a narrow path for Michael?
    Because I wanted to perpetuate myself in him.
    Why did I want to keep you to myself, Monica?
    Because I wanted you to give your life to adoring
    The man that I pretended to myself that I was,
    So that I could believe in my own pretenses.
    I've only just now had the illumination
    Of knowing what love is. We all think we know,
    But how few of us do! And now I feel happy—
    In spite of everything, in defiance of reason,
    I have been brushed by the wing of happiness.
    And I am happy, Monica, that you have found a man
    Whom you can love for the man he really is.
MONICA. Oh Father, I've always loved you,
    But I love you more since I have come to know you
    Here, at Badgley Court. And I love you the more
    Because I love Charles.
LORD CLAVERTON. Yes, my dear.
    Your love is for the real Charles, not a make-believe,
    As was your love for me.
MONICA. But not now, Father!
    It's the real you I love—the man you are,
    Not the man I thought you were.
LORD CLAVERTON. And Michael—

I love him, even for rejecting me,
For the *me* he rejected, I reject also.
I've been freed from the self that pretends to be someone;
And in becoming no one, I begin to live.
It is worth while dying, to find out what life is.
And I love you, my daughter, the more truly for knowing
That there is someone you love more than your father—
That you love and are loved. And now that I love Michael,
I think, for the first time—remember, my dear,
I am only a beginner in the practice of loving—
Well, that is something.
                    I shall leave you for a while.
This is your first visit to us at Badgley Court,
Charles, and not at all what you were expecting.
I am sorry you had to see so much of persons
And situations not very agreeable.
You two ought to have a little time together.
I leave Monica to you. Look after her, Charles,
Now and always. I shall take a stroll.
MONICA. At this time of day? You'll not go far, will you?
    You know you're not allowed to stop out late
    At this season. It's chilly at dusk.
LORD CLAVERTON. Yes, it's chilly at dusk. But I'll be warm enough.
    I shall not go far.   (*Exit* CLAVERTON)
CHARLES. He's a very different man from the man he used to be.
    It's as if he had passed through some door unseen by us
    And had turned and was looking back at us
    With a glance of farewell.
MONICA. I can't understand his going for a walk.
CHARLES. He wanted to leave us alone together!
MONICA. Yes, he wanted to leave us alone together.
    And yet, Charles, though we've been alone today
    Only a few minutes, I've felt all the time . . .
CHARLES. I know what you're going to say!
    We *were* alone together, in some mysterious fashion,
    Even with Michael, and despite those people,

Because somehow we'd begun to belong together,
     And that awareness . . .
MONICA. Was a shield protecting both of us . . .
CHARLES. So that now we are conscious of a new person
     Who is you and me together.
                         Oh my dear,
     I love you to the limits of speech, and beyond.
     It's strange that words are so inadequate.
     Yet, like the asthmatic struggling for breath,
     So the lover must struggle for words.
MONICA. I've loved you from the beginning of the world.
     Before you and I were born, the love was always there
     That brought us together.
                         Oh Father, Father!
     I could speak to you now.
CHARLES. Let me go and find him.
MONICA. We will go to him together. He is close at hand,
     Though he has gone too far to return to us.
     He is under the beech tree. It is quiet and cold there.
     In becoming no one, he has become himself.
     He is only my father now, and Michael's.
     And I am happy. Isn't it strange, Charles,
     To be happy at this moment?
CHARLES. It is not at all strange.
     The dead has poured out a blessing on the living.
MONICA. Age and decrepitude can have no terrors for me,
     Loss and vicissitude cannot appall me,
     Not even death can dismay or amaze me
     Fixed in the certainty of love unchanging.
                              I feel utterly secure
     In you; I am part of you. Now take me to my father.

CURTAIN

[343]

TRADITION AND THE INDIVIDUAL TALENT

By T. S. ELIOT

I

In English writing we seldom speak of tradition, though we occasionally apply its name in deploring its absence. We cannot refer to "the tradition" or to "a tradition"; at most, we employ the adjective in saying that the poetry of So-and-so is "traditional" or even "too traditional." Seldom, perhaps, does the word appear except in a phrase of censure. If otherwise, it is vaguely approbative, with the implication, as to the work approved, of some pleasing archæological reconstruction. You can hardly make the word agreeable to English ears without this comfortable reference to the reassuring science of archæology.

Certainly the word is not likely to appear in our appreciations of living or dead writers. Every nation, every race, has not only its own creative, but its own critical turn of mind; and is even more oblivious of the shortcomings and limitations of its critical habits than of those of its creative genius. We know, or think we know, from the enormous mass of critical writing that has appeared in the French language the critical method or habit of the French; we only conclude (we are such unconscious people) that

the French are "more critical" than we, and sometimes even plume ourselves a little with the fact, as if the French were the less spontaneous. Perhaps they are; but we might remind ourselves that criticism is as inevitable as breathing, and that we should be none the worse for articulating what passes in our minds when we read a book and feel an emotion about it, for criticizing our own minds in their work of criticism. One of the facts that might come to light in this process is our tendency to insist, when we praise a poet, upon those aspects of his work in which he least resembles anyone else. In these aspects or parts of his work we pretend to find what is individual, what is the peculiar essence of the man. We dwell with satisfaction upon the poet's difference from his predecessors, especially his immediate predecessors; we endeavor to find something that can be isolated in order to be enjoyed. Whereas if we approach a poet without his prejudice we shall often find that not only the best, but the most individual parts of his work may be those in which the dead poets, his ancestors, assert their immortality most vigorously. And I do not mean the impressionable period of adolescence, but the period of full maturity.

Yet if the only form of tradition, of handing down, consisted in following the ways of the immediate generation before us in a blind or timid adherence to its successes, "tradition" should positively be discouraged. We have seen many such simple currents soon lost in the sand; and novelty is better than repetition. Tradition is a matter of much wider significance. It cannot be inherited, and if you want it you must obtain it by great labor. It involves, in the first place, the historical sense, which we may call nearly indispensable to anyone who would continue to be a poet beyond his twenty-fifth year; and the historical sense involves a perception, not only of the pastness of the past, but of its presence; the historical sense compels a man to write not merely with his own generation in his bones, but with a feeling that the whole of the literature of Europe from Homer and within it the whole of the literature of his own country has a simultaneous existence and composes a simultaneous order. This historical sense, which is a sense of the timeless as well as of the temporal and of the timeless and of the temporal together, is what makes a writer traditional. And it is at the same time what makes a writer most acutely conscious of his place in time, of his contemporaneity.

No poet, no artist of any art, has his complete meaning alone. His significance, his appreciation is the appreciation of his relation to the dead poets and artists. You cannot value him alone; you must set him, for contrast and comparison, among the dead. I mean this as a principle of æsthetic, not merely historical, criticism. The necessity that he shall conform, that he shall cohere, is not onesided; what happens when a new work of art is created is something that happens simultaneously to all the works of art which preceded it. The existing monuments form an ideal order among themselves, which is modified by the introduction of the new (the really new) work of art among them. The existing order is complete before the new work arrives; for order to persist after the supervention of novelty, the *whole* existing order must be, if ever so slightly, altered; and so the relations, proportions, values of each work of art toward the whole are readjusted; and this is conformity between the old and the new. Whoever has approved this idea of order, of the form of European, of English literature, will not find it preposterous that the past should be altered by the present as much as the present is directed by the past. And the poet who is aware of this will be aware of great difficulties and responsibilities.

In a peculiar sense he will be aware also that he must inevitably be judged by the standards of the past. I say judged, not amputated, by them; not judged to be as good as, or worse or better than, the dead; and certainly not judged by the canons of dead critics. It is a judgment, a comparison, in which two things are measured by each other. To conform merely would be for the new work not really to conform at all; it would not be new, and would therefore not be a work of art. And we do not quite say that the new is more valuable because it fits in; but its fitting in is a test of its value—a test, it is true, which can only be slowly and cautiously applied, for we are none of us infallible judges of conformity. We say: it appears to conform, and is perhaps individual, or it appears individual, and may conform; but we are hardly likely to find that it is one and not the other.

To proceed to a more intelligible exposition of the relation of the poet to the past: he can neither take the past as a lump, an indiscriminate bolus, nor can he form himself wholly on one or two private admirations, nor can he form himself wholly upon one preferred period. The first course is inadmissible, the second is an important experience of youth, and the third is a pleasant and highly desirable supplement. The poet must be very conscious of the main current, which does not at all flow invariably through the most distinguished reputations. He must be quite aware of the obvious fact that art never improves, but that the material of art is never quite the same. He must be aware that the mind of Europe—the mind of his own country— a mind which he learns in time to be much more important than his own private mind—is a mind which changes, and that this change is a development which abandons nothing *en route,* which does not superannuate either Shakespeare, or Homer, or the rock drawing of the Magdalenian draftsmen. That this development, refinement perhaps, complication certainly, is not, from the point of view of the artist, any improvement. Perhaps not even an improvement from the point of view of the psychologist or not to the extent which we imagine; perhaps only in the end based upon a complication in economics and machinery. But the difference between the present and the past is that the conscious present is an awareness of the past in a way and to an extent which the past's awareness of itself cannot show.

Some one said: "The dead writers are remote from us because we *know* so much more than they did." Precisely, and they are that which we know.

I am alive to a usual objection to what is clearly part of my program for the *métier* of poetry. The objection is that the doctrine requires a ridiculous amount of erudition (pedantry), a claim which can be rejected by appeal to the lives of poets in any pantheon. It will even be affirmed that much learning deadens or perverts poetic sensibility. While, however, we persist in believing that a poet ought to know as much as will not encroach upon his necessary receptivity and necessary laziness, it is not desirable to confine knowledge to whatever can be put into a useful shape for examinations, drawing-rooms, or the still more pretentious modes of publicity. Some can absorb knowledge, the more tardy must sweat for it. Shakespeare acquired more essential history from Plutarch than most men could from the whole British Museum. What is to be insisted upon is that the poet must develop or procure the consciousness of the past and that he should continue to develop this consciousness throughout his career.

What happens is a continual surrender of himself as he is at the moment to something which is more valuable. The progress of an artist is a continual self-sacrifice, a continual extinction of personality.

There remains to define this process of depersonalization and its relation to the sense of tradition. It is in this depersonalization that art may be said to approach the condition of science. I shall, therefore, invite you to consider, as a suggestive analogy, the action which takes place when a bit of finely filiated platinum is introduced into a chamber containing oxygen and sulphur dioxide.

II

Honest criticism and sensitive appreciation is directed not upon the poet but upon the poetry. If we attend to the confused cries of the newspaper critics and the susurrus of popular repetition that follows, we shall hear the names of poets in great numbers; if we seek not Bluebook knowledge but the enjoyment of poetry, and ask for a poem, we shall seldom find it. In the last article I tried to point out the importance of the relation of the poem to other poems by other authors, and suggested the conception of poetry as a living whole of all the poetry that has ever been written. The other aspect of this Impersonal theory of poetry is the relation of the poem to its author. And I hinted, by an analogy, that the mind of the mature poet differs from that of the immature one not precisely in any valuation of "personality," not being necessarily more interesting, or having "more to say," but rather by being a more finely perfected medium in which special, or very varied, feelings are at liberty to enter into new combinations.

The analogy was that of the catalyst. When the two gases previously mentioned are mixed in the presence of a filament of platinum, they form sulphurous acid. This combination takes place only if the platinum is present; nevertheless the newly formed acid contains no trace of platinum, and the platinum itself is apparently unaffected; has remained inert, neutral, and unchanged. The mind of the poet is the shred of platinum. It may partly or exclusively operate upon the experience of the man himself; but, the more perfect the artist, the more completely separate in him will be the man who suffers and the mind which creates; the more perfectly will the mind digest and transmute the passions which are its material.

The experience, you will notice, the elements which enter the presence of the transforming catalyst, are of two kinds: emotions and feelings. The effect of a work of art upon the person who enjoys it is an experience different in kind from any experience not of art. It may be formed out of one emotion, or may be a combination of several; and various feelings, inhering for the writer in particular words or phrases or images, may be added to compose the final result. Or great poetry may be made without the direct use of any emotion whatever: composed out of feelings solely. Canto

XV of the *Inferno* (Brunetto Latini) is a working up of the emotion evident in the situation; but the effect, though single as that of any work of art, is obtained by considerable complexity of detail. The last quatrain gives an image, a feeling attaching to an image, which "came," which did not develop simply out of what precedes, but which was probably in suspension in the poet's mind until the proper combination arrived for it to add itself to. The poet's mind is in fact a receptacle for seizing and storing up numberless feelings, phrases, images, which remain there until all the particles which can unite to form a new compound are present together.

If you compare several representative passages of the greatest poetry you see how great is the variety of types of combination, and also how completely any semi-ethical criterion of "sublimity" misses the mark. For it is not the "greatness," the intensity, of the emotions, the components, but the intensity of the artistic process, the pressure, so to speak, under which the fusion takes place, that counts. The episode of Paolo and Francesca employs a definite emotion, but the intensity of the poetry is something quite different from whatever intensity in the supposed experience it may give the impression of. It is no more intense, furthermore, than Canto XXVI, the voyage of Ulysses, which has not the direct dependence upon an emotion. Great variety is possible in the process of transmutation of emotion: the murder of Agamemnon, or the agony of Othello, gives an artistic effect apparently closer to a possible original than the scenes from Dante. In the *Agamemnon*, the artistic emotion approximates to the emotion of an actual spectator; in *Othello* to the emotion of the protagonist himself. But the difference between art and the event is always absolute; the combination which is the murder of Agamemnon is probably as complex as that which is the voyage of Ulysses. In either case there has been a fusion of elements. The ode of Keats contains a number of feelings which have nothing particular to do with the nightingale, but which the nightingale, partly, perhaps, because of its attractive name, and partly because of its reputation, serves to bring together.

The point of view which I am struggling to attack is perhaps related to the metaphysical theory of the substantial unity of the soul: for my meaning is, that the poet has, not a "personality" to express, but a particular medium, which is only a medium and not a personality, in which impressions and experiences combine in peculiar and unexpected ways. Impressions and experiences which are important for the man may take no place in the poetry, and those which become important in the poetry may play quite a negligible part in the man, the personality.

I will quote a passage which is unfamiliar enough to be regarded with fresh attention in the light—or darkness—of these observations:

And now methinks I could e'en chide myself
For doating on her beauty, though her death
Shall be revenged after no common action.
Does the silkworm expend her yellow labors
For thee? For thee does she undo herself?
Are lordships sold to maintain ladyships
For the poor benefit of a bewildering minute?
Why does yon fellow falsify highways,
And put his life between the judge's lips,
To refine such a thing—keeps horse and men
To beat their valors for her? . . .

In this passage (as is evident if it is taken in its context) there is a combination of positive and negative emotions: an intensely strong attraction toward beauty and an equally intense fascination by the ugliness which is contrasted with it and which destroys it. This balance of contrasted emotion is in the dramatic situation to which the speech is pertinent, but that situation alone is inadequate to it. This is, so to speak, the structural emotion, provided by the drama. But the whole effect, the dominant tone, is due to the fact that a number of floating feelings, having an affinity to this emotion by no means superficially evident, have combined with it to give us a new art emotion.

It is not in his personal emotions, the emotions provoked by particular events in his life, that the poet is in any way remarkable or interesting. His particular emotions may be simple, or crude, or flat. The emotion in his poetry will be a very complex thing, but not with the complexity of the emotions of people who have very complex or unusual emotions in life. One error, in fact, of eccentricity in poetry is to seek for new human emotions to express; and in this search for novelty in the wrong place it discovers the perverse. The business of the poet is not to find new emotions, but to use the ordinary ones and, in working them up into poetry, to express feelings which are not in actual emotions at all. And emotions which he has never experienced will serve his turn as well as those familiar to him. Consequently, we must believe that "emotion recollected in tranquillity" is an inexact formula. For it is neither emotion, nor recollection, nor, without distortion of meaning, tranquillity. It is a concentration, and a new thing resulting from the concentration, of a very great number of experiences which to the practical and active person would not seem to be experiences at all; it is a concentration which does not happen consciously or of deliberation. These experiences are not "recollected," and they finally unite in an atmosphere which is "tranquil" only in that it is a passive attending upon the event. Of course this is not quite the whole story. There is a great deal, in the writing of poetry, which must be conscious and deliberate. In fact, the bad poet is usually unconscious where he ought to be conscious, and conscious where he ought to be unconscious. Both errors tend to make him "personal." Poetry is not a turning loose of emotion, but an escape from emotion; it is not the expression of personality, but an escape from personality. But, of course, only those who have personality and emotions know what it means to want to escape from these things.

III

ὁ δὲ νοῦς ἴσως θειότερόν τι χαὶ ἀπαθές ἐστιν

This essay proposes to halt at the frontier of metaphysics or mysticism, and confine itself to such practical conclusions as can be applied by the responsible person in-terested in poetry. To divert interest from the poet to the poetry is a laudable aim: for it would conduce to a juster estimation of actual poetry, good and bad. There are many people who appreciate the expression of sincere emotion in verse, and there is a smaller number of people who can appreciate technical excellence. But very few know when there is expression of *significant* emotion, emotion which has its life in the poem and not in the history of the poet. The emotion of art is impersonal. And the poet cannot reach this impersonality without surrendering himself wholly to the work to be done. And he is not likely to know what is to be done unless he lives in what is not merely the present, but the present moment of the past, unless he is conscious, not of what is dead, but of what is already living.

THE LIFE AND WORKS OF
T. S. ELIOT

By FRANCIS SCARFE

WE ARE ALWAYS suspicious of great men or "geniuses," while realizing that they are necessary to society. Not that their mission or function is always the same, for some come to preserve the past, others to destroy it, others to anticipate and plan the future. Among them T. S. Eliot holds an ambiguous position, for he brought what appeared to be a message of conservative traditionalism, yet he left the arts of theater, criticism, and poetry very different from what he found them. As in Eliot's case, the great man is not always what he pretends to be. Maybe the word "genius" is better dropped, for it is hard to find any common denominator among such minds as Dante, Shakespeare, Leonardo, Freud, Einstein, or Picasso.

The term "universal mind" attributed to Goethe and often applied to him, now sounds almost as pompous as "genius." Valéry's term "European mind" has its uses, but would also appear to exclude Eliot. There is a further category of minds: those who, while being neither universal nor strictly European, strive to define and maintain the notion of a Western civilization, among whom we would count such writers as Henry James, Ezra Pound, and T. S. Eliot. These men brought to their work—which

was remarkably European in many respects—all the vitality of the New World. Eliot was one of those few men who know how to build a bridge or link between several cultures. With admirable subtlety, he produced and defended an image of the European tradition which no European would have formulated in quite the same way. One might criticize his tendency to neglect or brush aside the popular or less sophisticated elements of European tradition. But in his efforts to define European culture, he also enriched it while at the same time enriching and in a sense educating the American mind.

T. S. Eliot had the advantage of receiving his education in several countries, acquiring enough languages to be able to approach both the ancient and modern classics in the original text. There was nothing secondhand about his thought. Poet, philosopher, teacher, businessman, he had direct experience in many fields. Through his many contacts with the society and intellectuals of different countries, he kept abreast of the current of ideas, although he was hostile to all revolutionary trends. Without having the range or energy of the greatest poets, he benefited by attaching his very personal and individualistic work to that of the great writers of the past. For instance, his dramatic work has its roots as much in the Greek as in the Elizabethan drama, and in it echoes of Racine and Claudel mingle with those of the commercial or boulevard theater. If he sometimes went astray in his critical work—for instance in underestimating Milton, Blake, Lawrence, and Yeats—his honesty very often led him to make amends. His greatest contribution in this field was a reformulation of many principles of literary creation. At the same time he reflected constantly on social problems. During the long period when he edited the journal *Criterion,* and in such works as *The Idea of a Christian Society* and *Notes towards the Definition of Culture* (1948), he was closely engaged in the contemporary world.

The basis of Eliot's conception of the poet and poetry is to be found in his essay "Tradition and the Individual Talent" which was first published (and presumably, written) in 1917 and which no poet or critic can safely ignore. It was subsequently reprinted in *The Sacred Wood* in 1922. *The Sacred Wood* was, with *After Strange Gods,* Eliot's most aggressive publication: in it he had harsh things to say about Milton, Blake, Dickens, *Hamlet,* Freud, and Bergson, while overestimating such minor figures as Remy de Gourmont, Julien Benda, and Maeterlinck. Although Eliot would subsequently modify the ideas expressed in this essay, he was convinced that the "individual talent" should be relegated to a very minor role in its relationship to the tradition. He was of course right in insisting on this concept of tradition, even if his definitions of it at that time were not very adequate, and in this way he struck a necessary blow against literary history. But his attack on individualism and subjectivity in the name of a theory of impersonality was farfetched, being accompanied by such biased (and pejorative) expressions as *"turning loose*

of emotion" and his injunctions to *"escape from emotion"* and *"escape from personality."*

His concept of "tradition"—so far as the Anglo-Saxon and American traditions are concerned—does not correspond to the fact that in English literature individualism has always been the rule rather than the exception; nor does it correspond to his own practice which in every direction was highly individualistic and original. But Eliot's criticism was markedly, at any given moment, an apologia for his own practice. He never lost sight of the quotation from Remy de Gourmont which he gave as an epigraph to his essay "The Perfect Critic" (not republished in the *Selected Essays*): "To set his personal impressions up as laws, is what a man will strive to do if he is sincere." In the circumstances it was fortunate for us all that Eliot's ideas were so sound.

T. S. Eliot was born on September 26, 1888, in St. Louis, Missouri, and he remained what E. E. Cummings had once described to me as "that little St. Louis boy." Because of the poet's reticence we know little of his childhood, but we can imagine him full of wonder before the huge Mississippi River, which runs vast and disturbing through his work.

He was the seventh and youngest child of cultured and well-off parents, and one of his forbears founded a university. His parents were conscious and jealous of their English origins, which might explain the attraction that England eventually had for him. Certainly, his parents fostered the formation of a conservative American mind which, like Henry James's, was to become more English than the English—and, therefore, a little exotic.

Eliot's mother had literary leanings and once wrote a poem about Savonarola. His father, an industrialist, was president of the Hydraulic Pressed Brick

Co. in New York. Their indulgence enabled the poet to spend about ten years at his studies in St. Louis, Milton, Harvard, the Sorbonne, in Germany, and at Oxford. He married in 1915, and after teaching in a school in Highgate and working for a period in Lloyds Bank, became one of the heads of the Faber & Faber publishing company. He acquired British nationality and joined the Anglican Church in 1927.

A great poet was evolving under this modest exterior. Philology, philosophy, ancient and modern languages, travel, all equipped him thoroughly for his task. Strongly influenced by Ezra Pound, he learned at an early stage to attach his verse to tradition, creating his own unique versification—an amalgam of Elizabethan blank verse and Laforgue's free verse—while incorporating in his work reminiscences from the classics and other sources. Pound taught him above all to strive for concentration and economy, which exactly suited his reserved and puritan temperament. In reacting against romantic verbosity, the artificial diction of the esthetic and decadent movements, and against the sentimentality of the Edwardian and Georgian poets, Eliot benefited especially from his knowledge of French symbolism. He also learned much from the contemporary Unanimist poets—Jules Romains, Duhamel, Vildrac—who strengthened his free verse and his use of realistic imagery.

Thus in his first book of poems, *Prufrock and Other Observations* (1917), Eliot had contrived a style which looked completely new but had its roots very strongly in the past. Perhaps most important, Eliot brought to poetry a strikingly *active* quality, which was also to dominate his *Poems 1920* and *The Waste Land* (1922). He not only tended to write through *personae* and thus dramatize his theme, but he wrote with a profoundly dramatic syntax. On the whole

he was using very modern methods to express conservative reactions against a modern world in which he found a lack of spiritual values. If his early works, up to *The Hollow Men* (1925), now appear to us somewhat negative and nihilistic, they revealed the presence of a man who dared to think for himself. At the same time, the poet's personal style and form revealed a talent destined for the theater.

In his early poems, Eliot employed a profound irony, which allowed him (like Henry James) to evoke a tragic climate or atmosphere while exploiting the techniques of comedy—situation, gestures, vocabulary, misunderstandings, ambiguities. In this he outstripped Laforgue and got back to the Elizabethans. Also, like Chekhov, he exploited silence itself, those terrible silences in which thought comes to life and dies without finding its expression, moments when the heart stands still and the soul seems to wither before monologue or dialogue starts up again. But most of all, the poem's structure or overall design—in the case of such poems as "The Love Song of J. Alfred Prufrock," "Portrait of a Lady," *The Waste Land*—is a neomusical form of composition in which it is possible to pass from one tone or theme to another as in a symphony or sonata. This is perhaps the most important (and most frequently neglected) legacy of symbolism; the discovery of a discontinuous poetry which we find not only in Laforgue's *Derniers Vers* or certain poems by Corbière, or in Rimbaud's *Illuminations* and Mallarmé's *Hérodiade* and *Après-Midi d'un Faune* but also in Pound's *Cantos* and *Mauberley,* Edith Sitwell's *Gold-Coast Customs,* Valéry's *La Jeune Parque* (written in *"îles"* or "islands"), as well as *The Waste Land*.

As for "The Love Song of J. Alfred Prufrock," which was written as early as 1910–1911 in Paris and Munich, the astonishment with which it was greeted by

Eliot's contemporaries and his difficulties in getting it printed show to what extent it appeared to mark a rupture with the English tradition. In this poem Eliot "cracked" the traditional versification and particularly blank verse with an amalgam of Elizabethan blank verse, Dante, and the free verse of Laforgue. Laforgue had already "cracked" the alexandrine with the help of Shakespearean blank verse, and particularly in his remarkable but unfinished *Derniers Vers* (something near to a verse-novel and which profoundly influenced Eliot) had invented a new type of internal monologue which was a great advance on that of Browning or anyone else. The nucleus of Eliot's two great monologues ("The Love Song of J. Alfred Prufrock" and the "Portrait") is to be found mainly in eleven lines of Laforgue's *Derniers Vers* (III):

Bref, j'allais me donner d'un "Je vous aime"
Quand je m'avisai non sans peine
Que d'abord je ne me possédais pas bien moi-même.

(Mon Moi, c'est Galathée aveuglant Pygmalion!
Impossible de modifier cette situation.)

Ainsi donc, pauvre, pâle et piètre individu
Qui ne croit à son Moi qu'à ses moments perdus,
Je vis s'effacer ma fiancée
Emportée par le cours des choses,
Telle l'épine voit s'effeuiller
Sous prétexte de soir sa meilleure rose.

On the point of giving myself with an "I love you"
It struck me, not without dismay,
I hardly "possessed" a self to give away.

(My Ego—Galatea blinding Pygmalion—
Could I presume to change such a situation?)

And so, threadbare, anaemic and third-rate,
My ego strutting only between acts,
I had to watch my Intended fade,
Drift "on the tide of events" as the saying goes,
Just as a thorn might witness the strip-tease
(Permissive twilight!) of its loveliest rose.

Here we see the difference between a *source* and a *cause:* just as Joyce's *Ulysses* does not have *Les Lauriers Sont Coupés* for its *source,* but rather as the *cause* of a certain technique of presentation, so, although Eliot never translated or adapted any of the above lines, they nonetheless dominate the import, style, and tone of his early work. The first line gives a basis of action for *Prufrock;* the second and third set the emotional reaction to the situation; the fourth is a key to the meaning of both "The Love Song of J. Alfred Prufrock" and "Portrait of a Lady" inasmuch as it indicates a personality split (what the French call a *dédoublement*) and hints that it is an idealized person, not the woman as she really is, who annihilates the poet or character.

Eliot's triumph in his exploitation of the Laforguian subject and technique, however, is not in reproducing and transposing Laforgue so much as in raising everything to a far more serious level, with a subtler modulation of tones and a more penetrating psychological analysis than the French poet's. This is particularly so in "Portrait of a Lady." It is astonishing that many years later Eliot could write that "dramatic monologue cannot create a character" (exactly the same comment that Arnold Bennett had made on Virginia Woolf's technique), when he had so perfectly demonstrated the very opposite: but Eliot's comment shows something fundamental about his work, which is that his career as a poet proceeded in fits and starts. He did not seem to have had enough confidence to retain a particular style for very long, and thus he gives the impression of restless experiment which often throws away the benefit of successful achievement. One rather disturbing aspect of Eliot's view of life remained a constant, however: the "romantic irony," as Irving Babbitt called it, persists down to the final plays where self-distrust is always very marked in his central characters. As it is, the early monologues remain too painful to be tragic.

Eliot's *Poems 1920* contains only one really satisfactory and important poem, "Gerontion," which marks a serious reorientation of style: maybe Ezra Pound was wrong (for once) in persuading Eliot not to include it in *The Waste Land,* of which it now appears to be an essential part. The break with the Prufrockian style is even more marked in the rest of this volume, where Eliot exploits the terse quatrain and bare style that Théophile Gautier had used for what we can only call nonsubjects in his *Emaux et Camées.* Actually, Eliot was not content to use Gautier's form as it stood, but strengthened it with elements of Corbière's. As an example, Eliot's "The Hippopotamus" is based to some extent on Gautier's "L'Hippopotame," a poem that does not rise above low comedy. Eliot, however, gave significance to what might have remained a superficial exercise by identifying the hippo not with himself (as Gautier did) but with the Church. The same remark applies to all the Sweeney poems in *Poems 1920,* which are important for several reasons. In them we see how Eliot used Gautier's quatrain in order to free himself from the

Laforguian technique; at the same time the inner approach to the character is abandoned and the symbolic character is portrayed and satirized from the outside, the roughneck Sweeney standing for all the vulgarity that Eliot could not accept in modern society and which he would further attack in *The Waste Land.*

These poems are also important for the germ they contain of that delightful unfinished dramatic fragment, *Sweeney Agonistes* (1920), which was a milestone in Eliot's progress toward the theater, though it proved also to be a dead end because he was to choose an entirely different dramatic form. The 1920 volume is marked by a profound feeling of disgust which the humorous veneer does not dispel: it is also notable for its half-mocking play on what we might call churchy matters, which shows how far away Eliot still was from any real conciliation with organized religion.

The Waste Land shocked the critics in 1922 with its unusual form and its apparent nihilism. Perhaps it was thought to be more obscure and hermetic than it really is. Because of the vast superstructure that the critics have built around it, and which now prevents us from getting at close quarters with it, it might appear naive to suggest that *The Waste Land* simply expresses that "philosophy of the Absurd," which Laforgue, Mallarmé, and many another end-of-the-century French poet had already espoused, largely under the influence of German philosophers. Yeats, also, was to consider the world (for a time) as nothing but "a bundle of fragments."

In spite of the introduction of a few anthropological references, and the legend of the Grail (divorced from its religious significance), and two or three words from the Sanskrit which have nothing to do with the Christian religion, there is nothing but cold comfort in *The Waste Land,* which shows an Eliot even more pessimistic than Mallarmé. Mallarmé at least thought that beyond the *néant,* or nothingness, man could build an esthetic world of his own. There is, of course, an element of pure estheticism in Eliot's poem, but his esthetic world is only a series of ruins and scraps; those thirty-five or so poetic tags which appear here and there would not be enough to shore up the ruins of even an esthetic world, let alone the one we live in. The scourge of nonspirituality with which *The Waste Land* deals is not changed by the symbol of the Grail, for Eliot stopped short of the theological solution. The legend of the Grail loses most of its symbolic value here, being reduced to an anthropological incident divorced from its profoundly Christian significance.

Perhaps *The Waste Land,* for all its power, energy, insight, and incidental beauty, failed to achieve a synthesis and remained in the state of a series of loosely related fragments; perhaps even the technique of writing in "movements" is unsatisfactory when there are such brusque changes of tone, manner, and even theme within a movement. This view is reinforced by the publication of certain passages that were omitted from the work, as well as the sacrifice of "Gerontion," the hesitation about including "Phlebas," and the fact that Pound referred to the work as a *series* of poems. Another thing that has come to light is that even if other pieces had been included, they would have done nothing toward diminishing the overall effect of disgust, disaster, and hopelessness, which pervades the work. Nor would they have in any way helped to cement its parts together. *The Waste Land* is an unfinished—and perhaps unfinishable—masterpiece.

Some critics claim that the quality of Eliot's poetic work declined after 1922. This is nonsense, although it is possible to understand that critics might regret the decline in concreteness, and the increasing abstractness of Eliot's work particularly after *The Hollow Men* of 1925. It is a mistake to think that in this reorientation, all the experience Eliot had gained in his early work was lost. Apart from its high quality in its own right, this work was to underlie his greatest achievements in the theater.

Up to and including *The Hollow Men,* Eliot had kept himself outside his poetry, though of course he could never have written the early monologues had there been no genuine affinity with Laforgue and his theme of failure (there is after all some psychological significance in the very fact that a writer selects one theme rather than another). It was only with *Ash Wednesday* (1930), that the "I" of the poem was no longer somebody else, but was openly identified with the poet himself. After denouncing the inferno of modern society, the poet now explored more publicly his own personal inferno. Thus with *Ash Wednesday* and *Four Quartets* (1943) Eliot's poetry became a kind of confessional. This was a surprising evolution for a poet who had declared in "Tradition and the Individual Talent" that the poet's task is to efface his personality, and who had so eloquently argued in favor of the "objective correlative" which is discarded in these works. But to be fair to Eliot, we also have to recall that he said that the poet's point of departure is his own sensibility. Now, his lyrical and meditative verse became more intimate and personal, while at the same time his "public" poetry for the theater, right down to his last play *The Elder Statesman* (1959), showed him to be no less obsessed by the problem of confession (and what, after all, were his youthful internal monologues but a type of confession?). *Ash Wednesday* was certainly influenced by the Abbé Bremond's thesis that poetry aspires to the nature of prayer: it is in fact the most sublime prayer in our language. It offered a brilliant reply to those who imagined that Eliot would never be anything more than a satirical poet, and even those readers who shun religious poetry cannot help admiring the purity of line and hard-won spontaneity of lyricism of this work. They were to be no more moon-struck Pierrots and Hamlets for Eliot, no more aggressive display of dilettantish learning for this poet who now appeared, suddenly, to have "grown up." *Ash Wednesday* placed Eliot squarely in the great English tradition of spiritual poetry; it also showed the fruition of Eliot's long study of Dante and the metaphysical poets.

Although Eliot turned from poetry to the theater in the years before the 1939 war, his finest and most profound poems, the *Four Quartets,* appeared during that war (with the exception only of "Burnt Norton"). It would be hard to explain to anyone who is not English what a deep and moving joy Eliot brought to his readers during those painful years. At a time when England was struggling desperately for survival, he brought us the consolation of these sublime poems with their unexpected and unhoped-for beauty. Eliot had already said in 1933 that he wanted to transcend or "get beyond" poetry as Beethoven had transcended music in his late works, and in order to do so he now adopted a neo-musical form. *The Waste Land, The Hollow Men,* and *Ash Wednesday* had already been composed in parts, or what might with some reservations be called movements, and Eliot was proceeding gradually to sonata or quartet forms. This he finally achieved in masterly fashion in the *Quartets,* which, in spite of the individual perfection of each, also hold together in such a way as to constitute one great work, a *magnum opus.* In his maturity Eliot was undaunted by the many tasks he set himself simultane-ously: to write a Dantesque poem; to follow Beethoven in his "musical" structure; to deal in turn with the four elements; to explore the concept of time and eternity in both a lay and a theological sense; to renew his vocabulary and versification; and to express his own mind while speaking directly to and for others. In this poem the creative side of Eliot's mind took over and overcame the sharp critical sense which, some might say, had so far inhibited his poetic gift. There is no need to agree with Eliot's views about life, poetry, religion, or indeed anything in the *Quartets,* in concluding that they form, together, one of the noblest and most necessary poems in the English language.

Long before he began writing and producing works for the stage, Eliot, as we have already remarked, had shown a strong disposition toward dramatic presentation of his ideas. As far back as 1922 in the "vulgar" parts of *The Waste Land,* he seemed to have created a form of free verse which could easily be adapted to the requirements of the theater. Then his *Sweeney Agonistes,* a dramatic poem or "fragment of an aristophanesque melodrama" as he called it, announced more clearly his desire to bring a whole group of characters into action and to find new rhythms and a new versification for that purpose. Had it been finished, that work would no doubt have been a ferocious adaptation of the tricks and gags of the music hall and the comic opera of Gilbert and Sullivan, as well as having its roots in Aristophanes.

When Eliot was asked in 1934 to raise funds for a church by writing the script or scenario for a pageant to be called *The Rock,* he experimented in a range of tones and styles which ran from a parody of the young Auden to the creation of serious choruses showing the influence of Paul Claudel. Although it was an adequate script for its purposes, the poet admitted that it was not sufficiently dramatic for the theater. But the preparation of this text brought Eliot closer to stage problems, and a year later he wrote one of his finest works for theater, *Murder in the Cathedral* (1935).

Eliot, who in his essay on "Poetry and Drama" gave a thorough critique of his theatrical works, reduced *Murder in the Cathedral* to the simple formula of a man returning home, expecting to be murdered, then being murdered. This is an almost laughable simplification, for in this case the man happened to be an archbishop; the event of his death was at once a matter of state, and a matter of sacrilege in the way it came about. The importance of the subject therefore speaks for itself. It has, of course, the disadvantage of any historical subject based on actual events in history—the data and the dénouement are already known and determined in advance. On the other hand, such a subject makes demands on the whole art of the dramatist.

In giving the play a static liturgical form, Eliot solved a whole series of problems. The action unfolds like an algebraic demonstration, following a ritual in which every participant is confined to a limited role. The king, the court, Rome, and so many incalculable elements which Shakespeare would have introduced to complicate the action, are omitted, but the enormous gaps are easily filled by the poetic evocation of an atmosphere of crime. An almost Jansenistic sense of predestination replaces the fatalism of Greek tragedy. The archbishop appears as monolithic as all those around him, but is none the less heroic for that. Eliot reproached himself for the hero's lack of inner development, but it is partly that psychological inevitability, the lack of division in Becket's personality that makes him a perfect symbol of the predestined martyr. Throughout the play,

Eliot showed a remarkable capacity for invention (which left him in his later works), as in the elevation of the poor women of Canterbury into the roll of "weepers" or professional mourners so that they dynamically re-create the essence of the Greek chorus.

The versification is supple, original, full of surprises, the vocabulary is rich, concrete, modern. In the speeches delivered by the murderous barons in their self-defense, he contrives in the most skillful manner to heighten the tragedy through a scene of bitter comedy, clashing the genres together much as he had done in *The Waste Land*.

Murder in the Cathedral is Eliot's most poetic play, and the one which brought him closest to the English public. It has the permanent advantage of adaptability, being so conceived that it can be presented either as a grandiose spectacle against the background of some fine cathedral, or be enacted in the open air. It can even be acceptable when played by amateurs in some local village hall. This play was the climax of Eliot's career in the theater, for in spite of constant development he was never able to produce another work so satisfying in every respect.

The Family Reunion has been more hotly debated than any of Eliot's other plays. The director of the Mercury Theater, Martin Browne, described it as a masterpiece unsuitable for the theater. The theme of the play has some relationship to the Oresteian trilogy, especially in the transformation of the Furies or Erinnyes into the benevolent Eumenides, but apart from the curse or malediction overhanging a whole family, the comparison with Aeschylus does not take us far. The thesis is rather Claudelian, being one of expiation and the ardent search for truth and redemption on the part of a man who appears to hold himself responsible for his wife's death—he "pushed her overboard in mid-Atlantic," or imagined that he did so.

In criticizing his own play, Eliot acknowledged the parallel with Aeschylus, but thought his own work remained imperfect for several reasons: the action is too slow in starting off, and leads to a too rapid dénouement; the protagonist's anguish is not sufficiently translated into acts; the public, unaccustomed to the conventions of the classical drama and also expecting more than a psychological development, finds it hard to understand whether the real drama is Harry's or his mother's, and so on. He added that the Furies raised a problem of verisimilitude which cannot be resolved in the theater, so that in spite of the producer's ingenuity they are open to ridicule.

Maybe Eliot was wrong in deprecating one of his finest works. Obviously a vulgar or popular audience will find it hard to appreciate all the import of an internal drama. But an intelligent audience will see *Bérénice* as the height of Racine's art and will not expect some bloody melodrama from Eliot. Martin Browne was bent on popularizing verse-drama, and no doubt he influenced Eliot in this respect. Whatever Eliot thought about his audience, this is a play which will appeal only to an élite. It is none the worse for that. Some critics also regard it as a highly successful radio play. But it is hard to accept Eliot's conclusion that it is impossible to present "supernatural" beings on the stage at a time when every possible technical device is to hand for such purposes. And as the dramas of mother and son are inseparable, there is no need for an audience to choose between the two; at the most, it might have been better if the mother's death had occurred before the son's departure, for

it is important for the principal character to dominate the final scenes.

Far more significant than all these objections was the outcry against Eliot's choice of a somewhat eccentric versification (which he more or less abandoned in subsequent plays) and the use of his characters in chorus fashion. Yet both of these elements are perfectly successful and serve their purpose in the structure of Eliot's last really "poetic" play.

It is always unpleasant—and perhaps presumptuous—to suggest that the evolution of a great writer is or was not entirely satisfying. But in the case of Eliot we are speaking of a writer whose entire production—and even those parts of it which we cannot accept or have criticized most severely—has an enormous *experimental* value. We cannot but admire the degree to which one man succeeded in imposing a new conception of poetic theater on the contemporary mind. The concessions he made to the public's mediocre taste were perhaps carried too far, and led him away from the sublime path that he had opened with *Murder in the Cathedral* and *The Family Reunion*. But his example remains to instruct and stimulate new generations of poets.

For the rest, the witness of all those who knew Eliot most intimately indicates a superior mind and an exceptional person: his "failures" were not the outcome of some personal weakness, but had much to do with the weakness of the age he lived in. He dedicated all his gifts to the examination of fundamental and enduring problems, and left our poetry enriched by his labors. That is why T. S. Eliot's work has no national frontiers, and why it will continue to compel the respect of all thinking men in the future.

Francis Scarfe, director of the British Institute in Paris, is a critic, novelist, poet, and member of the French P.E.N. Club.

THE 1948 PRIZE

By KJELL STRÖMBERG

ENGLAND'S share of the Nobel Prizes during the first half-century of the award's history was meager. Though in England both poetry and the novel flourished, the English novel had been honored by an award to only two writers—Kipling and Galsworthy. The two other Prizewinners who wrote in English—Yeats and Shaw —were Irish. Algernon Swinburne and Thomas Hardy had been regularly proposed as candidates by their English colleagues each year until they died at seventy-two and eighty-eight years of age respectively. Both had been the subject of lively discussions within the jury, but neither had received the award.

When T. S. Eliot received the Nobel Prize in 1948, it was not as the representative of a long and honorable tradition but—as was specifically noted in the official motivation—"for his outstanding, pioneer contribution to present-day poetry." In other words, in awarding the Prize to Eliot—born an American and a British subject by naturalization in 1927, when he was nearly forty—the Swedish Academy perhaps wished to honor not only a fine poet but a great international literary movement of symbolist origin which it had rather neglected until then. The Academy was subsequently to vote the award to poets from Spain, Italy, and, of course, France, the country where this esoteric poetic school had

been fathered by Stéphane Mallarmé and where it reached its culmination with Paul Valéry.

By the time Eliot became a serious candidate for the Nobel Prize, he had been at the peak of his fame for ten years.

Eliot had fervent admirers and highly competent translators in the Swedish Academy, but the first report prepared for the Nobel Committee was rather negative. This is scarcely surprising, for the author of the report was the venerable dean of the Academy, the former permanent secretary, Per Hallström, eighty years old and not very responsive to the enigmatic charms of the New Poetry. He was disturbed by this "flight over centuries and civilizations, religions and empyreans." On the other hand, several members of the Academy, including the new permanent secretary, Anders Österling (who incidentally had been the first to propose Eliot in 1945) backed his candidacy with enthusiasm. They won their colleagues over without too much resistance, not even from Hallström. The only really dangerous competitor was an earlier laureate, Thomas Mann (Nobel Prize 1929), to whom a strong minority wanted to award the Prize a second time in recognition of the substantial additions which he had made to his earlier work. The bylaws of the Nobel Foundation prohibit such an award, however. Among the other candidates there were four French writers—Georges Duhamel, Jules Romains, André Malraux and, for the first time, Colette. Their chances of being selected were minimal, since another French writer, André Gide, had won the Prize only the year before.

At any rate, Eliot was the great favorite of the better-informed Swedish critics, and if resistance within the Academy was overcome so easily, it was partly because so many public honors had been awarded him by different countries to the poet, who was nearing his sixtieth birthday. In 1948 alone, he was awarded honorary degrees from Oxford, Aix-en-Provence, and Munich, and in previous years he had received honorary degrees from Harvard and several other American universities. In that same year he was made a Knight Commander of the Order of Merit by George VI, and the President of France decorated him with the ribbon of the Legion of Honor.

Eliot's trip to Sweden for the awards ceremony was not his first. In 1942, at the height of World War II, he had braved the dangers of the trip to make a lecture tour in Sweden for the British Council. He had traveled in a Royal Air Force bomber converted into a civil transport. Then, the aircraft invariably flew at a great altitude and thus insured a fairly regular flight over the German lines. This time Eliot had no need of an oxygen mask while crossing the North Sea, but he almost arrived too late for the awards ceremony. A heavy fog prevented his landing at Stockholm, but, with the help of the British consul general at Gothenburg on the west coast, he managed to catch a fast train to the capital. He arrived just in time to change his clothes (he had picked up a new set of tails in London, together with his new decorations) and was off to the Concert Palace, the traditional scene of the ceremony.

Before leaving Stockholm, Eliot had the happy surprise of seeing a production of his play, *The Family Reunion,* at the Royal Dramatic Theater. At the end of the play a wild ovation greeted the author. Eliot was deeply touched.

Translated by Dale McAdoo.